CP. 1st 15ᵘ

# JOHN SUTTER

JOHN SUTTER
(Courtesy of Mr. H. K. Douglas Peachy)

# JOHN SUTTER

## RASCAL AND ADVENTURER

By

### MARGUERITE EYER WILBUR

*Based on Source Material, Manuscripts and Letters pertaining to Captain John Augustus Sutter, leading figure in the Gold Rush and the founder of Sutter's Fort.*

LIVERIGHT
PUBLISHING CORPORATION
New York

# CONTENTS

# ILLUSTRATIONS

# ACKNOWLEDGMENTS

THE RARE VIEWS of early California are taken from the Archives of the Henry E. Huntington Library in San Marino, California, through the courtesy of Dr. Leslie Bliss, and from *Das Burgdorfer Jahrbuch* for the year 1935. Permission to reproduce the original oil portrait of Sutter, painted in San Francisco in the fifties, was secured through the kindness of its owner, Mr. H. K. Douglas Peachy, of Los Angeles, California. Appreciation is also hereby expressed for critical readings of the manuscript by Dr. William Ashworth and Mr. Harvey Taylor, of Santa Barbara, and Mr. Peter Churchill, of Hollywood, California.

# NOTE ON SOURCES

JOHN AUGUSTUS SUTTER left only fragmentary records of his life in California—a brief diary, some business correspondence, a few letters to friends and relatives in Switzerland, and his *Reminiscences,* written in his old age when his memory was failing. Much of this has been published, notably in the *New Helvetia Diary,* in *Sutter's Own Story,* by Erwin C. Gudde, and in *Das Burgdorfer Jahrbuch, 1935.*

There is also available, however, considerable information, both published and unpublished, about the founder of New Helvetia. The most important single item is the record of Heinrich Lienhard, who lived for several years at the fort during the Gold Rush era. Sections of his verbose record have been published, but the balance of the manuscript contains a wealth of information about life at the fort. The Lienhard record is probably the most valuable item of Sutterana yet found. Of outstanding interest, as well, is the *Statement of John A. Sutter, Jr.,* edited by Allan R. Ottley, which supplements and clarifies Lienhard's story. There is also a mass of material of minor importance, such as business letters from Sutter to his associates and theirs to him, notably the Sünol-Sutter correspondence in French, and passing comments about Sutter in contemporary letters, journals, newspapers and magazines. In fact, practically every traveler to California during the Gold Rush had something to say about him.

Among the leading published records that contribute to our knowledge of Sutter are: John Bidwell's *Trip to California* and his *Echoes of the Past; What I Saw in California*, by Edwin Bryant; *Three Years in California*, by Walter Colton; *Recollections of the Past*, by Peter Burnett; *Seventy-Five Years in California*, by William Heath Davis; *Duflot de Mofras' Travels on the Pacific Coast; A Tour of Duty*, by Joseph Warren Revere; *El Dorado*, by Bayard Taylor.

These eye-witness accounts are enriched by the standard histories of California by Bancroft, Hittell, Cleland, and others; by such books as McGlashan's *History of the Donner Party*, Nevins, *Frémont, the World's Greatest Explorer*, the *Fort Sutter Papers*, edited by Seymour Dunbar, the *Report of the U. S. Senate on the Claims of General John A. Sutter*, the important volume by Gottfried Duden, *Bericht über eine Reise nach den westlichen Vereinigten Staaten*, and the invaluable *Quarterlies* of the California Historical Society.

Several excellent books have been written about Sutter: *Sutter of California*, by Julian Dana; *John A. Sutter and his Grants*, by John Lauftkötter; *Sutter's Gold*, by Blaise Cendrars; *The Life and Times of General John A. Sutter*, by T. J. Schoonover; *General Johan August Suter*, by Martin Birman; and *Sutter, the Man and his Empire*, by James Peter Zollinger, which contains an extensive bibliography.

# JOHN SUTTER

# CHAPTER I

# THE DARK FOREST

JOHANN SWIRLED a globe of the world between restless hands. He was sullen and angry with the unreasoning rage of the very young.

He looked rebelliously out of the study window in his father's house in Kandern, near the Black Forest, where he was confined by way of paternal chastisement for having stolen a book from a schoolmate, and he glared at the tall, darkish pines that surrounded the house, half hiding it. Today they infuriated him. There was a feeling of restriction, as if they were attempting to conceal from his sight the strange, alluring world beyond.

He was a chubby blond boy of about ten, with a mass of tousled curls. His face was round and ruddy with good health. His nose had the shapely classic lines of those found on Greek coins. His lips were sensually thick and inclined to droop at the corners. Although his body was broad and of good proportions, it was smaller than the average for his years. Altogether he gave the impression of a headstrong, buoyant personality that swerves readily between the bright peaks of ecstasy and the black abyss of despair. The self pity of escape in suicide obsessed his mind at times.

As he held the globe up to the light near the windows and tried to decipher the fine print, he wrinkled his brows in despair. Asia and Africa stood out clearly. He glanced indifferently at them, then turned to North America. It built images of explorers traveling down

1

the St. Lawrence, across vast prairies, high mountains, fighting Indians and wild beasts, in regions devoid of white settlements. He began to study the vast area marked the United States of America. He traced a route with his forefinger from New York west through Ohio, Michigan, Indiana. He paused and inspected a great waterway labelled Mississippi. It divided the United States as neatly as if cut with a knife, although not into equal halves. West of it stretched an enormous region called Missouri Territory. On the south it touched Old Mexico and on the north Oregon Territory. Its magnitude filled him with awe. He swung the globe back to Switzerland. By comparison it was a pygmy land. A feeling of consternation came over him; he had always believed his country was the center of the universe. The desire to know more about this strange remote country came to him.

Johann returned the globe to the shelf and began to search hastily along the capacious book shelves of his grandfather, Pastor Stober, that lined the study from floor to ceiling. Most of them dealt with religion, morals, philosophy or ethics, but scattered among them were a few standard histories and books of travel. They were classified with a precision that revealed the orderly habits of the pastor's mind. The histories and lighter works were less frequently read and so were placed on an upper shelf.

The boy dragged a heavy chair nearer and by standing on its arm he could read the titles—Epictetus, Goethe, Schiller, Martin Luther, Immanuel Kant, Descartes, Aristotle, Grotius, Marcus Aurelius.

Johann sighed. He could read neither Greek, Latin, nor English, for only French and German were taught in the village school. He searched among the books of travel. He discovered the narratives of Columbus, Magellan, Cortes, Cook, Vancouver in English. He was vaguely acquainted with their contents for his grandfather had instructed him in history and geography. Recently he had been telling Johann about the French explorers, La Salle, Cadillac and the Bienville Brothers, *Les Voyageurs*, he called them, who paddled in canoes down the St. Lawrence and Mississippi exploring new lands and bringing religion to pagan natives. The lad searched for the books from which the pastor had read. He could not find them. He pulled first one then another from top shelves, only to open them and fling them aside. He tried another. His eyes glowed with delight. It was in French, a language he could understand by Count Jean Francois de la Perouse. Happily he studied the pictures with French captions under them. One showed the Bay of Monterey on the Pacific Ocean in a place called California. He caught up the globe and located it. *Las Californias* covered an enormous area from the coast to the Rockies, north to Oregon Territory and far south until it terminated in a long tail he knew to be a peninsula.

Globe in one hand and book in the other, he was sitting comfortably in the pastor's large arm chair when the door opened.

Johann dropped the globe and book, and crimsonfaced jumped guiltily to his feet.

Pastor Stober looked sternly over his spectacles at his cringing grandson.

"Johann! Where is your Bible? Have you memorized the chapter from Psalms?"

The lad hung his head. "*Nein.*"

"Why not? You have been here for more than an hour."

The boy twisted his feet in embarrassment. "I . . . was . . . going . . . to . . . soon," he stammered.

Pastor Stober cast a hasty glance at the tumbled array of books. His eyes wandered to the volume lying, with crumpled leaves, at his grandson's feet. "Hand it to me," he said.

Timidly the boy placed it in the pastor's outstretched hands.

"*The Perouse*, I see. My favorite traveler. Put it back where you found it, Johann. And the others you pilfered. Then bring your Bible and follow me."

As he obeyed, Johann pondered over the sad, resigned way in which his grandfather had mentioned *La Perouse* and wondered why he called him his favorite traveler.

They went down a long corridor into a small back storeroom. It was a cheerless spot, lighted only by an upper window. The pastor indicated a low box.

"You will sit here for two hours, Johann, and learn two Psalms." He opened the Bible and indicated the passages. "Tomorrow you will go to your teacher and apologize for the trouble you caused her when you stole your schoolmate's book. I'm ashamed that a grandson of mine should so debase himself before God and man." Without further comment he left the room.

Left alone to his devices, Johann threw the Bible aside. From an inner pocket he drew a pencil and piece of paper. He began to cover it with crude pictures: young girls in the nude, boys in vulgar postures. When he had exhausted his supply of paper, he placed his artistic endeavors in an inside pocket, then stretched out on the box, cradling his curly blond head in his arm. Soon he was asleep.

He was aroused by the pastor shaking him violently. "Johann, wake up."

The boy rubbed his eyes. "What is it?" he asked.
"Repeat the verses to me."
Johann stared blankly at his grandparent.
"Have you memorized them?"
"*Nein.*"
"Then I must whip you, Johann. It is my painful
duty. Take off your clothes."

The lad removed them silently. As he slipped off his
jacket, his drawings fell from his pocket and fluttered
to the floor. Pastor Stober regarded them with a grim
and tight-lipped countenance.

Johann looked on in rebellious silence as the pastor
stuffed them into his vest pocket. He winced as the
heavy rope the pastor removed from an old box struck
his back. At the fifth stroke he began to whimper. As
the pastor appeared not to notice it, Johann began to
cry noisily.

"Well, Johann," said the pastor, "I have never
whipped anyone before. Your own father was always a
good, God-fearing son. I pray this will be a lesson to
you. He who sins will be punished. That is God's holy
law . . . Come. Kneel down before me. Let us ask God's
forgiveness. Let us beseech him to save you from Satan's
toils."

Bowing his head, Johann moved his lips obediently.
"Now let us repeat the Lord's Prayer together."

Our Father who art in heaven . . .

That evening Pastor Stober discussed with his
daughter Christine, and his son-in-law Johann Jakob
Sutter, the lad's parents, his anxiety over Johann's
immoral tendencies, his concern over his grandson's
disobedience, thievery, self-glorification, and his passion
for adventure.

Christine listened attentively but said nothing. Of her two children, Johann was her favorite. Friedrich, age five, was his father's. Brought up in the small town of Grenzach, she knew little of the moral impurities of the outside world. Her fortunate marriage to Johann Sutter, superintendent of the paper mill at Kandern, had only strengthened her belief in the inherent goodness of mankind. She could not believe that the traits that so distressed Grandfather Stober were present in her own son.

After listening to the conversation for a time, she slipped from the room and, carrying a lighted candle, went upstairs to the large nursery where the two boys slept. Tiny Friedrich was sleeping soundly, but Johann was wide awake. "Why are you not asleep, *Liebchen?*"

"I'm thinking," he said.

"Of what?"

"Indians. Traveling in a canoe down a river. I want to go to America."

He viewed her gentle laughter as tacit reproach.

"You don't believe me, do you?"

"Of course not, Johann. It's an immense wild country, not civilized like Switzerland. Besides this is our home. We Sutters have always lived here."

"In Kandern?"

"No. In the little village of Runenberg. It's in the hill country in the northwest. My own family came from Grenzach. Some day I'll take you there to visit."

"Tomorrow?"

"What an impatient child you are. We'll wait until you're older."

"I'm ten." He began to yawn.

"Yes. I know. But it's time to go to sleep now, *Liebchen.*"

Johann trudged reluctantly toward the schoolhouse the next day, lunch box in hand. The more he thought about the apologies he was obliged to make to his teacher, the more indignant he grew. He was neither sorry nor contrite. He was indifferent to his own delinquencies. He felt an antipathy toward his parents, especially his grandfather's puritanical view. But he had an intense curiosity about life, about the world beyond Kandern, which he had never seen.

Suddenly he remembered hearing his father at the table say that this was the day Napoleon's armies would cross the bridge that spanned the Rhine between Kandern and Basle only a few miles away. He longed to see his hero from earliest childhood. Down the road leading toward Basle a few wagons moved carrying country produce to the city. Impelled by an irresistible force he ran toward one piled high with hay and begged a ride. The driver invited him to climb into the seat.

After an hour they came to the Rhine Crossing. Johann thanked the driver and got off. He saw the river bank crowded with spectators, giving it the aspect of a holiday. He pushed his way to a place near the bridge.

The distant sounds of fifes and drums were audible. Johann quivered with excitement. He wiggled to a strategic vantage point. His feet tapped the ground in rhythm with the approaching drums. His eyes bulged in the delirium of delight. He craned his neck to watch.

"They're coming," called a shrill woman's voice.

The reck of a sweetish perfume made Johann turn. Beside him stood a flashily dressed woman. Her face was heavily rouged and her eyes were bold and black. She placed a wrinkly, heavily-ringed hand on Johann's shoulder and looked down at his inquiring face. "You're a pretty lad," she said, smirking at him.

He turned away as some dignified iron gray horses bearing elaborate plumed headdresses clattered across the bridge, carrying officers in handsome red uniforms. They sat stiffly, lances in hand, and looked neither to the right nor left.

Johann clapped his hands and cheered with all the power he could force from his immature lungs.

The drums beat louder. The bugles piped a stirring fortissimo. Foot soldiers, guns on their shoulders, marched by. An expectant hush came over the whispering crowd. "There's Napoleon." The woman clutched Johann's shoulder until it ached.

He saw a shortish man with a leonine head and heavy features, wearing knee breeches, a red coat and black tri-cornered hat, astride a black stallion. An array of medals formed three parallel rows across his chest. Taciturn and somewhat wearily he rode, as if oblivious to the world about him. He seemed as aloof, as remote, as unreal as if carved from stone.

As Napoleon came abreast of Johann his horse stumbled on a loose stone. The rider tightened his grip on his reins to prevent it from falling. As he did so, his eyes fell on the excited face of the lad nearby. He smiled at him, a somber but kindly smile.

Johann, half paralyzed with wonder and fright, hung his head. The woman clawed his shoulder.

"Smile back at him, lad. Don't you know it's Napoleon?"

He glanced timidly up but the rider was no longer looking his way. Ashamed by his lack of manners, he began to push his way toward the rear of the crowd.

The woman followed. "Don't you want to see all of

Napoleon's soldiers? They'll be crossing this bridge most of the day."

"No," he replied. "I'm tired."

He reached a road that led toward a thicket on the river bank. Tired and thirsty he stretched out on the ground and closed his eyes. He heard the woman lie down beside him. She moved over and put her arm around him, drawing him close. He could feel the warmth of her breasts pressing on his body, her breath hot above his lips.

"You're such a handsome boy," she whispered, fondling him.

He did not move but lay quietly on the grass responding instinctively to her progressive advances.

Hours later a small boy was seen trudging across the fields. Inside the lad the devil was at work. The dark entrails of guilt cast long shadows upon his conscience. It was Johann August Sutter going home.

Pastor Stober, his daughter and son-in-law were sitting, deep in conversation in the study.

"My Johann is late again tonight," Frau Sutter observed.

"His teacher may have kept him," said her husband. "The lad gives her endless trouble. I'm at my wits' end to know what to do with him. If it were not for Grandfather Stober's wise counsel . . ."

"Young Johann pays no attention to what I say," the Pastor replied. "If he keeps on the way he's going . . . well, I can't predict what will become of him. Satan's image is in his heart, not that of our gracious Lord."

Pastor Stober sat for some time, a perplexed wrinkle on his forehead. He could not decide how to deal with the wayward lad whose zest for adventure was leading him into devious ways. He regretted that Johann was growing so stubborn and rebellious. Yet he could be ingratiating and delightful when he tried. The pastor regretted, too, that his grandson was inclined to brag and to regale his schoolmates with fabulous tales of imaginary achievements. He also bullied his delicate and nervous brother, Frederich.

The pastor closed his eyes, and leaned back in his chair feigning sleep. His mind was centered on Johann. In his heart he felt a deep affection for the winsome culprit. He tried to discover the basis of the lad's perverse ways. Perhaps it was one reaction of modern youth due to changing times. Certainly the old Europe he was brought up in, was not the same nowadays.

Broadening horizons, the disturbing changes everywhere tended to make people restless. Emigrants by the thousands were leaving Europe. The amazing opportunities for independence and wealth across the Atlantic acted like magnets. They were discussed in every city and village, with the result that Swiss, German and French settlements had established their own colonies as far west as the Mississippi. Or was it the new freedom that was sweeping over Europe? Individualism, they called it, the right of every man to work out his own salvation. Its supporters lauded liberty, equality and freedom of speech. He was not sure that he wholly approved radical removal of the barriers of restraint. In France they called it *laissez faire. Liberté, égalité, fraternité.*

Individualism would have gone even further had it not been for the Napoleonic wars, and the French leader who had dominated most of Europe with his mad campaigns. Militaristic standards were poor spiritual food for youth. Perhaps that was behind Johann's inexplicable moods. Young boys were impressed by the external manifestations of war: uniforms, gold braid, loud bangs, the noise of gunfire. They did not see its terrors, the suffering of the innocent, sickness and death in the wake of war. What did it profit men to win battles if they bartered for it all the truly vital things? Pastor Stober could never reconcile himself to physical conflict. He believed that one simple code sufficed for all: Peace on earth. Liberty of thought was of value only as it emanated from God.

He wondered how he could convey this to his grandson. He remembered his own stormy youth, the same rebellion against parental restraint, the same self-confidence, the same haughty, unbending spirit, the same urge to seek adventure. He had once thought of hanging himself, or running off to Africa ... or was it South America? He had appeased his rampant spirits at twelve by dedicating his life to God.

At the creak of an opening door, he looked up. Johann, pale and with shifty eyes, idled at the entry.

"*Liebchen*," said his mother, kissing him.

"Good evening, son," said the mild-mannered father, scarcely noticing him. He resumed his reading of a trade bulletin to which he was a contributor.

Johann hastened to his grandfather's chair and lowered his head humbly.

"Why are you so late tonight, Johann? Were you kept at school?"

"*Nein.*"

"Well, then where were you?"

Johann shifted his feet nervously.

"I went to see Napoleon. Whip me, grandfather. I wish I were dead." Breaking into sobs, he rushed from the room.

## CHAPTER II

## BASLE INTERLUDE

IN THE GATHERING DUSK, Johann Sutter leaned far
over the side of the great bridge that spanned the Rhine
at Basle, horror and despair in his eyes. He stared at
the waters churning over the rocks. Thoughts of suicide
tormented him. He tried to gather strength to throw
himself into the icy waters but his knees weakened and
his body cringed. His hands, clutching the stone para-
pet, trembled and shook; despite the chill air they were
wet and hot. As he leaned dejectedly against the side
of the bridge, his harassed face, the dejected droop of
his head and shoulders were the epitome of frustration,
anguish, despair.

From a chubby boy, he had become, at twenty, a
slender man of medium height. His head large and well-
proportioned was topped by masses of curly blond hair.
The grandiose appearance it gave him was further enhanced by high-arched, bushy eyebrows and sweeping
lashes that formed an impressive frame around his
eyes, deep-set and sapphire blue. Above his full lips
a stiffly-waxed mustache fanned out symmetrically with
meticulous Teutonic neatness. Equally neat side-chops
extended from ear to throat, making more conspicuous
the high-boned cheeks, and a chin showing independence. The face was moody; it gave evidence of a character that pivots readily from regions of fancy to black
despair.

His apparel was that worn by most young men in

Switzerland in 1823: heavy laced boots, thick gray
woolen trousers, without shape yet durable, a striped
waistcoat, black coat and fresh white shirt, a flowing
bow tie. A black hat of broad brim and soft crown was
pulled over his forehead and he carried a voluminous
black wool cape.

As the damp air fanned his cheeks his tenseness began
to lessen. Except for a few loiterers at the far end, the
bridge was deserted. He looked down at the Rhine less
apprehensively now, with a dawning consciousness of its
strength. Since early childhood rivers had exerted a
peculiar fascination. They consoled him when depression came over him; yet, more than once, as tonight, he
had longed to throw himself into the Rhine, to seek
oblivion from this world in its clear cool depths. But
invariably, an urge to live restrained him.

With consummate weariness Johann dragged himself
from the end of the bridge, and began to move slowly
toward the south bank of the Rhine. At the end of the
bridge, reluctant to return to the small dismal room
he called home, he stopped uncertainly to contemplate
a small chapel. It was called Bishop Heinrich's chapel
in honor of the pious patriot who had foregone spiritual
pursuits to indulge in the more worldly occupation of
building this bridge.

He stood for a time watching the fading sun. Already
the waters of the Rhine were tinged with night. Now, as
the river flowed beneath the Bishop's masterpiece, it
exerted upon Johann a renewed desire to live.

As he walked on he felt hemmed in by the range of
mountains towering beyond Basle. Their icy barriers
chilled him. They seemed strangely to restrict him,
shutting out from sight the remote land, the unknown

people far beyond. He glanced back once more at the water. He vowed some day to follow it to the sea.

He began to stroll along a narrow street skirting the Rhine, the Rheinsprung, until he reached the squat stone buildings of the University. Looking at them he felt a supreme satisfaction in knowing that men like Holbein the Younger, erudite Erasmus, and the printer, Frobenius, had once studied here, in the thought that their spiritual presence gave intellectual integrity to Basle.

Proceeding on past the dingy cathedral he reached the municipal palace whose broad terrace overlooked the river and the city. For a time he looked meditatively off across the housetops of Basle.

Twilight, a medley of delicate pinks and violets and yellows, cast lengthening shadows on the distant, snow-capped peaks. As he watched, they became a mysterious grayish-black, shot through with faint flecks of color, as of rainbow tints at twilight. With the deepening dusk, along the sparkling Rhine a strange metamorphosis took place: its deep blue waters, dimming gradually, turned black, merging finally into the chasm engulfing them.

Johann turned up the collar of his coat and plunged his hands deep down into its comfortable pockets. He began to pace rapidly back and forth across the stone pavement of the terrace, feasting his eyes on the glow of the city lights. He hoped by violent exertion to exhaust the turbulent emotions within himself, so that he could return to his room and sleep.

Many things contributed to young Sutter's despair that night. Thurneysen, owner of the bookshop where he was employed, had reprimanded him severely that day, warning him either to pay more attention to business or he would be discharged. Furthermore, he was deeply in debt for books and beer. He was considerably depressed, as well, over the letters he had just received from home, refusing a request for funds. His father had written sharply about the danger of contracting debts. One from his grandfather, the pastor, was full of moral platitudes that had always annoyed Johann. Worst of all a letter from his mother, full of affectionate words, enclosed only one gulden and not the generous amount he had confidently expected. Their refusal to help him made him rebel against the world into which he had been born. He had always disliked the provincialism of his environment; from earliest childhood he had longed to escape its small town ways, excess of piety, its penuriousness and constant emphasis on morals and thrift. It was the reason why he had left home to work in Basle.

Johann recalled suddenly how in his adolescent years he had found relief by a boyish adulation of Napoleon. Ever since he had seen Napoleon in the full glory of his military uniform, ten years before, the memory of it was constantly with him.

He thought of it now as he strode across the terrace, deep pity in his heart for the man once the idol of his day, who had fallen so ignominiously, leaving behind him a chaotic Europe wrecked by war. He knew few even thought of Napoleon nowadays, that his amazing campaigns were almost forgotten. He was aware that a new era had begun, one in which men were absorbed in creating a new world based on *liberté, égalité, fraternité*.

He knew that freedom was what men were seeking. Indeed, it was what he himself wanted. He longed for freedom, adventure and prosperity, a position of importance somewhere in the world. He wanted power, titled admiration, boundless wealth. Now, at twenty, the dreams of his youth were stronger than before. With steadfast determination he hoped some day to attain it.

Absorbed in these thoughts Johann, stamping back and forth across the Platz, was aware that the wind was blowing sharply. He felt it sweep down from the mountains bringing with it the icy quality of snow-capped peaks.

He pulled his coat closer around his lean body. He started down the Rheinsprung toward the shabby building where he lived. As he entered his small, drab, unheated room on the third floor it seemed less inviting than usual. Shivering, he undressed by candlelight and crept into bed, only to toss restlessly for several hours. When he finally dozed off his rest was broken by strange dreams, chasing one another in senseless revolution.

The next morning, when he tried to fit them into some pattern, he recalled only a confused medley of fragments vague, chaotic, turbulent. He did remember clearly that he had been carried to some remote land across the seas, a country to which men seeking liberty and freedom were mysteriously transplanted, frantically searching for something vaguely precious, that despite herculean efforts invariably eluded him.

He was still trying to make order from the array as he entered the establishment of Emanuel Thurneysen, printer, publisher and bookdealer. He glanced at the clock; it was exactly eight.

"I'm glad to see you so punctual, Johann," said Thurneysen.

That day the drabness of his life as a clerk weighed with increasing heaviness upon Johann. He felt in the confining walls of the bookshop the same feeling of suffocation he experienced when he looked at the towering mountains closing in on Basle. But he found a relief from his cramped, poverty-stricken youth in voluminous reading. Books indeed afforded a wealth of knowledge, a spiritual satisfaction that gave him inestimable comfort. Thus the imaginative world overshadowing his true world as an underpaid clerk made him believe that the dreary routine was unreal and that what he had created within himself was the world in which he lived.

Johann was perhaps the best-informed clerk in Basle. He gleaned most of his information from the volumes on Thurneysen's shelves, for the bookseller carried a full stock of the standard authors as well as the newest books from France, Germany, Italy and England in demand at the university. He was a rapid reader and indulged in history and romance and adventure even during working hours, despite disapproval of Mr. Thurneysen. He continued to hide books in his desk and to sneak several volumes home at night.

Favorites were Voltaire and Rousseau, although he was almost equally charmed by Scott whose characters were more real to him than the men with whom he worked.

Voltaire's satire, logic and provocative verses aroused the spiritual kinship of a bosom friend. To Sutter, Voltaire was a cosmopolite, a sophisticate of fine manners and breeding to emulate. A favorite verse, one that Johann often repeated to himself, ably crystallized his search for the unattainable.

> "Last night in sleep I seemed a king,
> A crown of gold was mine . . ."

In Rousseau, on the other hand, Johann admired the paganism, the unabashed joy of life, the beauty in nature, and the cult of self-indulgence.

For several weeks Johann kept Rousseau's *Emile* under his pillow, reading it by candlelight and memorizing favorite passages. Fragments of these he repeated to himself as he fell asleep: "Passions are extremely violent; I am absolute stranger to discretion and decorum," and he would mutter drowsily to himself in that hazy borderland of sleep . . . "We have much in common."

It was this habit of day-dreaming that led to Johann's inefficiency, a habit for which Thurneysen had no sympathy. It was only out of respect to the young clerk's father, an old friend, as well as a prominent paper manufacturer with whom he had had extensive dealings, that Thurneysen restrained himself from dismissing the difficult son.

After an unusually trying day, the bookdealer gave vent to his feelings as he sat with his wife after dinner in the dining room behind the main office.

"That Sutter fellow. *Nicht gut.* All talk. Always his debts. *Gott.* And his accounts. Never do they balance."

"*Ja*, Emanuel. But he's young."

"Nonsense, Mathilde. He's unstable. He dreams. He runs after every *fraulein.*"

"*Ja*, Emanuel. Once you were young."

Thurneysen glowered. "I didn't expect you to side with him, Mathilde," he roared.

"But I like him, Emanuel," she remarked tranquilly.

"And why?" he asked.

"He's a dreamer, Emanuel, not a sound practical business man, like you, mine husband."

Mollified by the flattery, Emanuel's voice became less

rasping. "But he annoys me beyond endurance. He takes books all the time . . . and reads them when my back is turned . . . or so he thinks."

"What harm's there in that?"

"He should be working. Cleaning shelves. Checking sales. There's always plenty of work to do. Young Weber always finds some."

"Let him read, Emanuel; it's a harmless enough habit."

"I shouldn't mind so much if he had no other vices. But he has."

"What especially?"

"Spends money too freely."

"On himself?"

"For his own enjoyment, certainly. Taking girls to beer halls and picnics and sangerfests and walking parties. *Bois, chanté, aimé* . . . for these he lives."

"Let him drink, sing and make love. It's only natural."

Thurneysen lapsed into frowning silence.

Oblivious to the heated discussions about him, Johann worked languidly on. His day usually lasted from eight o'clock until dusk. Yet all he received were a few gulden for his needs and a suit of new clothes once a year.

One day five new novels came in from Paris. Joyfully Johann removed their wrappers and glanced with keen interest at the paper-bound backs.

"Sir Walter Scott. Look, some new Scott, Weber," he called to his fellow clerk.

His associate, who was bent over a ledger nearby, dropped his work and crossed the room indulgently. He was a slender youth, with dark hair and eyes, neatly, if soberly dressed. He peered closely at the volumes. "And five of them."

"Give me one." Johann reached for *Waverly*. He tucked it carefully inside his coat. "What luck to get it in French. English is hard for me."

"All good books come out sooner or later in French anyway. Or German. Take Goethe and Schiller. But poetry should be read in the original."

"But all good poets are German, Weber. I regret not being able to know the English ones, men like Byron and Keats and Shelley. Many critics consider *Don Juan* one of the finest things of recent years."

"Too modern, a year or so old. Too soon to tell if it will stand the test of time. I like the more seasoned writers," remarked Weber with a ponderous air.

"I prefer novels. Poetry is so mild."

"Like *Emile*, I suppose. I saw you reading it at the lunch hour. So did old Thurneysen."

"How could he? I had it under a newspaper."

"I don't understand why you like Rousseau, Johann. He's an atheist. Sensationalist. His characters are morally weak. His women are—well, words fail me." There was scorn in Weber's voice. "He preaches self-indulgence and freedom of conduct which no honest Swiss can condone."

"That's what I like about him," Johann replied. "He preaches liberty and equality and gives these the importance they deserve."

"Well, I haven't read him, nor do I intend to," Weber remarked. "*La Nouvelle Heloise* is nothing short of wanton, I understand. And so are his *Confessions*. He's vile. He has no sense of morals, of decency, or of man's duty to God and his country. I can't understand what you see in him."

"He believes man's first duty is to himself," said

Johann drily. "And I must say, Weber, I agree with him."

Annoyed by his friend's support of what he considered literary poison, Weber shrugged his shoulders, returned to work on his ledger.

Several hours later Thurneysen called Johann into his office, where he was sitting erect and forbidding behind an old pine desk.

"Scott's *Waverly* is missing from the shelves," he said frostily, "kindly tell me where it is."

"I don't know, sir."

"That's a lie, Johann. I saw you reading it not two hours ago."

"I . . . don't . . . know . . ." He wondered wildly how the man had seen him take it. Had Weber . . .

"No more lies, young man. I've had enough."

He reached into his desk drawer, removed a worn pocketbook and extracted two gulden. He handed them to Johann.

"I have no further need for your services," he said frigidly.

White-faced and silent, Johann brushed aside the money, bowed formally, turned, and left the room.

# CHAPTER III

## REVOLT

SOME FIFTEEN KILOMETERS southeast of Basle, situated in the lush valley of the River Wigger, a tributary of the Aar, lies the small hamlet of Aarburg. Like so many villages of a few hundred inhabitants, it is self-sufficient, subsisting on the produce of the surrounding farms. In Aarburg the world begins and ends within itself.

After six months of futile attempts to find work in Basle, Johann found employment here in a small draper's shop as a clerk. He found Aarburg inexpressibly dull. Scarcely a day's journey from the large city, for all practical purposes it might as well have been thousands of miles away, for Johann had neither the means nor the opportunity to leave. His salary was barely enough for subsistence. After he had paid for his shabby quarters in the village schoolmaster's house where he lodged and had his breakfasts, there was little left for himself. What he did have was spent on books sent direct from Paris, his sole means of escape from boredom.

Buried in the pages of historical romances, he could live freely in a world replete with exciting adventures and fascinating people, a delightful world that mitigated, although it did not alleviate, the drab life of an ill-paid clerk.

He derived from this fantastic realm a flood of incipient ambitions: the desire for wealth, for power, for a romantic marriage; the desire to lift himself from inhibiting mediocrity into a world where he could find for himself an exalted destiny of Napoleonic grandeur. The urge to escape from the treadmill circle with its poverty and restraint was becoming a mounting obsession. It was of this he thought as he clerked, as he ate his lunch of bread and hunks of Swiss cheese washed down with ale, as he drifted off to dreamful sleep late at night.

He was wise enough to conceal the turbulent spirit within himself, the dark moods, under a winsome, if somewhat labored smile. No one buying a yard of ribbon from the apparently cheerful clerk would have surmised beneath the courteous demeanor the visionary dreamer, whose pleasant blue eyes appeared to be focused on the purchaser, yet actually were not conscious of those whom he served.

Anna Dubeld, known as Nanette, who was visiting her cousins on the outskirts of town, was not aware of Johann's indifference when she stopped in to make a trifling purchase of some muslin she hardly needed. As a matter of fact she had come to the shop solely out of curiosity, because every unmarried girl in the town was talking about the handsome young man with city manners and charming ways.

Johann had been in Aarburg just long enough to have heard about every eligible girl in the vicinity and he was aware the moment he saw Nanette that the tall, dark-eyed stranger was not a resident. He knew she was the heiress from Burgdorf, twenty-three kilometers away; he had heard the schoolmaster mention her at the breakfast table as a marriageable girl with good prospects. Johann had pointedly inquired about her. He found out that Nanette's mother was a widow, more

attractive than her daughter, that she owned considerable property, including a flourishing restaurant in
Burgdorf. In fact, the Dubeld family, which included
a younger sister, had the reputation of being among the
richest and most substantial citizens in the entire canton of Berne.

As Nanette stood before him examining the muslin in
a leisurely manner, Johann looked at the Burgdorf
visitor with calculating appraisal. She was not pretty,
being tall, extremely thin, slightly stoop-shouldered,
and with thick brown hair which she wore around her
head in braids. Her eyes were her most attractive fea-
ture: they were brown, warm, deep. Her face, however,
was marred by the prominence of pitted and unsightly
teeth. The Swiss costume she wore, a blue skirt and a
white blouse embroidered in gay red yarn, was supple-
mented by a flattering and girlish flower-wreathed hat.

Her background of wealth and prestige interested
Johann. Eager for money, he was not averse to marrying for that alone. He decided to make himself agreeable
to Nanette. It was not difficult. She was a simple-
minded creature, vain, with an exaggerated idea of her
attractions.

Johann was sure that she was impressed by his graciousness, and as he talked to her about the delightful
years he had spent in Basle, he saw her face glow with
interest.

When the closing hour arrived they were still deep
in conversation and so, after he had barred the windows
and doors for the night, Johann escorted Nanette to
the house where she was staying. She was reluctant to
go inside and lingered teasingly over the parting, and
left him only after he had promised to call the next
evening. From then on, they were seen constantly to-

gether. Nanette delayed her departure for the single
purpose, according to local gossip, of being with the
romantic clerk.

Johann found in Nanette the diversions of companionship young men seek. It was not long before he
was escorting Nanette to picnics, dances, church socials,
not to mention the intimate long walks into the countryside. These jaunts became periods of loitering for hours
in isolated spots on dark nights. Johann was amazed at
the capacity of her passion. He had never met a woman
who responded so willingly.

He was annoyed at times and even repulsed by the
possessiveness of her love, yet he could not restrain her.
To escape was virtually impossible.

Before she returned home Nanette insisted that
Johann move to Burgdorf, where she assured him he
could secure work in a butcher shop at a salary better
than he earned. Indeed, the fact that he was a close
friend of Nanette Dubeld assured him a position in that
community without delay.

Burgdorf had about it none of the provincial flavor
of Aarburg. Johann found its airy streets, its neat
public plaza, its Seventh Century castle and the more
modern Fifteenth Century cathedral mildly exhilarating. But it was the River Emme that lured him, because
Burgdorf lay pleasantly placid on the banks in a manner reminiscent of Basle. He found a room in a house
near the square, and from its solitary window he could
see the waters of the Emme bounding by.

The square was pleasant, green and fragrant, with
shrubs and flowers. It had a *gemutlich* quality he liked.
Around its four sides rose the village church, the
steeply-pitched roofs of the shops, cafes and municipal
buildings. On the benches placed near its sidewalks

women with their knitting sat in gossip, observing children at mischievous play.

Even though she saw Johann every night, Nanette passed the shop where he was employed several times a day, basket in hand, ostensibly bound for the market where the women bought their fresh produce. Often she came into the butcher shop and made some inexcusable purchase for the Dubeld restaurant merely to talk to him.

He tried to avoid seeing so much of her, but she showered him with continuous invitations. He came finally to ask himself if he would marry for money a woman whom he no longer loved. It was clear that she expected it of him. As her physical charms faded he called only when she insisted vehemently. At such times he passed the evening with the entire family, usually at the restaurant where there were always crowds of people. He wished to avoid being alone with Nanette.

It was the Widow Dubeld, a vivacious brunette, capable and energetic, with whom he most frequently talked. Johann preferred her sane, unemotional outlook to the tyrannical ways of Nanette. Certainly Nanette was growing less attractive. She complained of ill health, was quarrelsome and disagreeable. She assumed that they were to be married immediately, an assumption all Burgdorf shared. Johann hardly led her to think otherwise. He merely delayed, offering his precarious finances as an excuse. The widow Dubeld gave what encouragement she could. "You're merely shy, Johann, my dear. Once you and Nanette are married . . . you'll be another man. You'll be happy, I know."

With a quiet firmness, Johann continued to elude this sympathetic widow and her tenacious daughter. "I must find a better position before I marry." He knew,

secretly, he did not love Nanette enough to marry her.
There were, of course, very pressing reasons why he
should.

A month or so later, one evening he heard footsteps
outside his door. An urgent knock followed. Johann
flung aside Rousseau's *Confessions* and threw a jacket
over the volume to hide it. "Come in."

The door opened, admitting two pompous middle-
aged men. Johann gasped slightly at the sight of such
important guests. The elder, the Reverend Samuel
Jaggi, a man whose stern manner was belied by sympathetic eyes, gave Johann a look of compassion. But his
companion, Dr. Carl Schnell, a handsome, alert-appear-
ing man and the leading attorney in Burgdorf, showed
no pity for the young man before him.

There was a long moment of awkward silence.
Johann's heart beat wildly.

"Please be seated, gentlemen," he said miserably.

They sat on the edge of an unmade bed, hats clutched
in their hands, as if fearful of contaminating them by
placing them elsewhere.

"Widow Dubeld, you know, is an esteemed member
of our church," the village pastor began. "We have
come to talk at her request."

"Nanette's mother?"

"Yes," said the Reverend Jaggi, "her mother."

From his coat pocket Lawyer Schnell drew a large
document and displayed it carefully upon his knee.

The pastor opened his mouth and seemed to grow an
inch or two in stature while he made ready for a pro-
nouncement.

"I must speak frankly to you, as father to son. You
have sinned, my son, against God, against Nanette and
my dear boy, against yourself."

Johann looked out of the window to avoid meeting the pastor's eyes, now watery from emotion.

"Yes." He paused. "I know."

"To admit sin is commendable," said the Reverend Jaggi. "However, the consequences of sin admit of no delay. You must marry Nanette within the month."

Johann Sutter turned toward him in misery and despair.

"But . . . I . . . don't . . . love Nanette . . ." he faltered. "At least, not now."

"That, my son, is of no importance. The responsibilities of parenthood alone demand it."

Johann clutched his hair with tense fingers. "I'd rather die," he muttered.

For the first time Lawyer Schnell spoke. "You prefer to go to prison?"

Johann stared with uncomprehending eyes.

"I didn't know . . . I didn't know I could be *jailed* just for that. Does Nanette . . . still insist on marrying me?"

"That I cannot say, son," said the pastor. "I talked only with Widow Dubeld. She demands the ceremony not later than a month from today."

He looked questioningly at the two men. "Is there . . . no alternative?"

"I believe not. Widow Dubeld is wealthy, as you know." Carl Schnell spoke deliberately. His manner conveyed all the respect a reputable lawyer feels for moneyed clients. "No, young man. It's the principle involved."

"But Nanette herself is penniless. I do not make enough to support her," replied Johann. "She is accustomed to luxury."

"Widow Dubeld tells me she will arrange matters," said the lawyer smoothly. "You will have a house of your own."

"Your signature on this document will indicate your readiness to marry Nanette one month from this day," continued the lawyer. He watched coldly as the young man wrote unsteadily on the line indicated, Johann August Sutter.

Johann dropped his pen hurriedly, and without speaking he walked dejectedly from the house. He crossed the square and soon reached the Emme. There he sat disconsolately on its bank, in a towering rage against Nanette, against Widow Dubeld, everyone in Burgdorf. There was no thought of compassion, nor of his duty in this crisis. He knew but one thing: he was in a serious dilemma. He looked at the turbulent Emme. Then he raised his head and looked at the hazy mountains beyond Burgdorf. They seemed to close in on his world.

He started back toward Burgdorf. He knew that he would be forced to marry Nanette. But somehow he would find the means to escape. Some day he would find relief from his agony. Somewhat revived by this consoling thought, Johann returned to his room.

For the next month he tried to avoid Nanette as much as he could. But living as close as he did he could not help seeing her almost every day. She came often into the store where Johann worked to make sundry purchases. She appeared not to notice his coldness, but radiated sweetness and affability. She spoke joyfully of the approaching wedding.

"I can't wait, Johann. I think of nothing else."

"You should stay indoors, Nanette," Johann said to

her crossly one day. Her condition was now so obvious as to prove embarrassing and he was humiliated by sly and whispered comments.

The wedding of Johann August Sutter and Anna Dubeld took place on October 24, 1826, at the Protestant church in Burgdorf. It was a simple noontime ceremony, attended only by a few witnesses, and members of Nanette's family.

After the guests had dispersed, Nanette, weak from exhaustion and excitement, sank into a chair in the pastor's study and burst into tears. Because of her condition emotional outbursts were increasingly frequent; Johann suspected that most of them were designed to focus attention upon herself. Unmoved he stood silently beside her waiting for her to calm herself. When she did not, he called the Widow Dubeld.

"Nanette insists in crying," he said indifferently. "Please try and stop her."

The widow leaned tenderly over the weeping bride. "What is it, darling?"

"I'm in agony," moaned Nanette. "It's the child."

The widow looked at her, startled. "It can't be," she said, soothingly. "Not for two months, you know. You're merely tired and excited, darling. Nothing more."

Nanette shook her head, denying her mother's words. "But I know."

They moved her to the Dubeld house and sent Johann for the midwife. After hours of endless confusion, broken by the screams of Nanette, at dawn the following day the widow called Johann into the bedroom where Nanette lay sound asleep. He came in hesitatingly. He looked reluctantly at the tiny creature. He realized as he looked at the baby, red and wrinkled, that only by an uncomfortably close margin had his boy been saved from illegitimacy—by a day.

"Your son," said the widow proudly. "Nanette has named him Johann August Sutter, Jr."

Hurriedly and half ashamed he held him. As if sensing his unappreciative attitude the infant gave a few feeble squirms. Swiftly Johann returned his namesake to the Widow Dubeld.

"I . . . don't . . . like . . . children," he replied tensely.

For Nanette, who had opened her eyes at the sound of his voice, he had not a word. The widow looked at him suspiciously. There was something strange, she thought, in a man not welcoming his first child. For a long time she had noticed how constrained John was in the presence of Nanette. Perhaps she had been unwise in insisting that the marriage take place. But Burgdorf was a small town with puritanical standards. Nanette could never have lived down the disgrace of a nameless child. It was better so. She called upon God to witness that she had done the best she knew how. Burdened with misgivings she returned the tiny bundle to Nanette, who accepted it in stoic silence. Unnoticed Johann had slipped from the room.

For the next few years Johann Sutter held himself to the treadmill, not happily, as did his neighbors, but with smoldering resentment that gradually built up a reservoir of unrest within him. He was like an incipient volcano too long confined.

Nanette, after the first shock of Johann's indifference to their marriage passed, seemed unaware of his discontent. She settled down almost contentedly to the routine of domesticity. There was an essential quality of earthiness in her that made life pleasurable. After young Johann August there came four more children.[1]

Had it not been for Frau Dubeld, John could never have survived these depressing years. She was a proud and ambitious woman and Nanette was her favorite daughter. With maternal devotion she aspired to see the young Sutters prosper. She felt confident that John, with his charm and faculty for making friends, and with the backing of the Dubeld family, might easily become a prosperous merchant and a leading gentleman in Burgdorf. She bought them property near her own on the Schmiedengasse. It was a two-story building with ample quarters for a store below and living quarters above. The store was stocked with miscellaneous merchandise and was known as August Sutter and Company. For a short time Johann's younger brother, Friedrich, who had meanwhile married Nanette's sister, Marie, was in partnership with him.

The store prospered, as the widow knew it would. Although some of its success was due to her friends, whom she persuaded to trade there, Johann attributed it solely to his own ability.

There was less time for dreaming over books than ever before. He worked industriously, although he never knew, any more than he had known when he clerked unsuccessfully in Thurneysen's bookstore, whether his accounts balanced, what he owed or what was owing him. Moreover, whenever he had money he spent it recklessly without thought of its value, buying clothes, books and luxuries for himself, Nanette and the children.

---

[1] On May 30, 1828 Anna Elisa arrived; January 16, 1830, Emil Victor; May 15, 1832, William Alphonse; and on December 26, 1833 Carl, who was to live less than a year.

Throughout Switzerland it was a time of easy money,
easy capital, ready credit, for as an aftermath of the
July Revolution in Paris free trade had been inaugu-
rated and, as a result, business flourished.

Johann rode high on the crest of this unsound commercial wave. His profits were tremendous. He found
stimulating and exciting the tang of speculation, the
activity of a steadily increasing business, the feel of
gold coins lying heavy in his pockets. Now, after six
years of marriage, he was accustomed, if not reconciled,
to life in Burgdorf.

Early in the spring of 1832, he made a short trip
with horse and wagon through the back country, selling
French ribbons, laces, silks and novelties at remote
farms and hamlets. Upon his return to Burgdorf he was
met at his door by a frightened Nanette. He kissed her
coldly on the forehead.

"Are you ill?" he asked with calloused indifference.

Sensing something amiss, he turned to enter his shop.

"Oh, Johann," she said, as she tugged pathetically
at his arm. "Don't go in. The bankers. They're waiting
for you in there."

He stopped on the threshold and glowered at her.
"Well, what do they want?"

"I don't . . . know."

"Yes you do," he said roughly. "What is it, Nan?"

"We've been robbed while you were away."

"Robbed?" he looked at her white face. "Who robbed
us?" His voice reverberated with rage.

"Your clerk, young Seelhofer. He's run off with most
of the stock and all the cash."

"*Gott!* And I trusted him. When did he leave?"

"A week ago. We have no money left, we can't pay

the banks for the goods bought on credit. Seelhofer ran out. The police can't find him anywhere."

With a curse John dropped onto the bench by the shop door. "We'll have to sell the house to pay our debts, Nan. There's nothing else."

Together they went into the store and mollified the impatient bankers by promising to pay their loans by disposing of their property. Widow Dubeld's resources were strained to meet this new demand on her purse.

Retrenching proved difficult for Johann as he had come to depend upon a bountiful table, upon choice foods and French wines. He also liked good clothes. Books, too, he must have, in fine French editions. Purse-proud and extravagant, he could not bring himself to reduce his scale of living. Inexplicably, he blamed Nanette for the dilemma they were in perhaps because she had been unable to secure from her mother funds to replace what had disappeared. Disgusted at John's carelessness in money matters, Frau Dubeld turned a deaf ear to Nanette's request. She thought Johann was old enough to manage his own affairs.

The Sutters quarreled frequently, for one thing over money, and more bitterly over the divorce of Nanette's sister, Marie, from hot-tempered Friedrich Sutter. Johann disliked arguments, especially those with his wife. He began to stay away from home to avoid them, frequenting the local taverns.

Bitter words were becoming habitual with them. Nanette was developing a sharp-tongued sarcasm that she unleashed upon the slightest provocation. Johann retaliated with scathing remarks more acid than her own, and wondered how much longer he could endure Nanette.

Johann's debts, by the turn of the year (1834), had

assumed staggering proportions. Without Frau Dubeld's aid, Johann knew and Nanette knew, they could
never be repaid. They appealed to her in vain. Coldly
she informed them that she had already considerably
diminished her own fortune in their behalf. It was all too
true, Johann admitted to himself. He also told himself
that poverty would be endurable, if he only loved Nanette.

Above all he felt the smoldering enmity of Burg-
dorfers. They felt that Johann Sutter had brought
only trouble and disgrace to the name of Dubeld and
that Nanette would be better off if he were dead.

As much to escape their idle chatter as to indulge in
the feeling of frustration to which he gave himself
these days, Johann spent long hours on the banks of
the Emme. He sat alone, a miserable, ruined man. Without love, without wealth, without ambition, what in life
was left? The thought of drowning himself mocked him
but he lacked courage to throw himself into an icy
stream. Jail was the alternative.

Days of anguish, nights made hideous by visions of
imprisonment took their toll. Johann's eyes grew heavy
and dull. Because he seldom smiled nowadays, his face
lost its former affability. He was too low-spirited even
to argue with Nanette.

"Don't be surprised if I disappear suddenly," he
told her one day.

Although he did not say so, he led her to believe he
meant suicide.

She did not reply but a moment later she flung her
arms about him. He looked at her in surprise. It had
been a year since she had shown the slightest affection,
the mainspring of her temperament.

"Don't kill yourself," she sobbed. "Think of the

children. We must raise them to be good citizens. We can, Johann. We can."

Somewhat roughly he pushed her away. "Keep still, Nanette."

He could not bring himself to tell her at that moment what was in his mind.

After long hours of deliberation, he had formulated a plan. He had harbored the outline of it for a long time. In Basle one of his friends worked in the government office that issued passports to Swiss citizens. He intended to go to him and secure a passport. He had no alternative; to leave the country or to go to jail for debt.

Already his preliminary preparations were complete. His old friend in Basle had agreed to assist. He could sell his clothes, books, his few beloved possessions for enough to pay at least part of his traveling expenses. That money would take him to Havre, where he would find some way to work his passage to New York. Once there, he would be safely beyond the law.

The night before he left he told Nanette vaguely of his plans, his desire to make a new life for himself somewhere in America. He promised to send for his family when he was established.

She wept and pleaded with him to remain, redoubling her efforts when he brusquely refused.

"But the bankers . . . what if they come to see me?" she cried.

"Reassure them. Tell them I'll pay my debts . . . that I'm away raising funds."

Unconvinced, Nanette lapsed into hysterics.

Johann slipped away and began to pack. Into a large bag he dropped his clothes, books and other personal belongings. In an old shawl he put a generous supply

SUTTER AS A YOUNG MAN

of bread and cheese. At midnight he slunk out of the
door and started on foot toward Basle. His belongings
became heavy and he made slow progress, being forced
to stop frequently to rest. Before long a team of horses
and a large produce wagon stopped. The driver offered
John a ride to Basle. He accepted gratefully, paying
for his transportation with a generous slice of cheese.

At Basle he procured a fictitious passport and bought
a third-class ticket to Havre. Toward the end of May
he found a berth as cabin boy on a small boat bound
for New York.

As he watched the French coastline recede into space,
carrying with it Burgdorf, Nanette, and his debts, for
the first time in six months he drew a long breath of
relief. A wave of confidence came over him. Ahead spread
the open sea through whose white-spumed waves the
vessel sailed.

He glanced at the mast head. From it floated an enormous pennant of red and white stripes, broken in one
corner by a square of blue, sprinkled with white stars.
It was the symbol of the United States, the thrilling
new land of freedom without end—of adventure, of
illimitable wealth. Voltaire's words rose spontaneously
to his lips:

> "Last night in sleep I seemed a king
> A crown of gold was mine."

There, in the New World, he knew, every man was king.

Weeks later, as Nanette was sitting with folded hands
beside her mother in the doorway of her house, she saw
the Chief of Police coming toward her. Nervous and
half ill from anxiety over Johann's abrupt departure,
a sudden fear swept over her. Had ... Johann ... been
caught by the police?

At the doorstep the Chief of Police stopped, and with a look of compassion he handed her an official document.

She clutched it, afraid to open it.

"I'm sorry, Nanette," he said, patting her hand in a fatherly manner. "Indeed I am." Then he moved quickly away.

Afraid to open it Nanette fell limply to the threshold, her breath coming in quick gasps.

"What is it?" asked the widow. "A letter from Johann?"

"Yes," sobbed Nanette. "The Chief of Police just brought me this note."

"Haven't you opened it?"

"No. I don't dare."

"Let me have it." Swiftly Widow Dubeld read it in silence. Her lips curled in disdain. "Listen, Nan." Slowly enunciating the words with sarcastic clarity, she read:

Berne, June 12, 1834.

Johann A. Sutter, merchant of Burgdorf, Canton of Basle, has secretly liquidated his assets and is believed to be on his way to America. He owes the sum of 6000 francs. The police are hereby notified to arrest him at sight and to notify the authorities at Berne immediately.

Widow Dubeld dropped the paper from her stiffened fingers. She knew the tragic inference of this legal notice. Death itself would have no such far-reaching implications. The stigma would last for generations.

Nanette leaned weakly against her mother, her face contorted with fear. "They'll catch him ... before he gets away ..." Her voice rose in hysteria.

"Be quiet, Nan," said the widow, putting her arms

around her daughter. "Perhaps they won't find him after all."

"If they do . . . and he . . . goes to jail . . . we'll all be disgraced for life." She pushed her mother's arms aside in a frenzy of fear. "Let me go," she screamed. Sobbing hysterically Nanette rushed to her bedroom.

# CHAPTER IV

# FABULOUS LAND

DURING THE LONG VOYAGE across the Atlantic John drew from his fellow travelers what information he could about the new country. He had no plans. He hoped ultimately, however, to reach the West coast. He found everyone highly enthusiastic about the untapped territory west of the Mississippi that had been gradually opened to colonization since the War of 1812. He had known vaguely about the purchase of Louisiana from France in 1803, but was surprised to hear that Napoleon, who had acquired it from Spain, had sold it to the United States for fifteen millions because he was afraid Great Britain might capture it when he was powerless to come to its defense.

He listened to the comments about the trans-Mississippi area, the free lands called Michigan Territory, Illinois, Indiana, Ohio, about southerly Texas, about Oregon Territory, held jointly by Great Britain and the United States, about the immense Mexican-owned California.

He heard talk of the small trading post called Chicago, of thriving St. Louis with its large German population. It was the rendezvous for trappers and traders going northwest into Oregon Territory, for merchants traveling into Santa Fe, for the explorers seeking overland routes across the Rockies to the coast.

There was discussion about Old Hickory Jackson, President of the United States; the rivalry between the affluent south with its new cotton gins and slave labor; and the agricultural west wanting cheap land, cheap goods, cheap money and cheap transportation.

He learned of Senatorial friction over "Balance of Power" between the northern and southern states, of antagonism between the commercial-minded east and the wheatlands of the west, of disputes over slave ownership. He was surprised to find that slave ownership had been prohibited north of 36° 30′ except in Missouri.

From New York in July, he started overland by way of Pennsylvania and Ohio with a group of German emigrant shipmates. One of them read incessantly a book published two years earlier in St. Gallen, by a German, Gottfried Duden. It was called *"Bericht uber eine Reise nach den westlichen Vereinigten Staaten,"* and described Duden's travels in America. The author was, at the present, engaged in founding a German colony in the farming country near St. Louis.

At St. Louis John found inexpensive lodgings at Hotel Schwyzerland, the gathering place for the local Germans as well as German-speaking Swiss. He enjoyed the gay group who spent their nights playing cards or discussing art, literature and politics. His vivacity and gracious manners won him many friends, not only among the Germans but also among the large group of French merchants.

"How would you like to go to Santa Fe with one of our caravans this spring?" one of them asked. "Pleasant trip. Seven hundred miles. Takes about six weeks."

He accepted with delight. He needed the money and yearned for adventure. It proved an invaluable experience. He learned the ways of overland caravans. He acquired a smattering of Spanish. He discovered how to drink heavily, to flirt, to dance, to drive a hard bargain. He returned to St. Louis, fired with ambition to head a caravan of his own.

During the following winter [1] he carried on an itinerant trade among the German population on the outskirts of St. Louis, handling goods he had bought while away. At the same time he tried to interest the farmers in the profits to be made in the Santa Fe trade. "There's a fortune to be had selling American goods. Santa Fe merchants have quantities of gold. The neighboring mines produce well. American-made goods are scarce."

Many to whom he talked were men who had prospered as the result of joining Duden's settlement in Warren County, Missouri and were willing to invest their surplus in the Santa Fe trade that had made many French merchants in St. Louis rich. John Sutter's fine presence and enthusiastic self-confidence won instant respect.

"Why did you leave Switzerland?" he was often asked.

Invariably he replied with an air of modesty, "I was an officer in the Swiss Guard of Charles X. The July Revolution of 1830 forced me to leave France. That's why I'm called Captain Sutter."

In the spring of 1836 John left for Santa Fe with several wagon loads of his own merchandise. But the trip proved a fiasco. New high taxes had been placed on American-made merchandise, most of the men were away fighting an Apache uprising, the gold mines were not producing well and rival caravans from Texas had begun to trade there. John drowned disappointment in a round of feverish gaiety. He drank and made love to the Mexican women, he danced and played cards. The

[1] 1835-1836.

day before he left Santa Fe he met a young French Canadian priest, Father Beaulieu, in the plaza.

Delighted to meet someone who spoke French, the priest talked to John for an hour. "The most interesting trip I've ever made in my life," he said, "was to California. It's a paradise. Not many people there. And the land! You never saw more fertile soil. Remarkable climate. Wonderful scenery. There's nothing like it anywhere."

Things were not going well with John. He had lost money at Santa Fe and to make a living he worked as a clerk in a small mercantile house at Westport, Missouri. It was a year of dreary labor. John was so unhappy that he talked to a fellow clerk about taking his life. Frightened, he urged John to try his luck further west.

With a solitary companion he set out on an Indian pony. The two travelers attached themselves for protection to a large caravan of the North American Fur Company that crossed the Rockies at regular intervals to collect furs from its trappers at isolated posts. The caravan traveled along the Platte River to Fort Laramie and on to Fort Hall, Fort Boise, and up the Columbia River to its mouth. There, just four years after he had stepped ashore at New York, John rode his Indian pony into Fort Vancouver, the largest fur post on the coast. John never forgot the great quadrangle enclosing the fort, its organization and excellent standards of living.

The settlement gave him his first taste of the exciting life of a frontier colony. He won the confidence of the chief factor, Sir James Douglas, who urged him to establish himself in California and raise wheat and livestock. "The safest, quickest way to reach there is to

take a boat to Honolulu. None go down the coast from
here," he said.

"Why not go overland?"

"November? It's the wrong time of year. No guide
would attempt it. The passes are already closed by now.
My advice, *Monsieur*, is to sail on the *Columbia* . . . She
leaves for the Islands in a short time."

Fortified by the letters of introduction Douglas gave
him, John boarded the *Columbia*. After a comfortable
passage of a few weeks he reached Honolulu. In a gala
French uniform that he had secured for a beaver pelt
from a Frenchman visiting at Fort Vancouver, John
paid formal calls on the British consul Mr. Pelly, on
the American representative, John Jones, and on the
merchant, William French, presenting his letters. Over
a period of weeks, while waiting for a boat for California, he enjoyed the social life of the Island, its
foreign colony always ready to include a charming
European in their gatherings.

John made every effort to ingratiate himself with the
merchant, William French, because he knew he had a
branch of his firm in California. He told him about his
own store in Burgdorf and, by exaggerating, made it
seem large and important.

"Perhaps we could arrange to do some business together, *Monsieur* Sutter," said Mr. French. "I'm about
to ship a cargo to our store at Yerba Buena, the Mexican port on San Francisco Bay."

"That, Sir, is my destination." John tried to restrain
the note of eagerness in his voice.

"Suppose I charter the *Clementine*? She's idling in
the harbor. I need to send a cargo to Sitka, as well.
The *Clementine* could go there first and catch the pre-

vailing winds to carry her south. Will you act as super-
cargo, *Monsieur* Sutter?"

"With pleasure. But please call me Captain Sutter.
It was my rank with the Swiss guards in France."

"Speaking French as you do, Captain Sutter, you'll
enjoy Sitka tremendously. The Russian colony there
uses French a great deal. A gay crowd. I'll give you
letters to Governor Kouprianoff in charge of the trading
post. He is in complete charge of the Russian-American
Fur Company's holdings in the Pacific. His territory
includes their little colony in California, called Fort
Ross. It's just north of Yerba Buena, about twenty
miles."

Sitka proved to be all that William French had
promised. An outpost with few contacts, the Russians
welcomed the gallant Captain Sutter. He flattered the
ladies and joked with the men. For a month, it was a
gay tonic to his growing self-esteem. With reluctance
he watched the rocky cliffs of the Sitka coast disappear
from sight as the *Clementine* with her master, Captain
Blinn, John Sutter, two German mechanics, ten
Kanakas, a bull dog and a load of merchandise for
Yerba Buena, set a course south toward California.[1]

Her sails puffed to tautness, the ship skimmed down
the coast as blithely as a stiff-winged sea gull. She was
a low-hung schooner, trim and fast; freighted heavily,
she rode the Pacific with equilibrium and grace.

So far the trip had exceeded his wildest expectations.
Good luck had played directly into his hands. In Honolulu he had made legions of friends. King Kamehameha
III had been especially gracious. He had supplied John
with the ten Kanakas now aboard the *Clementine*, as
well as a flattering letter of introduction to Juan Al-

[1] The fall of 1839.

varado, the governor of Alta California. John smiled to himself as he thought it was all a matter of a little stage acting. He accomplished it by creating the belief that he was a person of standing and importance in Europe, that he had been in the French army, a fact somewhat borne out by the distinguished manners he had thought it wise to adopt. And the worn French uniform had played its part. No one suspected that he had purchased it for a beaver skin. It lent pomp to its wearer and credence to the general belief in his military background. The officials at Fort Sitka had been especially impressed by its gold braid.

Yes, he mused, a little perfidy was more than justified by the deference paid him as an officer. And if he made a pretense of affluence, without having more than a few coins in his pocket, that, too, was justified. Pretense was an easy road to success. Had it not won for him the esteem and confidence of no less a man than William French, the leading merchant of Honolulu? So much so, in fact, that he had entrusted him with a valuable cargo of goods to be sold at Sitka and a commission to purchase other goods to be sold in California.

It amazed him to discover how he had only to smile and bow, and say a few flattering words, to win friends. Out here the chances of meeting anyone from Switzerland who might know about him were relatively slight. In fact he seldom thought of his own land or Nanette, or of his children, or of the warrant he suspected his wife had written him about that had been issued for his arrest. He had sent word to Nanette, at the time he landed in New York, promising to return some day when he had made enough to pay his debts. He had given her no return address, and so he had not received a reply. Widow Dubeld, he knew, would provide.

The patter of bare feet crossing the deck made John turn suddenly. He saw Manawitta approach. She was the captivating Kanaka girl he had brought with him from Honolulu. "Come here, Mana," he called. There was a subtle possessiveness in his manner.

As she moved gracefully toward him, he looked at her with absorption mixed with desire. Carefree, spontaneous, cheerful, she walked languorously, with the measured poise of Islanders, on small, bare feet, without apparent effort. She was a delicately-built creature, with black hair, yet fair-skinned. Her father had been an English captain on a whaling ship that called frequently at Honolulu. From him, too, came her blue eyes, brilliant under thick, black eyebrows.

Although but sixteen, she had, in accordance with the Island custom that favors youthful unions, already been married two years to a stalwart, brown-skinned youth, whom John called Kanaka Harry. He was an indolent creature and made no objections to the attentions the white man showered on his wife. In fact, he seemed to consider it a mark of distinction. With the lax attitude toward marriage prevalent in the Islands, John was in hearty accord. In a way it justified his feelings for Mana, toward whom he had had a European's dislike for the more permanent aspect of marriage. It was enough for him that Kanaka Harry bore him no ill will. He gave it little thought, preferring rather to drift into that placid acceptance of life characteristic of the frontier.

Now, as Mana dropped to the deck, near his chair, and crossed her legs beneath her, he was conscious only of her beauty. Masses of black hair hung to her waist, touching the deck behind her. From her ears hung small pieces of pink coral, crudely carved in the shape of tiny fish. A necklace similarly carved was wound around her neck. She was clad only in a loose wrapper, of a coarse native material, of brilliant coral color, interwoven with a design of soft green banana leaves. She was well-mannered, having spent three years at a Methodist school in Honolulu, at her father's expense.

"Are we almost there, Senor Juan?" she asked in Spanish. She was inordinately proud of her linguistic ability.

"Almost, Mana," he replied.

They sat for several moments without talking. Silence was somewhat habitual with them for John's knowledge of the Kanaka tongue, which Mana preferred to use, was negligible. Together they watched the infallible signs of land appear: masses of brown kelp drifted by; occasional flocks of land birds moved lazily through the sky. Presently she rose, stretched herself languidly, and sauntered off to the quarters she occupied below decks with her Kanaka friends.

John was about to retire to his own cabin when he saw the master of the *Clementine* leaning over the ship's rail. Captain Blinn was observing the depth and color of the seaweed. He was unusually companionable and jovial for a Scotsman, being portly, red-faced, and with the countenance of a benign Neptune. An excellent sailor, he felt completely at home upon the sea. He had run away from his home in Glasgow at the age of ten and shipped as a cabin boy. Now, at fifty, there were few parts of the world he had not visited, few sights he had not seen. He addressed John. "Within twenty-four hours, I can safely promise ye." He spoke with a rich, deep brogue.

"We'll be in Yerba Buena?"

"Maybe m' lad, with way m' darlin' *Clementine's* acting."

The captain burst lustily into song.

"Oh m' darlin', oh m' darlin', oh m' darlin' *Clementine*," he roared with delight. "Ye know the song, don't ye, John?" he asked. "Micht be the most popular in America. I've heard sailors and trappers and explorers sing it time and again."

"Never heard it before," replied John. He was unimpressed by it, or was it the strange sound of words colored by the captain's Scotch brogue? The English language was still difficult for him to understand at times, even after living in the States five years.

John's unconcealed lack of enthusiasm dampened the captain's spirits. He took from his pocket a blackened pipe and began to fill it with tobacco from a worn deerskin bag.

"Yes, *Señor* Sutter," he said, "tomorrow, I promise ye, we'll be dining on chili con carne at the home of *Señor* Nathan Spear."

"What's that?" asked John hopefully. He liked good food and he was now thoroughly tired of the jerked beef, dried salmon and hard bread on which he had subsisted since leaving Sitka.

"It's an excellent Spanish dish," replied Captain Blinn, who was not a connoisseur of good food, and so, overrated Spanish cookery. "It's meat, usually beef, cooked with red hot peppers. Chili con carne's served everywhere along the coast. It's the national Spanish food."

John shrugged his shoulders with a gesture of disdain.

"Are there no European cooks in Yerba Buena? I have a craving for a dish of *sauerbraten*, the kind we have in Switzerland—beef cooked in red wine," he explained, noticing the puzzled look on the captain's face.

"*Señor* Sutter, ye forget. Yerba Buena is most a wilderness. Only a few families. And at the most five or six houses. Shacks, most of 'em. As for European cooks . . ." the captain's voice trailed off into noisy laughter.

"But Admiral Kouprianoff, up at Sitka, told me it was an important place."

"That's because the good mon was niver there."

"Maybe not. But he told me it had several stores and fine houses," protested John.

"Russians are inveterate liars," said Captain Blinn. "It's high time, my dear friend, you found out. Liars, all of them, as you'll find out, my good friend. So they told you Yerba Buena was a fine place? Why, there's nothing there worth mentioning. A few houses, one store . . . the dilapidated mission across the sand dunes . . . an old wreck of a Spanish fort."

"But I've heard glowing accounts of California ever since I landed in New York."

"When was that?"

"Five years ago."

Captain Blinn shot a look of admiration at his passenger. He had all of a Scot's respect for determination and grit.

"Five years . . . it's a long long time. And now you're almost there. Well, I only hope you'll like it, m' lad."

A puzzled look crossed John's face.

"But everyone tells me it's the most fertile land in the west . . . especially along the Sacramento and the American Fork."

"So that's where you're bound for, m' lad? Well,

several have been there before you. That rascal of a Russian, Otto von Kotzebue tried it . . . but didn't get far."

"I know," interrupted John, "I've read his account of it. The governor of Sitka showed it to me."

"Then there was that stiff-necked English fellow, Sir George Simpson. And Belcher, who made a map of the Sacramento, two years ago in 1837. He didn't like it, I've been told."

"I have a copy of his map," said John, a look of satisfaction on his face.

"They weren't the first either. . . . Old Father Fortuni poked his nose up the river in 1811; he and Father Abella of Mission San Jose. The pious old chaps named it for the holy sacrament . . . *Rio del Santo Sacramento.* That's a terrible name for a river . . ." he sniffed with disgust.

"Are you by any chance a Catholic, m' lad?" asked the captain suspiciously. He had all the antipathy of a staunch dissenter for those who professed the Catholic faith, and his manner, hitherto warm, grew somewhat constrained as he waited for John to reply.

John sat for a moment in silence. An atheist, he did not intend to jeopardize his standing with the captain, so he said noncommittally, "Most Swiss, as you know, are Calvinists." It was a safe remark, one destined not to stir the Scotsman to ecclesiastical debate.

Captain Blinn failed, however, to note the ambiguity in John's remark, and he continued, "The Padres have their good points, of course. Not that I like them," he added hastily, as if afraid that John might wrongly evaluate his remarks. "For m'self . . . I'll take the trappers. There's real men for you. Men like Jedediah Smith, who crossed the mountains in the dead of winter

ten or twelve years ago. Just to hunt and trap along
the Sacramento. Injuns well nigh killed him, though.
But him and the Hudson's Bay men got all the furs they
could carry. Made 'em a fortune in gold."

"That's what I came for, too," John said enigmati-
cally.

Memories of the debt he still owed made his eyes grow
lightly moist. But he put these disturbing thoughts out
of his mind as the loquacious captain rambled on.

"Yes, m' lad. I know most of the foreigners out on
the coast. I've been up and down California for years.
I've been haulin' goods to the Islands well nigh twenty
years. Fine men, trappers. One of the best was Sylvest
Pattie. From Kintuck, I believe. Pattie came here . . .
let me think . . . about ten years ago. . . . Everyone liked
him. . . . Saved 'em from the smallpox plague."

"Smallpox? How did he save them?" asked John
aghast.

"Pattie vaccinated 'em. A new-fangled way. Treated
twenty thousand. Acted like a kind of magic. Hundreds,
most of 'em mission Indians, had died before he got
here. But he saved thousands." A sudden smile en-
livened the naturally wide mouth of Captain Blinn's
face.

After a brief pause, John inquired, "What are you
smiling at?"

"The Padres. That was a neat trick Pattie played.
The rascal asked the priests to pay him in gold for the
medicine."

"What was wrong with that?"

"Who ever heard a priest paying gold for anything?
But Pattie made 'em. . . ." The captain roared with delight. "First they tried to get him to take hides for the
cure. Pattie refused. He held out for gold. Yes, John,

SAN FRANCISCO BEFORE THE GOLD RUSH

he insisted on gold. But the joke was on him. You see, m' lad, out here, cowhides is all the gold we have. Only the demned trapper didn't know it."

A sharp wind had come up. To avoid it the two men got up and moved over to some packing boxes piled in a more secluded corner of the foredeck.

"What is your opinion of the Californians?" asked John respectfully.

"They mean well enough, *Señor* Sutter," said the captain. "But they're lack . . . a . . . dasic . . . cal." He fumbled clumsily over the long word; it was one he seldom used. "Too many fine words, m' lad. That's what I mean. Words, nothing but words . . . I can't fathom it. . . ." He shook his bronzed head. "*Dolce far niente,*" some people call it.

"*Dolce,*" repeated John, obviously mystified.

The captain emitted a gruff laugh. "You'll hear the words often enough in California. It's their national motto. Someone ought to paint it on the Mexican flag."

"Tell me, please, what it means."

"It's sweet to do nothing, that's what it means," roared Captain Blinn, slapping his thighs. "Remember. I've warned ye. And it's all ye need to know about them Californians."

"Is that true of all the people? The women too?"

"*Señors* is troublesome enough, m' lad, but *señoras* . . . heaven help us. Too brimful of fire. I've warned ye, m' lad. Don't be fooled by them. Imps of Satan, all of them . . . or worse." Captain Blinn shut his bulging Scotch lips in a firm line with the finality of closing a book. "Yer young, John Sutter, and I'll wager, attractive to women?" He jerked his thumb in the direction of Mana, who, having finished her siesta, had reappeared and now sat cross-legged on the deck nearby.

"Tell me, what'd ye intend to do in California?"
The captain looked quizzically at John.

"I want to establish a Swiss colony somewhere along
the Sacramento."

"Why?"

John looked dreamily off into space. "It's difficult to
explain. The idea came to me suddenly one night at
Fort Vancouver. We were sitting around the table.
Governor Douglas began talking about California. I
could not get what he said out of my mind. In fact, I
could almost see California. I began to long to go there.
One night I even dreamed I had founded a colony on
the coast. The idea still haunts me all the time."

"A Swiss colony, heh? I wonder what Governor Alvarado will say to that. Well, many's the foreigner who
has an eye on California. Take the English. Why do
ye suppose all these trappers come here? And the
Hudson's Bay Company's men swarm up and down the
coast like agile fleas. To annex it, of course. We British
are born colonizers," he announced sententiously,
thumping his chest. "Vancouver knew a good country
when he came here less than forty years ago. The
French want it, too. They've been sending fleets here
since the days of La Perouse. Let me see. He was here
in 1786, the first Frenchman to land on this coast. Yes,
France covets California to replace Canada and Louisiana—not that I blame her. She needs and wants new
colonies. Yes, France bitterly regrets the day she lost
Canada and especially Louisiana. What a fool Napoleon
was to sell all that fine land to the United States. And
for only four cents an acre," he sniffed with a Scot's
appreciation of a good bargain. "But ye and I know,
*Señor* Sutter, that Mexicans are the worst rulers on

the face of the earth. I, for one, expect, in the near future, to see California a British colony."

"Aren't the Americans interested in the coast?"

"Them Bostons, I suppose you mean, m' lad? Some, I warn ye, are as canny as a Scot. But they don't mean business. No one out here takes them seriously. They come to trade, that's all. Once they have a cargo aboard they all head home in those crazy whaling ships. They don't intend to colonize. Money's what they're after."

The captain rose, squinted at the weather and, with a wave of his hand, disappeared below.

Left alone with his thoughts, John strolled the foredeck of the *Clementine*. In his mind a picture of California began slowly to formulate. Colored inevitably by Captain Blinn's comments, yet it had in it much that he had gleaned elsewhere. Another few hours and he would set foot on the hallowed soil of California.

He went to find Mana who was stretched out comfortably on the sunny spot on the deck. Together they stood for a time near the rail. Land was faintly visible, a slender line, ephemeral, softly bathed in haze against the sky. John pointed toward it. "California, Mana," he said in a low voice, throaty with emotion, "*our* California. The land we shall call home."

She clutched his arm; tears flooded her eyes. Our own California!

He took her hand in his own and squeezed it. "To live with you always in California, Mana. That is my one great desire."

As he neared the Bay, Captain Blinn eyed its narrow channel queasily. It was the most treacherous gateway he had ever met. "The Devil's Gate," he scoffed. "Bonny name for a death trap. Scylla and Charybdis at their worst. Might as well be caught in lobster's claws. Many's the ship that's gone down trying to get through." He swore volubly. The free flow of invectives served like a tonic to brace him for the task ahead. "But we'll make it, you and I, Oh m' lady *Clementine.*" The ship lurched violently to larboard, as a sudden gust caught her, as if to dispute his words. "Come about," shouted the captain, "we've missed the channel. Try again." White-crested waves pounded heavily at the *Clementine's* sides; the roar of mounting winds drowned all but the captain's voiced commands. "Heave to. Reef the mains'l." The *Clementine* continued to heave and pitch crazily under the strain. Gears creaked and groaned. Boxes and bales stored on the upper deck clattered noisily. Sailors darted from sail to sail, obedient to the captain's orders. A chain, breaking loose, crashed against the rail. But the terrifying sound of the wind pounding against the sails, lashing and tearing at them with ever increasing force, dwarfed all other sounds.

Defying the elements, the *Clementine* tore swiftly through the waters; for an instant she seemed determined to throw herself wantonly upon the cliffs.

Perspiration dripped off John's white face as he watched. A nameless terror, as of the unknown, poured coldly through his veins. He focused his gaze on the narrow entrance that led into the Bay. The *Clementine* was moving directly toward it. But the closer she came the faster moved the ship. John grew rigid with fear. Death, disaster . . . lay ahead.

On and on sped the madcap ship, lunging swiftly ahead. Sheer, sharp granite rocks loomed ominously beyond, like impenetrable walls. Beside them, the *Clementine* seemed a toy, fragile, made of wood and canvas, buffeted mercilessly by the elements. Then Captain Blinn changed his course; the rocks, which had been directly ahead of the vessel, suddenly appeared off starboard, a clear passage was visible opening into the bay and the *Clementine* passed safely through. A moment later she glided into calmer water.

Sweat dripping from his forehead, Captain Blinn came over to John. He shook a clenched fist defiantly at the channel behind him.

"Ye kin thank yer God an' the angels," he said melodramatically. "Without 'em, the *Clementine* and all aboard would be greetin' Davy Jones."

Speechless with relief, John was too exhausted to bestow on Blinn's skillful seamanship the praise it deserved.

As the *Clementine* sailed on into the quiet waters of the vast harbor on which lay Yerba Buena, John looked curiously around. The bay, sparkling and azure, was bathed in lucent sunlight. Along the rocky shores hundreds of sea gulls nested. Beyond sloped tawny hills, gaily patched here and there with wild flowers, red Indian paint brush, blue and yellow lupin, orange poppies, and soft gray sagebrush.

On the right, nearby, stood the mud-colored walls of the old Spanish fort. Roofless and a prey to the elements, its crumbling adobes were only partially concealed by patches of weathered whitewash. Like an ungainly octopus, it spread its unsightly mass along a sunny knoll overlooking the bay. As the *Clementine* moved by, the guns of the venerable stronghold emitted two guttural booms, followed by two puffs of smoke. Captain Blinn dipped his colors courteously in reply. "That's the old fort. Most of it's in ruins. The Spaniards erected it some sixty years ago." [1]

[1] 1776.

"Where is the mission?" inquired John. "I can see no signs of it."

"Just across the hill. Everyone here calls it Dolores. The fathers built it about the same time. They named it *Los Dolores de San Francisco de Asis*, after some old saint in Italy. The name's stuck to San Francisco Bay ever since."

Rounding a bend in the bay, by noon, Captain Blinn, after a series of skillful maneuvers and considerable foul language, brought the *Clementine* safely to anchor. Lined up on the shore a few hundred yards away, John observed two officers and an escort of fifteen soldiers, holding cocked guns.

"Ship ahoy," called a voice in broken English, recognizing the British flag drooping lazily from the mainmast.

"The *Clementine*. Of Honolulu. In from Sitka. In distress," called Captain Blinn, in passable Spanish, hands cupped to his lips.

"You can't stay here. It's a closed port. Go on to Monterey. Get a permit to land. Then come back."

"But I must stay now. We're out of water," lied the captain courageously.

"It's a closed port. Governor Alvarado's orders. No one can land," shouted the Mexican official, a shade more leniently, for he had, by now, observed Mana standing on the foredeck.

"We can't make it. The ship's leaking badly," sang back Captain Blinn, winking at John as he talked.

John was fully aware that Captain Blinn was attempting to defy the Mexican law which made Yerba Buena a closed port to all foreign ships, except in emergencies, and that he intended to put his passengers ashore without going first to the capital of Monterey for a permit.

"We're coming aboard," the official tartly replied. A sound as of splashing oars came clearly across the water.

Presently a tall Mexican officer, a swarthy-faced individual, shabbily dressed but bedecked with ornate medals, climbed the rope ladder up the side of the *Clementine*, saluted Captain Blinn ostentatiously, gave Mana a lascivious glance, then swaggered over to John.

"*Buenos dias, Señor*," he said courteously.

John returned the formal Spanish greeting with equal decorum.

The official's spurs clicked sharply. He turned again to Captain Blinn. "Who's your distinguished passenger, captain?" he asked.

"A Swiss. John Sutter."

"What does he want?"

"He has a cargo of goods consigned to William French's agent at Yerba Buena. He has letters to Alvarado. Important ones, he said."

At mention of the governor's name, the official bowed. "You have other passengers," he said, indicating the two German mechanics and the ten Kanakas, who were listening intently to the Spanish words they could not understand. "And a dog, I see." He kicked a spurred boot viciously at Bull, sniffing inquisitively at his heels, then raised his eyebrows ever so slightly at Mana.

"You may land for twenty-four hours," he said condescendingly, "since you have letters to Governor Alvarado. Long enough to take on supplies and caulk the ship." Saluting, he descended the ladder into the boat manned by Indians and was rowed to shore.

The Indian skiff glided with a slow rocking movement over to the anchored *Clementine*. With alacrity John and Captain Blinn climbed aboard. Ten minutes later the skiff reached the official landing place known as the *embarcadero* and was pulled up on the beach by the Indian crew.

The Mexican official was waiting for them and in a pompous manner offered to accompany them on a tour of the Spanish port. They accepted immediately and with their guide started slowly along the waterfront.

Consternation spread over John's face at the dreary settlement stretched out before them.

Despite Captain Blinn's unflattering comments about Yerba Buena, he was not prepared for the mounds of sand and dirt, the shabby dwellings, the air of isolation and discomfort, apparent everywhere. Bewildered, he looked dejectedly around him.

"This is *Punta del Embarcadero*," announced the Mexican officer with an air of simulated grandeur, indicating the muddy bank where they had landed. Then he waved a gloved hand importantly toward five or six tiny houses half hidden by mounds of sand, dirt, weeds and debris.

"Welcome, *Señor* Sutter, to *El Paraje de Yerba Buena*."

"In English, it means the Place of Mint," observed Captain Blinn. "I'd as lief call it the place of flies." He brushed an insistent buzzer vigorously off his large nose as he talked, then another and another.

John, however, was looking unhappily at the panorama around him and so failed to hear what the captain said. On the northern tip of the small cove rose a range of low hills, several hundred feet high, which John, accustomed to the grandeur of the Swiss mountains and the vast height of the Rockies, found unimpressive.

"That tall one is Loma Alta," explained the Mexican, mistaking for admiration the puzzled look on John's face. "From its peak we can see every ship the moment it enters the main harbor."

Courteously, for John never allowed his inner feelings to mar his fine manners, the Swiss traveler murmured a few apt words of praise.

Flattered, the Mexican escort straightened his sword, then stood more erect, as if to impress through his personal appearance the Swiss guest with the superlative caliber of the Mexican official world.

"Come and see the town," he said to John.

They walked along the waterfront toward a group of five or six one-story adobe and frame houses.

"Don't forget, I warned ye, John," whispered Captain Blinn as he trailed behind. "It's one of the worst holes I was ever in." He brushed and slapped and cursed as the flies swarmed around his face.

It was only a few steps to a small dwelling whose door stood ajar.

"That's *Casa Grande*—William Richardson's house. He's in charge of commerce at the port, I understand. He's the man for you to meet," said Captain Blinn, between flies. "He handles all kinds of produce."

"What produce do you mean? Can anything grow here?" John looked at the mounds of gray sagebrush, scrawny, ill-nourished.

Captain Blinn's sides shook with mirth. "Don't look so dejected. Fortunately California's not all like Yerba Buena. Most of it's rich, yes, rich as Croesus. Enormous quantities of hides and tallow and beef come from the missions and *ranchos* around the bay."

They stopped before the open door of Richardson's

house and Captain Blinn read the terse note pinned to the doorframe. "Gone to Sonoma. Back tomorrow."

Captain Blinn turned thoughtfully toward John. "We must see him. We'll wait till he gets back. He's the man to supply you with what you need for your new colony. That is, if you still intend to start one."

The scoffing words had the effect of restoring at once John's dwindling self-confidence.

"I intend to start the moment I obtain a permit from His Excellency, Governor Alvarado," he replied.

They moved slowly on to the next building, a small frame structure that resembled a store rather than a house. Playing near it was a white baby about a year old. The Mexican captain patted the infant's curly head, then leaned over and kissed her on the forehead. "Come, Rosalia," he said, lifting her in his arms and carrying her to John.

She leaned toward him, gurgling happily. "She's Rosalia Leese, the first white child born in Yerba Buena," he told John.

The three men went on down the dusty road, until they reached another small edifice. "That is the house of A. B. Thompson," said the Mexican impressively. "John Fuller built those two over there." He pointed a gnarled forefinger at them. Before the smallest hung some carcasses of beef, black with flies. "He's the local butcher," joked Captain Blinn. "I see he sells meat garnished with flies."

John looked with a shudder at the unsightly array of overripe meat, darkly flecked with buzzing flies. Even after years spent in frontier camps he was still fastidious, and found Yerba Buena far worse than he had anticipated.

"Here's where William Sturgis Hinckley and Nathan

Spear live," said the Mexican. He stopped at a store bearing the sign: General Merchandise. "He owns a launch and several Indian crews. He rents them out when they're not in use. They handle all the produce around the Bay."

The trio looked inside: the store was empty, as was the adjoining house of the Frenchman, Victor Prudhomme, and the wooden structure used by the Hudson's Bay Company trappers and traders when in port.

"Is there a fiesta somewhere today?" asked Captain Blinn. He was well versed in Mexican customs, having visited the ports of Monterey and San Diego many times before.

"*Sí, Señor.* At Mission Dolores," replied the officer. He pointed to a dusty road that ran across sand dunes covered with stunted sagebrush. "Everyone's there."

A few babies were tended by Indian nurses. Several Mexican women, some slinking curs, cackling hens and mangy cats moved about. "They'll have returned at dusk, *Señor*," added the officer. "By then they'll have have had all the *aguardiente* they can swallow," he said with a tinge of humor in his voice.

"Would you not like to join them?" asked Captain Blinn, eager to be rid of him. "We have detained you quite long enough. Besides we should get back to our ship; she needs repairs, you know."

At the *embarcadero* they parted with bows and mutual protestations of admiration and goodwill. Even before John and Captain Blinn had boarded the *Clementine*, the Mexican officer and his solders were kicking up clouds of dust as they galloped away across the sand dunes toward the fiesta.

## CHAPTER V

# MEXICAN MONTEREY

GOVERNOR JUAN BAUTISTA ALVARADO stood curiously watching at the open window of his house overlooking Monterey Bay one day in early July.[1]

He was little more than five feet tall, with a massive head, thick with chestnut-colored hair, worn parted on one side and heavily oiled, deep-set gray eyes, a sharp aquiline nose and a firm full mouth and strong chin. Somewhat corpulent, he carried himself with the dignity commensurate with his office.

He accepted his gubernatorial responsibilities philosophically, giving to them a devotion that had won for him the confidence of the majority of Californians. For he had fought their battles valiantly, striving even before he became governor to achieve for them independence from their tyrannical parent, Mexico. This he had accomplished in 1836, at the age of twenty-five. Independence, however, had been of only short duration. With a political acumen far beyond his years, Alvarado soon realized that Californians were not yet ripe for self-government, and that they would not work harmoniously together. So, under his skilled guidance the land became once more part of Mexico, being known as the Department of Alta California.

The youthful governor watched with interest several figures moving slowly along the dusty road that led from the plaza of Monterey to the low, white-washed

[1] 1839.

adobe set on a knoll above the town. Long, sturdy, and commodious, his house with its broad front porch supported by columns placed at symmetrical intervals looked over the houses below, and across the sand dunes, their contours dramatically shadowed against the sky. Of all the houses in Monterey, his was the most pretentious.

Drawing away from the window, he addressed his secretary. "Finally they're coming. He said he would be here promptly at ten," he remarked with annoyance, "but it's long past that time."

The secretary stifled a mild yawn. "Yes, Your Excellency," he replied. "What does he want?"

"Like most men who come here, favors."

"To be expected," commented the secretary. He took from his desk several letters. "Have you seen these, Your Excellency?"

"What are they?"

"Letters of Introduction. Some twenty or more. Your tardy caller brought them from Honolulu. One's from John C. Jones, American Consul. Another's from the British Consul, Pelly. Here's one from James Douglas at Fort Vancouver, and a note from Governor Kouprianoff at Sitka. They all speak highly of Sutter; he must be all right."

Alvarado turned his back. "I've glanced through them. David Spence gave them to me yesterday at the Fourth of July celebration at Larkin's. I talked to Sutter. I rather like him."

"Why did he come to Monterey, Your Excellency?"

"Wants some land, I believe. I think for a French colony."

"But I thought he was Swiss. The letters say so," replied the secretary. He felt it incumbent upon himself to protect the all-too-amiable governor from potential imposters.

"I trust he is. Especially after that unpleasant affair with the French at Vera Cruz." His thoughts reverted to the sudden declaration of war on Mexico a few months before by the French and the unexpected bombardment of the port. He had heard rumors, too, that the French had designs upon California, enough so that in June the *Comandante* of Alta California, Mariano Vallejo, had issued a proclamation warning the people to be on their guard against French visitors. "I may be mistaken, perhaps he said the Swiss army. But he was wearing a French uniform. Here he comes now."

The secretary moved toward the window and peered over the governor's shoulder. "That's David Spence with him. And . . . And what is that?" He nodded toward a group immediately behind Sutter.

"They're Kanakas. Sutter brought them from Honolulu. He got them from the King. Look at that woman," he said motioning toward Mana. "There's something there." Alvarado spoke with all the connoisseur's appreciation.

"No Kanaka can compare with our Monterey *señoritas*," scoffed the secretary.

"Don't be too sure, young man." Alvarado crossed the room, and seated himself decorously in the gubernatorial chair.

An Indian servant opened the door to John Sutter, David Spence, the two German mechanics, then motioned to the others to remain outside.

Alvarado rose and bowed with the proverbial Spanish greeting: "*Mi casa es su casa, Señor.*" He observed with surprise that the French uniform his foreign guest was wearing was richly decorated with gold braid. It was, he also saw, topped by a broad beaver hat, obviously of English origin. By his side hung a gilt-handled sword. "It is indeed a pleasure, *Señor* Sutter, to welcome you to our land."

John acknowledged the courteous speech with a graceful bow. He was glad now that he had a passable command of Spanish.

"You desire, I believe, to make your home here with us?" Alvarado spoke with genuine hospitality, "You're a member of the holy Catholic church, I presume?"

John hesitated briefly. "Yes, Governor Alvarado." He would do or say anything to achieve his goal. "A good Catholic, Your Excellency."

Face aglow with cordiality, Alvarado continued, "*Amigo mio*, what then can I do for you?"

Warmed by the governor's attitude, John spoke without constraint.

"My wish is to settle in the interior of California. Near *El Rio del Santo Sacramento*. I hope to found a colony." He indicated his escort, loitering on the veranda. "I have some colonists with me, you see." He flashed the governor a flattering smile. "As a matter of fact, I have come, Your Excellency, to beg from you a land grant. A large one, if you please."

The governor gave him a look of gratitude. "We need settlements in the interior. The Indians are growing more surly and wild. Ever since the missions were sold out, five years ago, a wave of lawlessness has swept over Alta California."

"I heard about it in Yerba Buena."

"Yes, bands of them raid *ranchos*, steal horses, and maraude settlers around the bay. The natives in the Sacramento Valley are the most lawless of all. Most men want land near the coast. Why, *amigo mio*, do you prefer the interior?"

"I've heard about the river country," said John with one of his alluring smiles, "I like the wilderness and Indians. No, Your Excellency, that does not disturb me."

"They're dangerous, I warn you."

"Not for a soldier," said John, drawing himself up proudly. "I've lived among them ever since I reached America. It may be flattery, but I understand them."

"Your request comes as somewhat of a surprise, *Señor* Sutter. You see, we have so few European visitors. You are a Swiss, I believe? *El Comandante*, Vallejo, in charge of the frontier, does not welcome foreigners. I need time to think over what you propose. There's my uncle, Mariano Vallejo, at Sonoma to be considered." He rose and looked out of the window.

John let his eyes roam around the room with undisguised interest at the bare plaster walls hung with flags and images of saints. All that he had heard about Juan Bautista Alvarado, he told himself, was true. But there was even more that he had not heard about the forceful personality, almost Napoleonic in stature, before him.

He knew, as he studied him, that Alvarado was a patriot. He loved his land, his people; he strove to improve their lot. Thomas Oliver Larkin and David Spence had told him fabulous tales about the governor; how he had been brought up by the priests; how he had read every book he could lay his hands on; how he governed his country by precepts of scholastic wisdom.

John's glance fell on a heavy parchment scroll, with bold Spanish lettering that hung above the governor's chair.

LIBERTY, PEACE, AND UNION ARE THE TRUE INTELLI-
GENCE BY WHICH OUR DESTINY IS TO BE GOVERNED. LET
US PRESERVE INDISSOLUBLE THIS UNION—THE SACRED
ARK IN WHICH LIES ENSHRINED OUR POLITICAL REDEMP-
TION. THE TERRITORY OF ALTA CALIFORNIA IS IMMENSE.
ITS COASTS ARE BATHED BY THE GREAT OCEAN WHICH,
BY PLACING US IN COMMUNICATION WITH THE NATIONS
OF THE WORLD, GIVES ENCOURAGEMENT TO OUR INDUS-
TRY AND COMMERCE, THE FOUNTAINS OF WEALTH AND
ABUNDANCE. THE BENIGNITY OF OUR CLIMATE, THE
FERTILITY OF OUR SOIL ARE PRIVILEGES CONFERRED BY
THE OMNIPOTENT. LONG LIVE THE NATION. LONG LIVE
LIBERTY. LONG LIVE UNION.

The governor was speaking again. "The land I will
grant you. But only when you are a citizen of California. Not before. You must remain here a year at
least. You must show me that you can live harmoniously
with the Indians, that you are capable of establishing
a colony. Come back a year from today. At that time,
if you still want to make your home with us, all the land
you want in the Sacramento Valley will be yours."

"One year from today," said John, "I shall return."
He rose to depart, when the governor indicated by a
sign of the hand that he was to remain longer. "My
friend, David Spence," he said, indicating the Scotsman who had remained silent during the interview,
"tells me you would like a permit to land and transact
business with French and Company at Yerba Buena.
Well here it is." As he talked he scribbled hastily on a
slip of paper, then handed it to John. The governor
rose, and with innate courtesy bowed his guests out.

Leaving the Kanakas and dog to stroll along the
waterfront, the men returned to the house of David

Spence with whom they were staying at Monterey. They were joined at dinner by Captain Blinn and Father Real from San Carlos church. It was a well-ordered and attractive home, for the Scotch merchant, who supplied the neighboring *rancheros*, had prospered since he had come to the Mexican capital of Monterey.

During dinner the Father delighted John with his sparkling talk, at times focused on serious topics, again lightly whimsical. He discussed the intimate life of the colony.

"You have seen Monterey, *Señor* Sutter?" he asked.

"Yes, Father. *Señor* Spence has been a generous host. He has taken me everywhere."

For a time John regaled the priest with his impressions of Monterey, although he could not tell what he truthfully thought; the old Spanish capital disappointed him as much as Yerba Buena. He found it unimposing. Its main streets were dusty and unkept; the houses were crudely made of adobe bricks, inadequately covered with a veneer of whitewash. They seemed unlivable for they had nothing but dirt floors and glassless windows protected by iron bars. In and out of the doors, usually ajar, ran chickens, cats, dogs and naked babies, watched with complacent unconcern by colorfully-dressed women, elaborately costumed in contrast to the austere interiors of their *casas*.

"It's a remarkably fine place, with the bay, and the pines, and the mountains all around. No wonder foreigners flock here," John said tactfully.

"We have an extraordinary climate," said the priest, "there's nothing better along the coast. Yes, *Señor* Sutter, we have quite a colony of foreigners living in Monterey. Fifteen or twenty families, I should judge.

There is Thomas Oliver Larkin, who lives in that pink adobe below Alvarado's house."

"We attended Larkin's party on the Fourth of July," said Captain Blinn. It was a foine feast, mon."

"We've visited several of the foreign residents. I wanted our two guests to meet them," said David Spence, "William Hartnell and Don Juan Cooper . . . ."

"We saw a bull and bear fight from Juan Cooper's balcony this afternoon," said Captain Blinn, "better than any horse race. I bet on the bull, but the fat old bear won."

"Then we went to call on the Serranos, the Amestis and the Vallejos," said David Spence. "I had hoped to stop in to see the Abregos as well but it was too late."

"Fine people," observed the priest, "as good Catholics as you'll find anywhere. They attend mass regularly, and give their tithe regularly to Our Lord."

"It's a fine building, San Carlos church," said John endeavoring to comment favorably on the unimpressive town. "David Spence took me inside for a few moments after we left Cooper's."

"San Carlos is where the first settlers worshiped," said the Father. "It's rich in tradition and history."

"Father Real knows more than any one else about old Monterey. Don't you, Pat?" observed David Spence. "He has read all the early records and diaries kept by the first priests and explorers who reached this coast. Am I correct?"

"Many of them I've read, *hijo mio*," replied the priest. "Many of them. Junípero Serra's letter might well have been penned by a saint. Certainly the accounts by Pedro Font and Juan de Anza and Gaspar de Portolá and Miguel Costansó are the most thrilling stories I have ever heard. Great men, these Spanish explorers.

May their souls rest in peace," he said softly, making the sign of the cross with a withered forefinger upon his shabby brown robe in the vicinity of his heart.

Captain Blinn, David Spence and John Sutter looked with deference at the erudite priest. All three had a profound respect for scholarship, the two Scotsmen instinctively, like most of their fellow-countrymen; John because of his early life in Basle.

It took only a little urging on their part to induce Father Real to impart to his eager audience fragments of the colorful beginnings of Monterey. "It was like this, my sons," he said, settling himself comfortably in his chair, and looking off into space. He told of the ardent desire of Spain, after the discovery of the new world by Columbus, to bring the teachings of the holy church to the pagans across the sea. "They came first with Hernán Cortés to Mexico, and subdued and brought under their control the idolatrous Aztecs under Montezuma, who sacrificed human beings to their gods. Among the heathens they established churches, schools and monasteries.

"The conquest of Mexico led on to that of California, once believed to be an island inhabited only by black women and ruled over by a queen called Calafía. At least that was the way the Portuguese writer of romances, Ordoñez de Montalvo, described it in *Las Sergas de Esplandian*, which was published in Seville ... about 1508, I believe. Although California was only a poetic figment, yet, curiously enough, men came to believe that it actually existed. They began to search everywhere for it. All they knew was what Ordoñez wrote:

'Know ye that on the right hand of the Indies, there is an island called California, very close to the side of the Terrestrial Paradise, and it is peopled by black women, without any man among them, for they live in the fashion of Amazons. They are of strong bodies, of ardent courage and great force. Their island is the strongest in all the world, with steep cliffs and rocky shores. Their arms are all of gold, and so are the harnesses of the wild beasts which they tame and ride. For, in the whole island, there is no metal but gold. They live in caves wrought out of the rock. They have many ships with which they sail to other countries to obtain booty.

'In this island called California, there are many griffins, on account of the great ruggedness of the country, and its infinite host of wild beasts, such as never were seen in any other part of the world. And when these griffins were yet small, the women went out with traps to take them. They covered themselves over with very thick hides and when they had caught the little griffins they took them to their caves, and brought them up there. And being themselves quite a match for the griffins, they fed them with the men whom they took prisoners, and with the boys to whom they gave birth, and brought them up with such arts that they got much good from them and no harm. Every man who landed on the island was immediately devoured by these griffins.

'Now, there reigned in this island of California a most beautiful Queen, very large in person, of blooming years, strong of limb and of great courage, in her thoughts desirous of achieving great things.' "

As Father Real paused to sip a glass of water, John could not refrain from expressing his delight in this fragment of the fairylike legend of California.

"There is much more to it than I have time to tell you, my sons, tonight. The tale, briefly, concerns the fight of the Christians and the Infidels before Constantinople, in which Queen Calafía plays a major part. Of course it ends, as a good romance should, with our dusky queen falling in love with an English prince, leader of the opposing forces. The romance quickly terminated the war. I wish all great conflicts could be so easily settled."

"Tell us more," said John, captivated by Father Real's skill as a raconteur.

"It was conceivable," he went on, "that at the time Hernán Cortés conquered Mexico he or his men had with them a copy of *Las Sergas de Esplandian*. He built ships on the west coast of Mexico with the purpose of exploring the coast further north. They never got beyond that long peninsula that hangs below San Diego. So far as they could determine, it was an island. Someone, no one knows who or exactly when, called this land California. Spaniards are romantic creatures and I suppose they hoped to find there more of the gold and treasure so abundant in Montezuma's fabulous land. But Baja California, as it is known today, proved to be almost sterile. Its Indians were little better than dumb beasts, the land itself had so little rainfall that nothing but cactus and weeds could survive. Even the missions that Father Salvatierra founded there a century and a half later were never self-sustaining. In fact I have read somewhere, possibly in Father Palou's history, his *Noticias*, that Father Salvatierra, close to starvation, lived for a time on rats.

"That, my sons, was where the name California originated."

"Have you a copy of the romance, Father?" John inquired. "I'd like to read it sometime."

"I only wish I had. But romances, you know, are banned from church libraries. It was before I became

a priest that I had a chance to peruse such frivolous
works."

"Did Cabrillo also use the name California," asked
John, glad now of the scrap of information he had
gleaned from Captain Blinn. "He was the true dis-
coverer of this land I've been told."

"You, too, love history, I see," the Father observed.
"Juan Cabrillo, yes. A great man he was. His voyage
up our coast in 1542 went a short distance beyond Cape
Mendocino. After that, the country was vaguely known
as Las Californias. But Spain was slow in taking possession of this remote land. Finally, about sixty years
later, in 1602 to be exact, Sebastián Vizaíno was sent
from Mexico to search along our coast for harbors. In
those days Spanish galleons were sailing annually between Acapulco and Manila and needed ports *en route*
where they could take on food and water and send
ashore to recuperate, sailors afflicted, as most of them
were, with scurvy."

"I don't wonder Cabrillo missed Monterey and San
Francisco; on foggy days I can never find them, either,"
said Captain Blinn.

"Vizcaíno was more fortunate; at least he found
Monterey. In fact he gave it its name; his patron, you
recall, was the Count of Monterey, ninth Spanish vice-
roy of Mexico. Spain finally had located a safe port.
Then she lost it again," he added.

"What do you mean by that, Father? How could
anyone lose a great harbor like Monterey?" asked John.

"That is what I am about to tell you," Father Real
replied. "Again Spain procrastinated in colonizing this
new outpost. She was engrossed with wars at home, I
presume. I can never understand why God's creatures
spend so much time and strength and money in such

senseless undertakings as wars. If they would only spend the same amount of energy in spreading the light of the holy gospel there would never be another conflict. Forgive me, if I digress, *hijo mio*. But the subject is one no good Catholic dares ignore.

"But we were talking of Monterey. Spain delayed colonizing for one hundred and fifty years. Then in 1769, four expeditions, two by land, and two by sea, were sent to Alta California. The day they left Mexico was a great one," he remarked jubilantly, "a great one for the Franciscan order. To us was entrusted the spiritual conquest of California. Blessed Father Junípero Serra was at the head of it. May his soul rest in peace.

"Don Gaspar de Portolá had charge of the land columns, soldiers and colonists and priests. They came overland by way of Sonora, stopping to rest at the missions Father Kino had founded in Pimería Alta, land of the Pima Indians. Juan Perez headed the expeditions that came by sea. They met, after a safe journey at San Diego, and founded a colony on the shores of the bay. From there they pushed north, by land and sea, stopping at places now familiar to all of us, La Ciudad de Los Angeles, San Buenaventura, Santa Barbara, which they named for the saints of our holy church. But for a long time they could not find Monterey, not until after several discouraging weeks of search.

"At last, on May 24, 1770, they reached Point Pinos, just across the hill, and on the third of June, Father Serra celebrated mass and Captain Portolá took formal possession in the name of the king of Spain under the same oak where Vizcaíno held divine services in 1602. It was a momentous day, *hijo mio*. I have heard the Franciscans discuss it many times. Under the great oak —the one standing at the present day in the courtyard near the door of San Carlos church—Saintly Father Serra, wearing his best alb and stole, cross in hand, knelt, and implored God's blessing on the land. Beside him also knelt Portolá and the soldiers, heads bent in prayer. Then they rose and sang together *Veni Creator Spiritus*. Having finished, they nailed the cross to the tree trunk, and sprinkled holy water on the place where they stood. On this site, said Father Serra, let there be erected in God's name a church to be called *San Carlos de Monterey*. This they now christened by chanting together, *Te Deum Laudamus*.

"Their next act was to unfurl the royal standard of Carlos III and select a site for a *presidio*. They chose the land lying on the little knoll above the estuary, not far from the church. Before long they had erected a simple palisade of poles and a series of crude huts for the settlers.

"Monterey prospered from the first. Colonists continued to be sent up from Mexico. The *presidio* expanded. A staunch adobe wall surrounded it. In the enclosure were built houses for the governor, the officers, soldiers and their families, warehouses, stores and a blacksmith shop."

"Did the Indians give them any trouble?" inquired John.

"Not the slightest, my son; the Fathers made friends with them immediately. Converting them was not difficult. The natives around Monterey are docile, childlike creatures. Before Mission San Carlos Borromeo del Carmelo, across the valley, was secularized, meaning that the Fathers were forced to relinquish properties they had devoted their lives to conserving for the benefit of their Indian converts, it had nearly four thousand neophytes. The Franciscan order did not deserve the unjust treatment it received at the hands of the Mexican government. It was an evil day when Mexico declared its independence from Spain in 1821 and severed all ties from its illustrious parent in Europe," said Father Real, tragically.

"But it's growing late, I must leave. I have some sick parishioners to see."

Then he rose and smiled gently, raising his hand to bless them as he moved out of the door.

Captain Blinn and John stood as the priest departed. "We are most grateful for your kind hospitality," said John. They left and strolled down Alvarado Street to the custom house. It was patrolled by six Mexican soldiers. Along the waterfront they came to their skiff drawn up on the shore. Two Kanakas were standing beside it. They rowed out by the light of a full moon to the *Clementine*, moored a few hundred yards off shore, and climbed wearily aboard.

"At sunrise we'll push off," said Captain Blinn as he bade John good night. "If the wind's right, we'll be back in Yerba Buena before long."

# CHAPTER VI

# HAMLET ON THE BAY

JOHN WAS IN high spirits when he reached Yerba Buena the next day, consumed with eagerness to begin plans for his new colony. At the *embarcadero* he watched the *Clementine* discharge her cargo for French and Company, take aboard hides and tallow for the Islands, and make final preparations to head west across the Pacific. As she left port twenty-four hours later, John stood on the beach until the ship disappeared from sight. Mana, who was with him, wept as the ship disappeared. John, too, felt somewhat depressed, for with the *Clementine's* departure was severed the last tie that bound him to the civilized world he knew. Now, alone except for his two mechanics and his ten Kanakas, he had only the resources of his own fertile brain, the brawn of his own hands with which to carve a new life for himself in the wilderness. The thought of it sent a chill of apprehension through his sturdy frame.

To divert his mind, he walked over to the General Merchandise store run by Hinckley and Spear. They greeted John jovially.

"We want you to be one of us," they said.

For several moments the three men chatted pleasantly on trivial matters, then John told them of his plan to establish a Swiss colony in the interior.

They listened in silence. Then Nathan Spear remarked, "Look here, *Señor Juan*, if I may speak frankly, what you intend to do is ... well, I won't say impossible . . . but, to put it mildly . . . somewhat dangerous. These Sacramento Indians are treacherous . . . They'll attack you like a mountain lion, behind your back. Besides, I can't arrange to rent you any boats for at least another month. I've contracted to move cattle for Jose Martinez across the bay."

"Not for a month?"

Nathan Spear viewed his crestfallen countenance with surprise.

"But you need that month to become acquainted with the settlement around the Bay. Why not visit Vallejo at Sonoma? He's an important man for you to know. And you should visit the Russians at Fort Ross. And the larger *ranchos* around the Bay."

John had heard desultory conversation and bits of gossip about many of them: Don Salvador Vallejo in Napa Valley; the vast *Rancho* Pinole owned by Ignacio Martinez south of the bay; the fertile San Antonio held by Luís Peralta; the San Leandro of José Estudillo; Los Meganos owned by the Bostonian John Marsh, an eccentric recluse who practiced medicine.

John followed their advice and visited the large *ranchos* near the bay. After learning the ways of the Californians, he decided to visit Sonoma and Fort Ross. As he traveled in Indian boats, manned by natives, across the bay toward the *embarcadero* at Sonoma, John speculated as to how to ingratiate himself with the *comandante*, Mariano Vallejo, head of the *Frontera del Norte*, as the country around Sonoma was called. Eager to make a good impression, he had on his French uniform, for everyone at Yerba Buena had warned him that if he intended to found a settlement in the interior he must win the support of the *comandante* who was as powerful as Governor Alvarado.

John knew that Vallejo had built for himself a principality over which he ruled with an iron hand, and that his self-imposed task at Sonoma was to ward off the encroachment of foreigners and to establish a sound frontier beyond which no one might trespass. That was why he had been sent to *Frontera del Norte* by Alvarado; that was why he had been granted the immense Petaluma ranch fifteen years before; that was why he had been placed in charge of the abandoned mission of Solano used as quarters for his officers and men. The immense power of Vallejo in the north not far from where he himself hoped to settle, made John apprehensive. What if Vallejo resented a Swiss colony adjoining his own? Anxiety was apparent in the deep furrows on John's forehead. He knew he must assume a bold front, a self confidence he did not feel, drawing on every ounce of bluff and showmanship he could muster.

Some two miles from Sonoma the travelers disembarked in a small cove. At a corral nearby they secured from a *vaquero* some horses which Vallejo kept solely for the use of guests. On them they rode swiftly along the dusty trail toward Sonoma de Vallejo. Upon reaching the plaza they dismounted and went to call upon the *comandante*.

They found him lunching in the officers' quarters at the old mission. He insisted that John and Captain Wilson join him in the hearty meal of chili con carne, tamales, frijoles and chocolate. As he ate John wondered how the Mexicans could endure such heavy fare in so warm a climate. But they seemed to enjoy it and thrive on it.

John, meanwhile, cast sidelong glances at Vallejo. He was impressed by his tall and distinguished presence, his patrician bearing. He saw that everyone saluted *El*

*Comandante* and took off their hats in his presence. It was a small thing, but it indicated the importance of the man.

After the repast, Vallejo escorted his guests around the town. Only twenty-five families lived in small adobes around and near the plaza, in all not more than one hundred and fifty persons, twenty of whom were foreigners. John enjoyed especially a brief chat with the local schoolmaster, Victor Prudon, a scholarly Frenchman with whom he conversed in his native tongue. From him John learned that Vallejo had a garrison of more than fifty men who lived in and near the decaying mission in quarters once occupied by the priests. He was surprised at this information; the *comandante* had led him to believe his military forces were at least twice as large.

As John, accompanied by Captain Wilson and *Comandante* Vallejo, strolled around the plaza he could not fail to see that it was a squalid, hot and dusty town. What did interest him was the enormous ranch house Vallejo soon took him to see some distance beyond Sonoma. At least a hundred workmen were engaged laying adobe bricks and although only partially completed, from materials filched from Mission Solano, it was the largest and most pretentious building John had seen anywhere. Vallejo was inordinately proud of it, pointing out its broad balconies and huge windows. He showed them his gardens, orchards, and grainfields; John saw growing in them wheat, barley, oats, beans, peas and other produce being raised by six hundred Indian workers. It was a princely domain that filled John with a brooding urge to create for himself a similar one in the wilderness.

Wisely he did not allow an inkling of his secret envy
to cloud his gracious manner.

"We have nothing finer in Switzerland, Your Excellency."

By this time Vallejo had come to like his distinguished foreign guest, with his cosmopolitan manners
and urbane carriage.

"Would you consider settling somewhere near me,
*Señor* Sutter? I understand Governor Alvarado is willing to grant you land along the Sacramento. Why not
find something nearer Sonoma?"

"That is indeed gracious of you, *Comandante* Vallejo," John answered. "You flatter me. There is nothing
I should like more."

He concealed his inner conviction that he wished to
be far away from the dominating man he knew Vallejo
to be. Independence—that to John was the most important thing of all. Moreover, a fact that disturbed him
more than he cared to admit, he saw in the *comandante*
a future rival. "That is indeed gracious of you," he
repeated with a smile.

"You might induce Captain Wilson to sell you his
holdings, *Señor* Sutter," continued Vallejo. "He owns
one of the largest *ranchos* in Sonoma Valley, don't you,
Wilson?" The captain nodded assent.

"Wilson runs several thousand head of cattle. He
might part with his holdings at a low price. Would you,
captain?"

He named a ridiculously low figure. "You may pay
me at your convenience," he added. It was apparent the
life of a *ranchero* was distasteful to him.

John, with exaggerated courtesy, declined.

Vallejo seemed annoyed at John's failure to accept
his suggestion. In his mind there rose the faintest sus-

picion that this foreigner might prove a rival some day. What if he founded a colony on the Sacramento? What if it flourished? For the first time he looked suspiciously at his Swiss guest and did not speak. Frenchmen had been on the coast before. What if he were a French agent and not a Swiss after all? He feared French designs on California, even more than he feared the Hudson's Bay men or the Russians. Following a lull in the conversation, he remarked, "You are on your way to Fort Ross, *Señor* Sutter, I understand."

"Yes, Your Excellency," John replied. "We leave this afternoon. We intend to pass the night at the home of Peter Kostromitinov."

At dawn John parted from Captain Wilson who galloped off to look after affairs at his own *rancho*, having first secured for his Swiss comrade the services of a competent Russian guide who spoke French to take him to Fort Ross.

John and his guide chatted gaily together in Spanish as they rode along. John found his huge Russian comrade both entertaining and surprisingly well-informed. "*Si, Señor*, La Bodega, the harbor for Fort Ross where we have our warehouses, lies just north of the great bay of San Francisco, in a small cove," he replied to John's query. "It's where all the Russian ships that come down from Sitka anchor. They carry back sea otter pelts to be shipped to Europe and grain for the Alaskan colony."

John listened with keen interest to the guide's incessant talk.

"You know, *Señor*, all about Nikolai Rezanov, the first Russian to come to the bay, don't you?"

"I heard Captain Blinn mention him once or twice."

"*Si, Señor*, he was a fine man, handsome as a god.

He was Russian ambassador for a time at the Japanese court; that was long before he came to California. He was one of the officials of the Russian-American Trading Company sent out to Alaska to inspect their trading posts. They were having trouble getting food for them; nothing much grows in Alaska. Well, Rezanov had heard about California. How everything grew there. So he decided to see it for himself. In the spring of 1806, in May, I believe, he anchored in San Francisco Bay near the old fort. No one stops there any more; the anchorage at Yerba Buena is so much safer. He was fascinated by California; by the seals and sea otter; by the forests of magnificent timber; by the grain and livestock everywhere. From the moment he landed he was eager to build a Russian fort somewhere along the coast. Yes, he fell in love with it, especially the women, one in particular. You've heard about that, I suppose?"

"Not a word," replied John.

"Poor Rezanov." The guide gave a long sigh. "It was sad, *Señor*, extremely sad. He fell in love with Concepción Argüello. She was the daughter of José Argüello, the captain of the port. A lovely young woman. Typically Spanish, with luscious, dark eyes. You know the kind I mean."

"Yes," said John, "I know."

"Well, *Señor*, they were to be married. But first Rezanov had to return to secure permission from the Czar. *La Señorita* promised to wait. She waited a long time. One year, two years, perhaps more. She grew thin and pale and listless as young women in love will. She wasted away. But he never came back again."

"Did *La Señorita* marry someone else?" John inquired curiously.

"No. She was faithful to Rezanov. She would look at no one else. It was sad, very sad." A sympathetic tear rolled down his rough cheek. "No. She drooped and pined. Finally she became a nun. It was a decade or more before they told her that Rezanov had died in the snow while crossing Siberia."

"When did you come?" John inquired.

"Almost thirty years ago in 1808. With Ivan Kuskov." He drew himself up proudly. "That was on the *Kadiak*. Kuskov came to select a site for a colony. We stayed only a short time. Four years later we came back. That was when we settled at La Bodega, *Señor*. Port Romanov we named it, for the Czar."

Now and again John nodded with sympathetic understanding; otherwise he did not interrupt.

"*Sí, Señor*," went on the voluble Russian, "we brought ninety-five Russians and eighty Aleut hunters with us. And many small boats. Aleuts are remarkable fishermen. Week after week, they brought in hundreds of skins; most of them from the bay and the Farallon Islands nearby."

"The Spanish authorities did not stop you?" asked John in surprise.

"Certainly not, *Señor*. They had no settlements in those days that far north. In fact they were glad we had come."

"Fort Ross, I understand, has been here a long time," remarked John.

"*Sí, Señor*. Since 1812. We began work on it in March. *Fuerte de los Rusos*, our Spanish neighbors call it."

They soon reached the top of a dome-shaped hill. As his glance fell on the panorama below, John turned to his comrade, motioning to him to stop. For ten minutes

or more, he sat contemplatively in his saddle, eyes fixed
on the walled bastion below.

John could clearly discern the palisaded walls and
bastioned turrets of Fort Ross, that stood on a bluff
overlooking the Pacific. Almost square in shape, it was
about three hundred feet on each side. Every few feet,
he saw loopholes for cannons; further protection was
afforded by a pair of octagonal turrets, twenty feet in
diameter, two stories high, on which were mounted guns.

"You're well armed, I see," observed John, as the
two travelers began the descent.

On all sides fertile lands lay lush and mellow under
golden sunlight, lands that gave forth promise of
abundant harvests of barley, rye, buckwheat, maize,
flax, poppy. In small, neatly fenced gardens, were
ripening pumpkins, turnips, beets, peas, beans, melons
and any number of rare fruits and vegetables seldom
used by the Californians.

John viewed them hungrily, with the approval of a
gourmet.

"Most of these," said his guide, "are shipped north
to the Russians in Sitka. We also give them most of our
fresh fruits, too. We have twenty varieties of fruits,
Señor, and grapes of all kinds."

The envy within John made him slightly ill. He realized at this moment that he coveted Fort Ross more
than he had ever coveted anything in his life before. If
I could only build one like it, he sighed to himself. As if
visualizing a wilderness retreat already completed, one
over which he ruled regally, he unconsciously squared
his shoulders and elevated his head. A wave first of envy,
then of self-confidence poured through him. What the
Russians have done, I, too, can accomplish.

At the gate armed guards admitted them into the

enclosure. Greedily John thrilled to the exhilarating scene spread out before him. He saw housequarters for the officers and soldiers, an arsenal, storerooms, and the Greek chapel, a simple wooden structure adorned with bells. There were also kitchens, a blacksmith shop, bakeries, gristmills, stables, dairy houses and eight large bath houses. It was a miniature world, complete within itself. John was enraptured by the civilized comforts he saw at Fort Ross.

They rode on until they reached a large house. "*El Gobernador*," said the guide with a flourish of his huge hand toward the front door. "I must leave you now, *Señor*."

The servant ushered John into a large room, elaborately furnished. "I will announce you to the Count, *Señor*."

As John glanced around he saw on all sides evidences of affluence and luxury. Hundreds of leather-bound books in French, German and Russian lined the walls. A piano, on which lay open a minuet by Mozart, was placed by a sunny window, curtained by silk draperies of a golden color. Turkish rugs covered the floor. Roses in silver bowls were placed on inlaid commodes. Soft couches and comfortable lounging chairs were grouped near open windows, whose lace curtains flapped in the breeze.

It's like being in Europe or at the Russian court, thought John. He recalled that the guide had told him that Alexandre Rotchev had married the Czar's niece, Princess Hélène de Gagarin; that they had, in fact, eloped, for the Count, erudite, cultivated and engaging as he was, was not considered a suitable match for one of royal blood. That was why they had been sent far from official circles to the comparative wilderness of

Fort Ross. Apparently they had made a success of their marriage; the house radiated well-being, in that subtle way dwellings have of disclosing the private lives of their occupants.

Presently the door opened and Governor Rotchev entered the room. He welcomed John with the utmost cordiality.

"I am indeed glad you have come," he said, in French. "Governor Kouprianoff wrote me about you. The letter came in from Sitka less than a week ago. You must be my guest. Stay with us as long as you find it convenient."

They talked together for an hour or more. At dinner Princess Hélène joined them, gracing with animated conversation and rare charm, a dinner table worthy, John thought, of St. Petersburg itself. Fascinated by the lace table cloth, lighted candles in great silver candelabras, the food and wine of superlative quality, John felt as if he had been transplanted into a magic world. After dinner the princess played to them Chopin, Beethoven, Mozart and the quaint melodies of Couperin. The setting, the dinner, the music, was of a quality rare in California; indeed, they could be found only at Fort Ross. In all his life, John had never known an evening like it.

With a feeling of profound regret, after a thorough inspection of the fort, the outlying *isbas*, or peasants' houses, the huts of the Aleut fishermen, the outlying farms, the fields, brooks, and pasturage, John left the following day for Yerba Buena. Visiting Fort Ross had inspired him with new ideas; he was eager to start a colony of his own modeled along similar lines.

At the Bay settlement a cordial welcome assured him of co-operation and support from Hinckley and Spear.

Impatient of each day's delay, John at once accosted
Nathan Spear who was knee deep in bales of hides and
casks of tallow, which he was preparing for shipment
to Boston, via Captain Arthur's *Munsoon*, at anchor
off shore.

"I shall need some supplies," said John. "In a day
or so."

"What especially do you want?" asked Spear. He
had been expecting John for some time and had already
discussed with his partner how much to advance him on
credit.

"First of all, food," John replied. "And plenty of it.
Then tools, the kind used by blacksmiths and carpenters. Agricultural implements. Seeds. Lots of them.
Some used rifles and muskets. With a large quantity of
ammunition."

"It's well to be prepared," said Nathan Spear. "Most
of these things I can buy on the *Munsoon*. Anything
else?"

"Three cannons, if I can get them."

"Captain Arthur does not carry them. But I may
be able to get some old ones in Yerba Buena. They
might be bought cheap."

"I have no funds," said John morosely. "At least not
enough for my purpose. I must ask for credit."

Nathan Spear hesitated briefly, "Hinckley and I will
stake you to what you need, *Señor* Sutter. If you will
sign a note to repay us in a year's time. Beaver furs
and deer fat will be quite acceptable. We can also
supply you with boats and Indian crews to take you up
the river. We have the schooner *Isabella* and the
*Nicholas*, and a four-oared pinnace for lease. With
crews, of course." He looked somewhat skeptically at
the amiable Swiss stranger standing before him, so

courteous, so enthusiastic, yet so casual in his attitude toward financial matters. An inner voice warned him to be more cautious.

"I assure you I will repay you a year from now," said John, as if he could read Nathan Spear's inmost thoughts. With a flourish of the pen, he signed the slip of paper the Yankee merchant spread before him, in a somewhat bold handwriting.

That night aboard the *Munsoon* a farewell dinner was given by Captain Arthur in honor of John and his colonists who were starting at dawn on the first lap of their journey up the Sacramento. The men drank deeply and freely. The evening grew hilarious as the hours passed. Finally the captain rose, swayed for an instant, then steadied himself.

"A toast to our good friend, John," he bawled, lifting his capacious mug of *aguardiente.* "May he, may he," he finally forced from his uncontrolled lips a few garbled sounds, "tame . . . the . . . wilderness . . . and all . . . of California, too. Tame . . . the Indians . . . make slaves of 'em . . . and . . . the Indian . . . women, God bless 'em."

Roars of appreciative laughter greeted his ribaldry.

"What do you intend to call your new settlement, *Señor?*" asked William Hinckley.

John rose, steadied himself. "New Helvetia," he shouted happily. "I intend to call it New Helvetia!"

# CHAPTER VII

# DEEP WILDERNESS

DAWN CREPT SOFTLY over *El Rio del Santo Sacramento*. Watching night merge into day that August morning in the year 1839, John felt a chill creep down his spine. Awed by a growing dread of the primeval wilderness around him, he stood upon the deck of the schooner *Nicholas* that had been moored to the bank for the night, gazing at the dense forests, wondering what dangers they harbored. Then he glanced at the muddy river, moving sluggishly downstream. He fancied he saw Indian skiffs carrying armed men lurking in the shadowy distance.

He was grateful that night was over. Dawn drove away much of the fear bred by night, making the towering forest less awesome by daylight. Apprehension merged into mixed feelings of curiosity and excitement so that the sunlit river began to lose its forbidding aspect. With lessening tension he gazed down at the ripples of light flecking the waters.

The Sacramento reminded him strangely of the Rhine. Yet there was little actual resemblance between the swiftly moving river vital with traffic he had known at Basle, and this sluggish waterway, rank with decaying vegetation and choked with patches of tule reeds. Since the days of Caesar, men had known and subdued the Rhine; but here was an untamed river, alluring, mysterious, its course uncharted and virtually unexplored.

The passion of possessiveness came over him with appalling force. The desire to conquer it overwhelmed him. Since childhood, rivers had inspired him with strange urges. They had mocked and challenged him with sirenic force. Now, suddenly, his youthful passion for the Rhine was transmuted into an obsession for *El Rio del Santo Sacramento*. He felt that this virgin river was his own, that he held its destiny in his hands.

Somewhere along its banks he would found a colony, a second Switzerland, a Utopia patterned after the ideals of Rousseau and Voltaire. What they had dreamed and written he would transform into reality. Here in the wilderness of California he, John Augustus Sutter, would build an ideal community, based on freedom and tolerance for all. Here men could live in peace and comfort far away from the restraints of the civilized world. He would create for his fellowmen an Arcadia. A Paradise in the wilderness.

His brain teemed with the spirit of the pioneer. Dreams of a halcyon community dedicated to what each desired, a place free from the inhibitions of his own restricted youth, swept over him. Visions of wealth, grandeur, power, crowded into his mind. They obliterated all thought of the perils before him.

Steeped in day-dreams, John was scarcely aware that the chill of dawn had vanished, giving way to mid-August warmth, that a rising land breeze carried drifts of heat across the water and stirred the forests, making the leaves rustle with crisp, metallic sounds.

Indeed, he was not conscious of the outer world until Kanakas and native sailors began to come up from below decks, stretching and yawning. He watched Captain William Heath Davis, dressed in a neat uniform, on foredeck directing the crew to unfurl the sails pending departure.

Presently the *Nicholas* cleared its moorings and began to nose upstream. The boat was one of the two small schooners John had secured from Hinckley and Spear, together with a rowboat, a native crew, food, trinkets for the Indians, seeds, tools and agricultural supplies for his colony, all on credit.

After the ship was under way Captain Davis, leaving the wheel in charge of a pilot, went below for a cup of tea and a plate of jerked venison and highly seasoned Mexican beans whose spicy aroma came from below deck. He reappeared just as John, impatient at the slow progress, was boldly assuming the prerogative of a captain. He was directing some sailors to bring the rowboat, that was towing astern, alongside the schooner so that he could board it. He had one foot on the rope ladder when Captain Davis, obviously annoyed, rushed over. "Sutter, why in the name of Christ do you want to travel in that small skiff?"

"I don't like the way the *Nicholas* crawls along. The rowboat will move five times as fast. What we need is a breeze."

The captain retorted sourly, "That's God's task, not mine. Besides, no one ever hurries in California."

John climbed down the rope ladder into the skiff. "That's the trouble with them," he called back. "Dawdling doesn't suit me. I want to move ahead. As fast as possible." Observing the worried look on the captain's face, he added, "I promise not to get out of your sight. All I want to do is to explore the mouths of some of the side streams we pass."

"Come on, Mana," he said. She began timidly to follow him.

"I warn ye, it's dangerous business."

"I'll risk it. There's not an Indian in sight."

"If the natives shoot you, don't blame me," the captain shouted as the skiff, rowed by four armed sailors, moved away. "But I can see you don't want advice."

The further the skiff moved away from the *Nicholas,* the more the captain's warning words disturbed John. The explorer in him was anxious to move ahead, but the colonizer in him longed to avoid hostile encounters with the natives. Conflicting aims, urgent and impelling, made him gloomy and morose, so that he sat rigidly and increasingly apprehensive in the prow of the skiff.

He listened intently as forest sounds drifted across the water. He heard a coyote emitting a wail like a sick child. He heard bluebirds chirp their throaty seductive call. From afar came the muffled roar of a wild beast. But except for these occasional brief disturbances, he found no signs of life anywhere.

Suddenly John saw white feathers fluttering from trees along the riverbank. As he watched them move rhythmically in the breeze, the belief that they were sinister Indian symbols filled him with foreboding. Anxious to find out about them, he tapped one of the boatmen on the shoulder.

"Pull over to the bank," he said quietly. He pointed to a large sycamore nearby.

The sailors guided the boat in toward shore. John reached out and grasped a bunch of feathers from an overhanging branch, soft bits of fluff, apparently off wild geese.

"What are they, Mana?" he asked, handing them to the blank-faced Kanaka beside him, a frightened look in her eyes.

"I don't know," she replied.

Unable to restrain himself, John cupped his hands, placed them to his lips, and shouted to the foremost of two schooners nearby, "What are the feathers for, Davis?"

From the deck of the *Nicholas* a few hundred feet away came a loud guffaw. "Indian message. Saves 'em buying pen and paper. No readin' or writin' needed."

"What do they mean?"

"They want food. They're asking the gods to send it. Fish, I suppose. And acorns. And grasshoppers. That's what most of 'em eat."

"If that's all, we can move ahead," replied John. "I thought they were danger signs." He dubiously directed the native boatmen to proceed slowly upstream. So far, except for the occasional howl of a wild beast, or the flutter of birds overhead, the trip had been singularly uneventful. Yet John had the queasy feeling of Indians, secreted in the underbrush, watching him from ashore.

Suddenly they rounded a bend in the river. He heard hideous shrieks, accompanied by drum beats. He saw Mana turn white with fear, hiding her head against his shoulder. He shook her off.

He began whispering to her in muffled, jerky, hurried undertones. "Don't—be afraid—Mana. They won't hurt you— I'll protect you— Pretend you're not afraid. We mustn't shoot. Remember—I promised Governor Alvarado—I'd make friends with them— Then he will give me the land he promised— All those thousands of acres—Mana—for us—a year from now—if I tame the natives. We mustn't kill a single Indian, not one— Smile at them, Mana— Smile— Smile— Keep the guns under the seat— Don't let the men touch them until I say so. Just smile, Mana— Smile."

A single thought pounded through John's brain—
peace. He must keep his own men from firing, and he
must contrive to keep the Indians also from shooting.
But how? What if they were allies of *Comandante*
Vallejo himself, sent in a burst of jealous rage to ex-
terminate a potential rival? Even so, at all costs he
must preserve the peace. A single shot and the empire
of his dreams would vanish in a cloud of smoke. The
irony of it was not lost on John: that if his own men
fired, he faced ruin; if the enemy attacked, he faced
death. His mind grasped clearly the salient fact that
hostilities were suicidal, that in peace alone lay success.

Mana's trembling presence, her hand gripping his,
eased somewhat the tension. He knew she trusted him.
He knew he must make no decisions, commit no acts that
would endanger her, Captain Davis or the crew. But
he knew there was not time to deliberate. Already the
four sailors were reaching under the seat Mana occupied, looking for the guns. She tried to stop them but
they grabbed them away and pointed them at the
Indians.

"Drop those guns," snapped John. He sat in the
bow of the skiff, watching.

In an open clearing near the riverbank he saw the
dark bodies of hundreds of Indians gleaming with red
and yellow and white paint. They were armed with bows
and arrows which they shook defiantly at the intruders.
Bending low they formed a huge circle which pivoted
slowly in rhythm. Shrill cries alternated with low guttural sounds. Staccato head tones contrasted dramatically with the throaty war chants.

Suddenly the circle broke. The Indians rose to their
full height. With threatening gestures they crowded

the riverbank. They hissed ominously, like angry hornets.

"Watch out, Sutter," Captain Davis shouted from the deck of the *Nicholas*.

Not a muscle in John's face twitched. A moment later he signaled his boatmen to put in to shore. Reluctantly they obeyed. Ten yards off shore he whispered, "I'm going to land without a gun. Don't fire unless I'm attacked. I don't think they'll kill me."

Meanwhile, the head oarsman, who had been taught by the priests at Mission Dolores, had been scrutinizing the warriors closely. He now turned to John and said, "*Señor* Sutter, some are Christians. I recognize them. They're from Mission San José."

Reassured, John stepped ashore, forcing an ingratiating smile. He held out his hands indicating that he was unarmed.

Two men, wearing the feather headdress of chieftains, approached. They threw their bows and arrows at his feet.

They proved to be Christianized natives, just as the boatman had said. For several moments John conversed with them in Spanish. "I have come to live among you in peace, to be your friend. I have brought gifts. Mana, where are the presents?"

She rose timidly from the cramped position where she had remained out of sight and leaped ashore, graciously extending a small parcel to the taller of the two chieftains. "*Dios va con Usted.*" After thus invoking God's blessing upon them, she returned hurriedly to the skiff.

The natives unwrapped the package swiftly, making animal-like sounds of pleasure as they inspected its contents: glass beads, looking glasses, pocket knives, tiny bells. "*Bueno, bueno—good—good*," they repeated over and over, fingering the beads joyfully.

After inspecting them to his satisfaction, the taller chieftain placed a string of red beads around his bronzed neck and came closer to John. He was handsome with a stately carriage and his face reflected kindliness and good-will. "*Dios va con Usted*," said the chief with decorum.

The thought came forcibly to John that this man was unlike any other Indian he had ever seen. He had no rings in his nostrils like the Nez Percés, he did not have the flattened head like the Columbia River natives at Fort Vancouver. He scrutinized the strange dark countenance before him, unable to decipher the thoughts behind it.

"*Dios va con Usted*," John responded with all the dignity he could command. He liked the ecclesiastical mode of address the fathers had taught their brown neophytes: God be with you. It warmed the heart.

"*Yo soy* Anashe," continued the chief, wrinkling his face into a smile.

"So your name is Anashe," Sutter paused, then attempted flattery. "Anashe, Anashe," he repeated slowly, "I like the name."

The chief grinned with delight. Then he motioned to his brothers, hovering indecisively in the background, to approach. They swarmed around their chief, curiously inspecting the gifts. "*Amigo, amigo*," they said from time to time, pointing grimy fingers at John.

"Tell your good brothers it is growing late," said John. "I am tired from traveling all day. I need sleep. Tomorrow I will come back with gifts for all. Tell the men to bring their squaws and children, too."

John returned to the skiff which now moved slowly

out toward the schooner. As he sat silently in the prow, his thoughts were of his first encounter with the Indians and its peaceful termination. Grateful as he was, he did not allow himself to be lulled prematurely into a feeling of security. He had heard too many tales of Indian treachery for that, too many tales of Apache uprisings, Navajo hostilities, raids by the unpredictable Nez Percés, ever to trust them. What if these first gestures of friendship hid a deep-seated plot to annihilate him further up the river? Still brooding, minutes later he boarded the *Nicholas* with a sigh of relief.

Captain Davis, who was waiting for him on the foredeck, pounded him jovially on the back. "Glad to see you with scalp still intact."

As the schooners proceeded upstream, John swept the shoreline with his eyes, searching for a desirable site on which to camp for the night. He decided not to stop until he found a knoll sufficiently wooded to provide protection in case of an Indian attack in the night, yet far enough in from the bank to escape some of the swarms of gnats and mosquitoes and flies that made sleeping aboard ship unendurable in the damp August nights.

The *Nicholas* had traveled two hours when John pointed to a small hill near the shore. "That looks like a good place, Captain. Let's stay here all night."

The travelers moved their bedding ashore and after a supper of frijoles, Mana and John unrolled their blankets on a bed of river rushes and with the bulldog beside them soon fell into the slumber of utter exhaustion. At daybreak John heard the dog growl ominously. He sat up and looked furtively around. A few hundred feet away he saw Anashe standing with folded arms, watching him. He grabbed his gun, then dropped it for

The California Indians

The California Indians

he saw the chief was grinning and extending his hand
in a gesture of friendship. Cautiously, John returned
the greeting. He looked around to see if Anashe was
accompanied by his friends, but no one was in sight.
"What do you want?" John asked.

He listened with surprise as Anashe explained that
he had come to guide the white chief up the Sacramento,
familiar to him since childhood. After deliberating a
moment, John accepted the offer though not without
misgivings. Advantageous as was the presence of one
who knew every bend, every cove, every affluent of the
river, he could not free himself from the suspicion that
Anashe might be leading him into a trap. He confided
his fears to Captain Davis who did little to alleviate
them. He shook his head. "Never trust an Injun.
They're as treacherous as hell."

Under Anashe's guidance the expedition left the
shore and moved upstream. As before, John watched
every bend in the river. Once they passed the mouth
of a large stream coming down from the north. Where
it joined the main channel stood a large Indian village.

He viewed the settlement apprehensively, wondering
if the hordes of natives, who crowded the banks when
the schooner appeared, would shoot. He saw with relief
that the Indian greeting Anashe gave as they glided
past reassured them.

For the next few days the *Nicholas* and the *Isabella*
moved slowly past the densely wooded banks of the
Sacramento, exploring its main channel and innumerable affluents with utmost caution. But the terrain they
passed afforded few suitable sites for a settlement. Most
of the ground was low, marshy and overgrown with
underbrush. High open spaces, breeze-swept and
sightly, that could be cleared easily for planting crops,

with fresh water and timber accessible, apparently did
not exist. Disheartened by the lack of suitable locations,
the colonists proceeded steadily ahead, grimly determined to find an Arcadia in the wilderness.

Presently they discovered a large river pouring in
from the east. Up this stream Anashe now piloted them.
"*Aquí está tierra muy buena*," he said in halting mis-
sion-taught Spanish.

He waved a hand toward the right bank. Here rose
an open knoll, devoid of trees and underbrush. "*Buena
allá*," he repeated. "*Vamos.*"

As the schooners neared the sloping banks and
dropped anchor in the tule reeds a few yards off shore,
John looked hopefully at the site. Evidently an abandoned Indian camping ground, it seemed ideal for his
purpose.

"Here is where we land."

After watching the skiff and the schooners tie up at
the bank, Anashe accepted the two knives and a glass
necklace John gave him. He glided off through the
forest toward his own settlement, promising to return
in ten days or two weeks.

Deftly the Kanakas and Indian crew removed the
tents and supplies from the boats. John directed them
in the task of pitching a temporary shelter, and helped
them roll ashore the two small cannons he had bought
in Yerba Buena.

For a time the men worked diligently, inspired by
the novelty of their tasks. Among them, however, were
several adventurers who had come aboard at Yerba
Buena slightly drunk and full of promises to help found
a new settlement. John had looked askance at them,
uncertain of their integrity and sobriety, but he needed
colonists desperately and white men were difficult to find.

Now, just when he needed help, he found them talking sullenly to the crew. "What's the trouble here?" he asked.

"Don't like it," one, Joe Nevis, replied.

"But I thought you wanted to get out of Yerba Buena. That's what you told me. Don't you like this place?"

"No, I don't," replied another, Jack O'Dell. He was a pasty-faced, squint-eyed Irishman, loquacious and irritable. "Who would, for Chris' sake?"

"Why not?"

"Skeeters and those damned Injuns. Not much food. No licker. Goin' back to Yerba Buena."

John looked gravely at the enraged O'Dell. He must have men. He observed the morose faces before him sadly. They had a savage look in their eyes, corroborating what they had said. Fear for his own and his Kanakas' safety swept over John. He dismissed it swiftly from his mind. He did not reply. Should he get rid of them?

Nevis and O'Dell and the others went away grumbling sullenly among themselves. John watched their retreating figures with alarm; the shuffling feet, the defiant way they carried their heads spelled disaster. Mutiny was an ugly word.

"Let 'em leave, the yellow snakes," he said to himself. "I'll manage somehow. The first thing tomorrow morning I'll ship the bastards back where they belong. A good riddance."

This decision materially strengthened his self-confidence, bolstered by seething wrath. He was too tired to do more that night than to sink into a haggard sleep on the improvised bed of rushes close to Mana's prone body.

The following morning, John, still incensed, ordered his puerile passengers gruffly aboard the *Nicholas*.

"Davis will take you back. This is no place for such God-damned dogs."

They sauntered aboard, hanging their heads meekly as if in shame. They had not expected to be deported with such alacrity by the determined Swiss. Three of them hesitated, as they reached the deck of the schooner, then turned around and went ashore.

"We'll stay, Cap'n," said one of them.

John extended his hand. "You'll never regret it, Frederich Hugel. Nor you, Louis Morstein. Nor you, Henry King." He beamed gratitude and pressed their hands one by one in a firm grip. Then he ordered Captain Davis to delay his departure for another twenty-four hours in the hope that more might change their minds.

By dusk the nucleus of a camp had been completed. Reed huts had been erected. A large area to be enclosed later by a palisade had been staked out. The cannon had been moved into place and ammunition piled nearby. An improvised cook house had been devised from stones left by Indian campers.

John viewed it with the pride of an artist who had accomplished what was before only a mental image. Meticulously that night by candlelight, with gnats and mosquitoes thick about him, John Sutter wrote proudly in his diary: Today,[1] with the help of ten Kanakas, three white men and a bulldog, I founded a colony, called New Helvetia.

[1] Monday, August 13, 1839.

# CHAPTER VIII

## LAND UNTAMED

THE *Nicholas*, the *Isabella* and the skiff weighed anchor the next morning and moved slowly downstream. On the banks of the river the weary colonists stood mournfully. John would not admit his depression, although anguish tore at his heart. He knew he was completely alone now, the future of himself and his group lay solely in his own hands. He tried to visualize the day when the river would move with flourishing traffic, when boats bound for the Bay would be freighted with his own produce. He turned and looked upon the wide expanse of virgin land around him. Here he would be lord and master of New Helvetia, with his servants, his private army, his servile colonists, and his Mana.

Mana edged closer to John, her face pallid with fear. Struggling to keep back her own tears, she gulped miserably, then hid her face against his coat sleeve. "I'm afraid," she sobbed.

"Of what, Mana?"

"Indians."

"Nonsense," said John, with an attempt at gaiety. "Why, there are only a few. Mostly squaws."

She peered around somewhat furtively. In the distance she saw a few curious loiterers, some of them carrying papooses.

"I know the men are hiding somewhere in the forest. They might kill us," she whimpered.

"Don't worry, Mana, don't you know that Anashe

told them we intended to be their friends? Come, be
brave. What will the squaws think of you? Look! One
of them wants to make friends." He indicated with a
wave of his hand a handsome young squaw who had
moved within a hundred yards of where they stood,
eyeing lasciviously the comely contours of Kanaka
Harry.

Mana lifted her head timidly as she contemplated
the advancing overtures of the squaw toward her former
spouse. The episode served to divert her, so John
slipped quietly away.

He felt the imperative need to drown his own dark
mood of depression and anxiety in activity of some kind.
His eyes were on the two venerable cannons, standing
with their rusty muzzles pointing ominously forestward.
Nearby stood Fred Hugel, somewhat superciliously inspecting them. A thought flashed through John's mind.

"Let's fire them off by way of a parting salute," he
said. The young German stepped closer to the firing
mechanism and tested it. "Are you ready, *Señor?*"

"All ready, Hugel. I doubt if the natives have ever
heard a cannon before."

Hugel pulled the lanyard. Fire and smoke belched
forth. The thunderous reverberation of gunfire pierced
the air. By comparison the profound silence that followed was intensified. John looked around, baffled, aston-
ished. He wondered if the natives had heard his salute
to the primeval forest.

"Fire again," he shouted, "and again and again,
Hugel. Show Captain Davis he didn't leave cowards
behind."

The great guns roared out nine salvos of farewell to
the ships disappearing from sight.

As the last echo merged into space, pandemonium

punctuated by shrieks and cries rent the skies, the dark figures of frightened Indians appearing mysteriously, scampered from treetrunk to treetrunk seeking shelter. Timber wolves set up a low mournful wail. Deer and elk mad with fright leaped from their hiding places and bounded through the underbrush. Birds rose in agitated groups swiftly skyward. Even the rank undergrowth that hid all manner of silent observers quaked with sudden life, as if electrified by the magic of gunfire.

The unexpected animation and activity absorbed the attention of the stranded colonists. They had no time for nostalgic thoughts, no time to indulge in the luxury of self pity. Mana rushed wildly over to where John was standing with Hugel near the cannon.

"The Indians," she screamed. "I saw hundreds of them."

"They've left, Mana," he said. "Can't you see they're afraid? They think we're gods, I suppose. Or evil spirits who can work magic. They'll be back, Mana *mia*. They'll come cringing to us. Watch and see."

Late that afternoon, John saw a few timid natives cautiously advancing, with gifts of venison, fish, fruits, acorns and berries which they carried in baskets on their heads. By way of encouragement he held out to them strings of beads. They made shy gestures of friendship. Although Mana still regarded the natives timorously, she made every effort to be courageous and proceeded to cook the meat they had brought over red-hot ashes until it was crisply brown. John praised her cooking; he could not recall a time since he had left Europe when he had dined so well.

While the white men ate, the Indians looked on in stolid silence, a quiet broken only by the native babies clamoring for food. John gave them bits of cooked meat. When the meal was over he distributed pieces of bright cloth, mirrors, glass beads and a limited number of knives. Grunting their appreciation the Indians glided away. John was relieved to know that these were peaceful mission Indians. The strain of their sly-eyed attendance was disturbing and Mana shuddered whenever a squaw, moved by curiosity, touched her dress. After they had vanished no one could find Kanaka Harry. John suspected that he had followed the young squaw into the brush, although he did not tell Mana.

The real work of building a settlement began. John, his three white assistants and several Kanakas cut a trail from their camp to the river and began to clear away trees and brush. John, unused to manual labor, was so exhausted by nightfall that he could not eat; he dropped wearily down on the pile of rushes Mana had placed in a corner of their hastily erected reed shelter and fell sound asleep.

Days and weeks of back-breaking toil followed. Before long a good road connecting Sutter's camp with the *Rio Americano* was completed. Over it supplies brought in by schooner every two or three weeks from Hinckley and Spear's store at Yerba Buena could be carried to their camp. A stout palisade was begun, for even though the Indians appeared quiet and friendly, John was reluctant to trust them. After the first month some of them were bribed by Fred Hugel and Henry King to make adobe bricks. They were slow and clumsy at first. John was anxious to begin the house, mainly because it would provide protection in case of attack. He kept his brooding fear of Indian treachery from Mana, who would never move away from his side unless she had the bulldog beside her. The dog was worth his weight in gold, John had told her. The Indians were afraid of his ferocious barks and his glistening white teeth.

"He's your bodyguard, Mana," he said, "don't go anywhere without him."

Time passed swiftly. John was happy with the thousand and one tasks necessitated by the building of the settlement. It was no longer laborious; he could toil from sunrise to sundown and not tire. Joy came upon him as he saw the forests cleared and small areas planted with grain. A few head of cattle purchased on credit from Ignacio Martinez near the Bay were finally delivered and two of them were slaughtered to provide fresh meat.

Slowly walls of his adobe house began to rise. It was a large one-story structure, forty feet long and twenty wide, to contain a blacksmith's shop, kitchen, and his own quarters. It would be the first permanent part of New Helvetia.

When it was ready to be occupied, John turned to other exciting tasks. There were huts to be built for newcomers who began to drift in now from the Bay whenever the schooner made its run to Sutter's settlement. He asked no questions of their past. What did it matter? Brawn and courage alone counted.

At times he found a good audience among the new settlers to augment his imaginary days as an officer in the French guards. With a growing flourish he told of his importance in Switzerland, and of the glories of his accomplishments in the Napoleonic Era. He was Captain or even Colonel to his colonists. He signed letters, "Captain John Sutter of New Helvetia." He was determined to place his colony on the high level of fine living that had deeply impressed him at Fort Ross. He wanted at dinner lighted candles in silver candelabras, stimulating talk about world events, books and music in the evening, with a beautiful woman playing Chopin's fabulous nocturnes. Often he was repulsed by the sight of Mana on the floor picking at raw brook trout with her chubby fingers. For a while at least he would tolerate the uncouth habits of the adventurers: men without home, country, or any moral code.

Dreams like these carried John over the crude days inseparable from pioneering. They glossed over the hardships of a primitive camp life. He suspected that, like himself, many came to New Helvetia with some crime to hide. They drank heavily, they bragged, and annoyed young Indian squaws with lusty abandon. But John was used to it. It was the same everywhere, from Santa Fe to Sitka, Alaska. He accepted it philosophically.

He felt most at home with the French Canadian trappers sent down by the Hudson's Bay Company. John tried to prevent them from trapping in territory he considered his own. He could not stop them, even by plying them with home-distilled grape brandy. He was forced to admit their right to trap there. Years before Governor Alvarado had licensed them to hunt along the Sacramento. They were convivial and entertaining guests, full of song and repartee. They gave the settlement some of that cosmopolitan flavor John craved. Also they were more diverting than the childish Mana, or the phlegmatic trio, Fred Hugel, Louis Morstein and Henry King, with all their sturdy qualities, whom he had appointed to supervise all work.

John found these three colonists invaluable, especially for the aid they gave him when he built his first adobe. The local way of making bricks was new to him.

For weeks they labored to complete the house, before the winter rains began.

The day he moved into his first home he experienced a feeling of gratification. He whistled and sang as he and Mana arranged their scanty household possessions against the clean white-washed walls—a bed made of lumber, a table, two chairs and three seaman's chests. He recalled that he had never felt any affection for the house in which he lived with Nanette in Burgdorf. This was different. He glowed with pride. Toward the end of the day just at sundown he lifted Mana and carried her across the threshold, placing her on the dirt floor in the largest of the three rooms. "It's an old European custom, Mana *mia*," he told her.

They were laughing gaily when a shadow darkened the door. It was Kanaka Harry. Sufficiently full of brandy to be insolent he demanded that Mana return to him. When she refused, he became violent. Flying into a towering rage, he threatened to take her by force. John was half afraid he would harm her and stood firmly between them.

"Where's your squaw, Harry?" he asked. "You told me only yesterday you liked her better than anyone else."

"She's left," snapped Harry sullenly. "For good, I hope." He made a move as if to seize Mana.

"Get out, Harry," John said indignantly. "Come back when you're not so drunk. Then we can talk."

"No. Give me Mana now. She's my wife," shouted Harry, teetering from side to side. "My squaw's gone."

"Why did she leave?"

"Too much drunk, she say," replied Harry.

"Come back tomorrow, Harry," said John in a soothing tone. He handed him a bottle of home-distilled grape brandy and shoved him out.

Relieved, John slammed shut the door and bolted it. Then he turned and faced his trembling mistress.

"Do you want to leave, Mana?" he inquired.

"No. No. I'm afraid of him."

She hid her head on her sleeve like a small girl and wept.

"Stop it," said John severely. He had the typical masculine distaste for tears. In fact the only trait in Mana that ever annoyed him was her constant sniffling in which she indulged upon the slightest excuse. "Stop it at once, Mana."

She made a feeble effort but without success. John thought, as he watched her, how listless and irritable she seemed these days. Perhaps she was homesick for the Islands.

"Do you want to go back to Honolulu, Mana?"

"No, never," she blubbered. "I can't leave you."

"Are you happy, Mana?"

"Yes, yes."

"Then why do you cry?"

"I can't help it. I'm going to have a baby, *Señor Juan.*"

John looked at her in stunned silence. I might have known, he thought miserably. He had always felt a certain fastidious distaste for half breeds, too prevalent at every trading post. Speechless, he stamped from the room. At the waterfront he sat down dejectedly and listened mechanically to the ebbing tide. Somehow the possibility of a child had never occurred to him. Faced now with it, he realized the shame and disgrace. He reproached himself bitterly through the night. Toward sunrise he rose and walked back to his house. He must keep the true state of his feelings from the trusting Mana.

One warm spring day, a week later, John sat sunning himself near the door of his adobe. He had on his working clothes, a pair of Indian moccasins, faded blue cotton trousers, and a loose red shirt open at the throat. His pipe angled from the corner of his mouth. John let his glance linger on his first crop of ripening wheat stretching before him. Hearing shouts and cries, he turned to watch a herd of his own sheep and cattle being driven by laughing vaqueros.

Mana came from the house. John and Mana sauntered past the waving wheat into fields knee-deep in yellow mustard, blue lupin and poppies. Mana filled her arms with flowers to decorate the house. When she was not chattering, she hummed little snatches of Hawaiian songs. Occasionally John accompanied her with his good bass voice.

In the late afternoon they returned to their adobe. Mana arranged great bouquets of the flowers in Indian baskets which John had traded for a few beads. They made a splash of color against the austerity of the whitewashed interior. "Like Honolulu, John," she said. She addressed him now by the English form of his name after he had protested against being called *Señor Juan.*

From beneath the oak table John pulled out a dingy barrel that had been converted into a chair. He sat down, and spread out a large sheet of old paper covered with drawings.

Critically he studied the plan of his New Helvetia. With a pencil he inserted wall lines here and there, releasing others. New ideas had just come to him and he was anxious to convey them to paper. After an hour he ran his fingers through his curly hair with a gesture

of weariness, then held up the paper studying it for
defects. He found several flaws. Again he began diligently to insert changes. Darkness descended. He lit
two stubs of tallow candles.

Mana, who had fallen asleep on the floor, woke and
came to help him. He patted her moist cheek with a
gentle hand.

"Come here, Mana *mia*, and look at it. I'm finally
satisfied. It will be finer in every way than the Hudson's
Bay forts. Or even Fort Ross, I trust, when it's completed. This is the way it will be, Mana," he said tracing
imaginary buildings in mid-air with a rough index
finger. "The walls will be eighteen feet high and two or
three feet thick, for safety. I'll have the workmen make
extra-large adobe bricks. These two corners will be
bastions. With extremely thick walls. Let me see, I
believe we'll make them two stories high. That will leave
room for a jail underneath."

"For bad Indians?"

"For bad men of all kinds, no matter what color,"
he replied with a smile. Although mystified by the lines
he indicated, she was quick to nod approval.

"It will be large? Like King Kamehameha's palace?"

Amused by her naïveté, he continued, "It will be far
finer, Mana. There will be nothing like it anywhere in
the west. It will be three hundred feet long and almost
as wide."

She clapped her hands gleefully. *"Hombre muy
grande.* You are a very great man."

He leaned over and brushed an appreciative kiss
across her forehead locks. She had expressed what had
long been his basic conviction. Mana was right. Everyone at the fort looked up to him. Captain, *comandante,*
or some other term of homage came naturally when they

addressed him. Only to Mana was he known as John, though she preferred on occasion to call him *Señor Juan*. "*Hombre muy grande*," she repeated softly.

He kissed her again; this time on her languid lips.

"And here, Mana," he said turning again to the paper, "are the houses. Barracks. A bakery."

"For tortillas?" She spoke disdainfully, not liking the flattened corn cakes of Mexican ancestry which had become so popular in California.

"No, Mana *mia*. For making bread. Real bread. The kind we have in Europe."

His mouth hungered at the memory of the hot rolls and fragrant loaves baked daily in the Dubeld household in Burgdorf. Lack of good food was his only criticism of the west, in fact of all America. He intended to serve on his future table only the choicest viands and wines, as was done at Fort Ross.

"You'll learn to like my kind of food, Mana."

She shook her dark head, then wrinkled her nose disdainfully. "I like poi," she announced.

"Here is a mill for grinding wheat. And a factory for making blankets. And here, Mana, are the small houses for the vaqueros. And still more for soldiers and workmen. I want them to live inside the fort. Mere stalls, I'm afraid. But our own house is large and commodious. We may need it, you know, Mana."

She hung her head in shy self-consciousness.

"See. It's in the center. Opposite the main entrance." He showed her the paper.

She looked vaguely at the thick penciled lines, over which John continued to rhapsodize. She tried vainly to imbibe some of his enthusiasm. To conceal her failure she asked hopefully, "Will there be a church?" Despite the unconventionality of her personal life, she still retained at intervals an inner urge to attend Methodist services.

John realized with a start that he had neglected to provide any kind of a place of worship.

"Yes," he lied glibly, being adept at simulation when the need arose. "Yes. One with real bells."

"When will you start the fort?" asked Mana.

"Soon, Mana, soon I hope."

How could he tell her that at least one year, maybe two, would elapse before the fort would be ready for occupancy. He glanced around the room where they sat. After all they were comfortable here. And reasonably safe.

"*Sí Señor.*" She walked across the room intending to arrange more gracefully a bouquet of flowers that seemed overcrowded. She could not live without flowers around her. Midway, she stopped. "What was that?" she asked stepping toward the half open door. "It sounds like the bulldog."

They listened intently. The low guttural sounds continued. Then a voice shrieked, "*Señor, Señor, Señor!*"

"That's Custot," said John, as he rushed toward the door. He could not afford to have anything happen to Octave Custot, one of his few reliable white men in New Helvetia. "Go back, Mana." He grabbed a loaded gun, hanging nearby, and rushed outside.

Trembling, Mana peered through a loophole in the wall. Although the area in front of the house was dark, a young moon cast a faint light on the fields beyond. She saw figures running away, pursued by John, gun held in front of him, followed by Bull. As she watched she saw one of the figures trip and fall; from his terrified cries she inferred that Bull had his teeth in him. John did not stop.

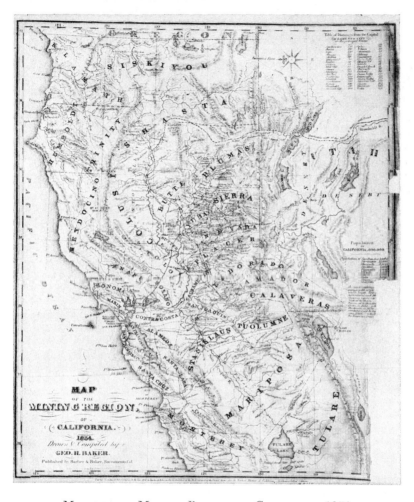

MAP OF THE MINING REGION OF CALIFORNIA 1854

An instant later a shot reverberated through the night, then another, and another. Mana clutched her throat in terror. "God, oh God," she moaned.

The moon drifted behind a cloud. Darkness brought with it fresh terror. "Our Father who art in heaven . . ." The words froze on her lips. She listened intently. From afar she heard Bull's vicious growls. Then she heard footsteps outside. At the same time Bull's growls stopped. John's voice came clearly to her through the night. "Let go, Bull! Get up, man! Come! You're not hurt much." She saw two figures, one limping badly, come toward the door. She opened it cautiously, peeking out through a crack.

"Open it wide, Mana; don't be afraid."

She flung it open, then stepped cautiously to one side. The two men entered.

"What happened?" she asked weakly.

John gave a short, bitter laugh. "Nothing much, Mana. Just a friendly little brawl. The kind that happens all the time at frontier posts. You'll get used to it. I can't promise it won't happen again." He tried to speak reassuringly, but she could hear the catch in his voice and knew that he was hiding something from her.

"What happened?" she repeated.

"Well, if you must know, some Indians attacked Octave Custot."

"Did they try to kill him?"

"I'd hardly say that," John responded slowly. "Perhaps they just wanted to fight. They'd been drinking too much *aguardiente*, I suppose. Is that so, *amigo mio?*" He turned to the silent Indian who was standing beside him, eyes on the ground. "*Aguardiente?*"

The Indian grunted but did not raise his head.

"They steal it from Custot. That was what all the

trouble was about. He found out about it and started
after them. Several of them tried to surround him. They
might have killed him if Bull hadn't given the alarm.
That was when Custot called to me. I fired at several,
but missed. I couldn't see well enough in the dark. This
rascal, the one I have here, has Bull's teethmarks all
over him. Get some rags, Mana, and a basin of water.
He needs bandaging. Indians appreciate any little attentions. We'll make a friend out of him yet."

Between them they made the wounded culprit as comfortable as possible, then provided him with a bowl of
hot gruel. He ate it noisily, lapping it greedily. Then
wiping his mouth on the sleeve of his deerskin jacket
he grunted with satisfaction, went outside, stretched
himself at full length near the door and was soon sound
asleep.

John locked the door securely behind him, leaving
two cocked guns nearby.

Silently, Mana, white-faced, watched. She went over
to a Spanish seaman's chest Captain Blinn had given
her when she landed at Yerba Buena in which she kept
her treasures. She opened it and extracted a shabby
Bible. It was the one the Methodist minister in Honolulu
had given her the day she married Kanaka Harry. She
sat down on the floor and turned the pages for a time.
Finally she found what she was seeking: "Protect us
from evil, God," she prayed, "give me strength and
courage. Save me from evil Indians."

John, who was cleaning some extra guns in an opposite corner of the room, glanced at her curiously now
and again, but did not interrupt. It was the first time
he recalled having seen her with a Bible. He was annoyed at her devoutness.

John's supreme self-confidence left no room for faith

in Deity, and he did not intend to encourage in her an almost forgotten devotion to the Methodist church.

"Put that book away, Mana," he called in annoyance.

If she heard him she did not reply, but continued to read on until the wax from the candle formed a thick mass around the sputtering wick. She removed her robe and, with her Bible in her hand, climbed into bed. She placed it under her pillow, and was soon asleep. John extinguished the smoking candle, hid the pistol under his pillow and endeavored, too, to sleep.

A coyote screamed in the night. John tossed restlessly. A few drops of rain hit the roof. A muffled drum beat out a sinister rhythm from a distant hill. John lay in tenseness trying to fathom the message. There was a long silence. Another drum caught up the same beat. It was closer. For hours the steady beats reverberated from one hill to another. For a moment John wondered if they were poundings from his own mind. He lay for hours, staring into the blackness of the room. Mana peacefully asleep lay warmly close to him. Would this be his end? Would he never build his great fort? Was it foolishness not to have accepted Wilson's offer? Would he have been happier in the Sonoma Valley? Suppose they found out about him. Suppose a French frigate should bring a warrant?

A quick flash of lightning flared outside and for that moment the room was in stark whiteness. Thunder clapped heavily. Mana stirred beside him, breathed heavily, and gave a little start of fright. He put his hand on her shoulder and she lost her tenseness. Another flash of lightning and a rumble of thunder and the storm seemed to go. Was this a message? There was no more sound of war drums. The night was silent.

The pink of an early sun poked through the barred windows. John awoke with a start. He must have slept somehow, but it seemed like a nightmare. Shall I tell Mana? What would her life be without me? He woke her.

"Mana, we must get up at once. In an hour I leave for Monterey."

"But the boat isn't back from the Bay," she protested.

"I can't wait, Mana. I'm going on horseback by way of John Livermore's ranch, from there over to Mission San Jose. I'm taking you along, Mana *mia*. I must get that land grant right away."

"You are going to see His Excellency, Juan Alvarado?"

"Yes, Mana *mia*."

"Will he give it to you, John?"

"I believe so. I cannot start building the fort until I know the land is my own."

## CHAPTER IX

# UNCROWNED KING

SINCE JOHN'S RETURN from Monterey late in June, land grant in hand and with the title bestowed upon him by Governor Alvarado: *Representado del gobierno y encargado de la justicia en las terrenas del rio Sacramento*, he had been a changed man. It was indeed a signal honor serving as the Governor's representative in charge of the administration of justice along the Sacramento. It was enough to turn any man's head; in fact it made him almost as powerful as *Comandante* Vallejo himself. That, in addition to the grant of land, 48,818 acres, eleven leagues, the largest amount Alvarado was empowered to give, made him a person of influence in California. Perhaps that was why he walked so pridefully, forced his men to work so endlessly. He swelled with vanity when they called him *Señor Comandante* of New Helvetia.

Mana knew only that John was immensely pleased and flattered by the confidence the Governor placed in him. She was only mildly interested in the letter from His Excellency which John read aloud to her. Every white man at the fort knew about Alvarado's letter to John. He appeared now reading the letter. . . .

"You have demonstrated your ability to pioneer; you have proven yourself industrious, determined and kindly toward the natives. I predict the success of New Helvetia. Because of my confidence in you, I am granting

121

you the largest amount of land it is in my power to give."

John kept the Alvarado grant on his table and often reread its formal wording, "Whereas Don Auguste Sutter, a native of the Swiss Republic, and naturalized in the Mexican Nation, has solicited, according to the law of 18th of August, 1824, and in the ordinance of 21st of November, 1828, for his personal benefit and that of twelve families, eleven leagues of land on the borders of the river Sacramento in the vacant lands of the northern frontier, in order to colonize and foster them, for which end he has sufficiently proved his assiduity, good behavior, and all other qualities required in those cases, having already anticipated his increased efforts, his constant firmness, and his truly patriotic zeal in favor of an institution, having reduced to submission a number of savage Indians born in those frontiers; and this government being sufficiently informed that the mentioned land does not belong to the property of any private individual, town or corporation, and that in consequence thereof it is specified in the aforesaid laws, and in conformity with the power conferred on me, in the name of the Mexican Nation, I have granted to the said Señor Don Auguste Sutter, by these present letters, for him and his settlers, the said land called *La Nueva Helvecia*, subject to the approval or disapproval of the Superior government and of the departmental assembly under the following conditions:

(1) He may fence it without injury to the adjoining land and, above all, to the trade and navigation of the river.

(2) He shall maintain the native Indians of the different tribes in these places in the free enjoyment of their possessions, without troubling them, and he

may only reduce them to civilization through prudent measures and a friendly intercourse; he shall not cause them hostilities of any kind, without previously obtaining authority from government.

(3) The land of which donation is made to him is of the extent of *eleven sitios de ganado major* (eleven square leagues). It is bounded on the north by *los tres pices* (the three summits), and 39° 41' 45" north latitude; on the east by the borders of the *Rio de las Plumas* (Feather River); on the south by the parallel of 38° 49' 32" of north latitude; and on the west by the river Sacramento.

Therefore I order that, this title being held as firm and valid, the same be entered in the proper book.

John B. Alvarado, Commandant General of the department of the Californias, has ordered and signed it which I certify.

Monterey . . June 18, 1841."

The heat of summer descended relentlessly upon the fort. New Helvetia wilted like a fading leaf under the scorching sun. Its hot blasts sent their withering breath across the fields of young corn, searing them until their weakened stalks fell limply to the ground. Trapped in the fiery heat, cattle and horses stood dejectedly under what shade trees they could find. Indians and their white overseers worked listlessly at their enforced task of making adobe bricks for the incompleted buildings inside the fort. They worked from necessity, not from choice, for they knew that Captain Sutter would severely chastise those who lagged. To everyone it was apparent that his insistent aim was to rush Fort Helvetia to completion.

Mana sat contentedly at the door of their house, one

day not long after John's return from Monterey, meticulously sewing new stripes of gold braid on his threadbare French uniform. John reposed on a wooden bench, reading some papers. Now and again she stopped long enough to wipe the film of moisture from her own face and to fan the flies off the naked infant lying in the Indian basket beside her. The child's blue eyes smiled. She leaned over him, patted the chubby brown arms, and brushed back from his forehead the yellow curls so like those of John. Then she resumed the dainty stitches, humming happily as she worked.

The sultry heat reminded her of Honolulu. A nostalgia for her birthplace came to her. She could see its palms swaying gracefully in the breeze, the red cupped-flowers of the tulip tree, the pink and yellow of the shower tree, spectacular, dramatic and redolent with perfume. The fancied sound of waves breaking on the shore made her quiver with delight. As she sewed, she dreamed of her Island's sandy shores, touched by the eternally blue sparkling ocean. She fought back the longing. An Island song sprang to her lips: it was one sung by Hula dancers as they waved their arms to simulate fishes swimming, and swayed their hips to imitate the rhythmic movement of the sea. She recalled how often she had danced it for Kanaka Harry in the days when he was courting her. John had never seen her dance. She wondered why he had not asked her. Perhaps she had forgotten the steps. She looked quickly at John and saw he was absorbed in documents. She laid aside the coat, and began to rehearse the favorite dance of the Islanders, meanwhile singing softly to herself the accompanying refrain.

"*Aloha oe, aloha ae, E ke onaona a noho; ka lipo.*"

John glanced up. "Mana, what are you doing?"

She stopped abruptly at his critical tone.

"Just dancing," she said meekly. "I thought you might like to see me dance. Hawaiian dances, I mean."

At his failure to take further interest in her, she sat down and resumed her sewing.

"Is the coat almost ready?" he inquired absent-mindedly.

Hurt by his indifference, Mana forced a strained smile. "Almost," she replied, plying her needle with unwonted speed.

Without further conversation, John went past her into the house.

Mana heard him draw up a chair with a scraping sound. She heard the rustle of papers, the scratching of a pen. The smell of smoke from his pipe came through the open door. A labored sigh was faintly audible.

She got up and glanced anxiously inside the door. John was sitting glumly before a table, looking into space. She saw him ruffle his hair with nervous fingers. He took a pencil from his pocket and began to add up what seemed to her to be a long column of figures.

Mana covered the baby with a piece of netting John had bought from a Yankee trading ship when he was in Monterey. She tiptoed in.

"What is the matter, *Señor Juan?*"

"Debts, Mana *mia*, just debts," he said, grateful for the solicitude. "A staggering load. I can't seem to pay them. If I settle some, I have new ones. I don't know what to do. Since I got the land grant, my creditors are pressing me more and more. I can't meet my debts, Mana, at least not now."

She patted his cheeks gently, in an effort to divert him. Business problems usually did not interest her, but these seemed serious.

"Debts? What debts? Who is bothering you?"

"That miserly John Marsh at Los Meganos. And old Bob Livermore down the valley. Ignacio Martinez; I still owe him for the cattle he sent me eighteen months ago. Worst of all are the back bills from Spear and Hinckley. I've never even paid them for the use of the boats and all the supplies they sent us when we started, Mana."

With a reassuring smile, she replied, "I know you will find a way to pay them."

"I don't know. They're pressing me more and more. Not that I blame them. On the whole they've been extremely generous. That is, all except John Marsh. Don't worry, Mana *mia*, we'll manage. I've been short of funds before and always got along somehow." He leaned over and listlessly kissed the young girl at his feet. "Don't worry, Mana. Promise. Run along now and look after the baby."

After she had left John sat with bowed head clasped in his hands, thinking over the hardships of pioneering, indifferent to the mass of bills lying nearby. He knew that his troubles sprang primarily from the great Hudson's Bay Company, whose forts extended from the Atlantic to the Pacific and whose trappers and traders, seeking fur skins, penetrated even into the Sacramento Valley where they outbid him with the natives. Although he took what pelts remained, there were not enough to satisfy his creditors. Worst of all, he had recently learned that this Northern company intended to open a new post, in charge of William Glen Rae, in Yerba Buena. He sank back into his chair and lit his pipe. Since he had contracted his bills in good faith, promising to pay his creditors in pelts, he would have to write once more and ask them to renew their old notes. Puffing

vigorously, he took his pen and began to write feverishly.

Although Sutter had spent almost two years at New
Helvetia, he had few real friends to count on. There was
a continuous disturbance among the hangers-on, the
deserting sailors of dubious character, Yankee trappers,
seeking a good season and ample reward for the least
labor. Then there were vagabonds of nomadic wayward-
ness, without morals and given to heavy consumption of
liquor. There was a constant undercurrent of dissatisfaction, morose complaints, fights over the few desirable
squaws, and gang brawls. These drained Sutter's
strength and weakened his morale.

A problem even more disturbing came from his nearest neighbor, *Comandante* Vallejo. His lack of friendship had its source in a smoldering jealousy. Many
rumors had come to Sutter and he had finally accepted
them as bearing facts. Vallejo had been writing scathing
letters to the head officials in Mexico City. He had ex-
coriated the Swiss pioneer, saying he appeared to be a
French agent, sent out from Paris to report on conditions along the West Coast. He repeated the warning
of France's aim to acquire California.

John felt some security in the land grant Governor
Alvarado had awarded him. Their friendship had come
from a unity of aims about protecting the frontiers
against marauding Indians who stole horses and cattle.
John also believed that Alvarado had confidence in his
manner of dealing with the friendly tribes who had
proved so helpful the first months at the fort. Even
after two years they remained faithful to him.

The most favorable factor toward the development
of the fort was the calibre of some of the pioneers who
came to settle there permanently. To insure their loyalty

and dependence upon the fort, he had given them generous land grants in the surrounding country and had helped them stock their ranges.

Work on the fort progressed with annoying slowness. John took his gun and went off across the fields on a tour of inspection.

It was the noon hour. Near the place where they were making adobe bricks he watched the Indian workers, lined up beside a trough, similar to those used to feed cattle. They were shoving a thick mush enriched with scraps of beef into their mouths. They ate noisily, with hog-like grunts. He watched them gorge themselves to satiety. Having scraped the last mush from the trough, they lumbered over to some oaks, stretched out at full length on the ground and slept.

Meanwhile, Mana, relaxing in the heat, whistled to Bull, who was romping outside to come in, laid aside her work, moved the baby inside the house where the air was somewhat cooler, stretched out on the dirt floor near his basket and soon fell asleep.

An hour later she woke up with a start. The baby was screaming. Bull was tugging frantically at her dress. Sitting up, she rubbed her eyes. Clouds of smoke darkened the room. They were so dense she could scarcely see. From the dry tule roof, tongues of flame crackled noisily upward. Panic swept over her. She tried to rise; the smoke choked her. She fell, then tried again. She heard the baby choke and gasp for breath. She covered her smarting eyes with her hands, then in a daze pulled herself to her feet. Now fully awake, screaming with fear and blinded by the heat and smoke, she snatched the baby in her arms, and ran hysterically to the door. At the threshold she stumbled and fell; the child freed from her grip rolled to safety outside. Behind her Bull, unable to escape, collapsed on the floor. He gave a weak pitiful moan and was silent. For several seconds Mana lay where she fell; then as the heat grew more and more intense, she pulled herself, and crawled out of the door.

"John, John, John," she sobbed. She fainted.

Presently she regained consciousness and saw John running at top speed toward her. She saw him stoop and pick up the child. He carried it to a safe place then came over and lifted her to her feet.

"Our house . . . it's gone, John . . . it's gone."

He could force no words of reply through his parched throat. His anguish was too deep, wordless. He merely held her closely to him.

After a dazed interval he murmured breathlessly, "But never mind the house. All I care about is that you and the baby are safe." His strength restored her composure.

"Those living near the fort, Mana, I consider our friends. But the Cosumnes, the ones living across the Sacramento have threatened to destroy New Helvetia." He felt a shiver go over her as he finished speaking, but she did not answer him.

Together with a crowd of Indians and white men from the fort they stood at a safe distance from the burning house, watching the tule roof turn to ashes and spill its charred timbers into the shell that remained. The adobe walls, blackened and hot, did not burn; denuded of their wonted covering they stood alone unmoved by the holocaust around them.

When the smoke finally subsided John placed Mana and the child in a grove of sycamores under which the natives soon erected a simple rush hut.

It was a week before John could resume his normal business of bartering beads and trinkets, secured on credit at Yerba Buena, for pelts brought in by Indian trappers. Then, worried again about his constantly increasing debts, he decided to go to a neighboring Indian settlement to look for his old friend, Chief Anashe, from whom in times past he had often secured high grade skins.

On the way he met his friend Octave Custot, who was blithely whistling a French *voyageur's* song as he walked.

"Have you seen Anashe lately?" inquired John. "I'm in desperate need of some pelts."

"You have obligations, perhaps, *Señor Juan?*" asked the Frenchman suspiciously.

He was well aware of Captain Sutter's financial difficulties and not too sympathetic with them; in fact, he considered the Swiss a poor business manager, a dreamer and a spendthrift, a man woefully lacking in common sense. Thrifty, like most of his countrymen, he despised John's habit of constantly straining his credit.

"Yes," said John morosely. "Especially John Marsh."

"How much do you owe him?" asked Custot with a frankness bred of close association.

"I'd rather not say."

Custot laughed, a merry, boisterous laugh. He knew from John's attempts at concealment that the bills were high.

"Well, and so you want to see Anashe, I believe?" he said. "I saw him less than an hour ago. He's over there at the Indian village. They're having an Indian ceremony, I understand. I'd advise you to keep away, *Señor Juan*. At least today."

"But I'd like to see it," John replied.

"There's no use concealing it, Captain," Custot said

morosely. "The Indians say a chief was killed by a white man here at the fort."

"Why wasn't I told?" John's face took on an ashen hue.

"It was an accident, I believe. Both men were drunk. They got to fighting over a keg of whiskey. Both men wanted it. The Indian was hurt in the fight. No one thought it was serious, at first. But he must have struck his head when he fell. He died without regaining consciousness. I saw it happen. But we have no Indian witnesses. That's the difficulty. I'd advise you to keep away."

"I can take care of myself, Custot. I've known Indians for years." He spoke with an outward air of assurance he did not feel.

Custot returned to the endless task of supervising the making of adobe bricks; John walked slowly on toward the Cosumnes village a mile away.

Even before he reached it, John saw signs of funeral preparations, men in ceremonial costumes, carrying loads of wood. He loitered unnoticed on the outskirts of the village until it was dark. As the moon rose he saw around a huge fire, burning brightly, dark silhouettes. As he moved closer John heard them groan, cry, yell and make weird gestures with their hands. There followed, with equal suddenness, a profound silence. The lull lasted only a short time. Again lamentations rose skyward. Again dark figures moved in weird pantomime around the blazing fire. By now the rhythmic tramping of feet was plainly audible. John heard it with increased distinctness, the closer he approached.

A gust of wind sprang up. John sniffed the strange odor that filled the air again and again. Something strange was burning; for an instant he could not detect what it was. Then a look of horror crossed his face. He knew now what it was: the smell of human flesh. His stomach gave a sudden wrench. His head swam dizzily. An urge to vomit came over him. He swallowed quickly; his mouth had a furry feeling that stifled him.

He turned and walked with rapid steps back in the direction of New Helvetia. Halfway along the narrow Indian trail that led to the fort he saw Octave Custot coming swiftly toward him again. In his hand he carried a long hairy object.

When they came face to face, the Frenchman exhibited the gruesome object he was carrying. John cried, "It's the head of an Indian. Look, the long, black, matted hair is still clinging to it."

"God, Man! It's the chief's," said Custot, knowing that further words were superfluous.

"Where did you get it?"

"I found it . . . found it . . ."

"Go on," urged John.

"Hanging to the door of your new grass hut."

"Did Mana see it?"

"I don't think so. I looked inside. She was asleep on the floor with the baby at her side."

"*Gott sei Dank,*" breathed John spontaneously.

"Promise me you won't tell her, Custot. This comes too close after the burning of our house. But I *can't* take chances. I can't live outside the fort any longer. I'll make some excuse and move inside. I'll find a place where we can camp until the new house is ready to occupy. Drop everything else and finish it, Custot. I'm desperately afraid of an Indian uprising."

CHAPTER X

# SINISTER SHADOWS

CALIFORNIA WAS SLOWLY emerging from the pastoral lethargy characteristic of Mexican rule. There were signs of it everywhere, notably in the growing interest of foreign nations in this land with its rich natural endowments, its salubrious climate.

Alien nations were casting covetous glances toward new land. They were quietly sending out men with military and political training to inspect it. Foreign ships and overland expeditions traveled up and down the West Coast from Oregon to Lower California.

Three nations vitally concerned themselves with the possibility of acquiring this potentially rich terrain. England hoped to add it to her northern territory, with its valuable chain of Hudson's Bay Company fur trading posts. France, forced out of North America after a long hard war, by the loss of Canada to England, and forced to sell Louisiana after the disastrous Napoleonic wars to the United States, hoped to regain her lost prestige by new colonies on the Pacific Coast. And in the United States since the turn of the century, westward expansion, the keynote of her new prosperity, was bringing men closer and closer to the West Coast.

Who, indeed, would not covet this *Tierra Dorada*, this golden land? Potential wealth lay veiled within it. Vast acres capable of supporting millions of head of live stock skirted the Pacific and the inland valleys. Immense virgin forests covered the mountains. Rivers,

133

in which the mission fathers had already found traces of gold, watered plains lush and ripe for all manner of crops. The promise of mineral wealth lay in deserts and mountains, in bitumen pits, in traces of asphalt.

The ocean revealed its source of wealth: sea otter, whales, salmon, and the lesser fishes. Inland the furs of wild creatures were already supplying the marts of London, St. Petersburg and New York.

For the most part indifferent to this wealth around them, the Californians lived in serene happiness. Nature supplied them with what they needed: fish and game. Moreover, cattle, sheep and horses roamed the land and multiplied so amazingly that the *rancheros* could sell enough hides and tallow alone to the Yankee ships that put into ports along the coast to buy all the household supplies they needed. Indian labor was bountiful and cheap. In this blissful Arcadia, to work diligently was futile.

Most of the indolent Californians did not concern themselves with *mañana;* they were grateful for the bounties of nature and for the chance to live freely and happily on their great *ranchos* or in the few small towns that had grown up around the missions and presidios. *Meriendas, fandangos,* bull fights and church festivals afforded varied recreations. Physical pleasures satisfied them. They knew no other way of life. For Californians *dolce far niente* became the keynote of their existence.

A few of the more erudite, thoughtful Mexican leaders, men like Governor Alvarado and *Comandante* Vallejo, although political enemies, agreed as to what lay beneath this pastoral surface. What they beheld confused and alarmed them. They began to suspect the true designs of those about them, the motives of the suave-tongued Hudson's Bay Company agents, the purpose of the French ships which touched now and again at Monterey, the desires of the American trappers, traders and settlers who were infiltrating the coast.

Alarmed over all this, *Comandante* Vallejo wrote to the Minister of War in Mexico City:

"Sutter, styling his place the Fort of New Helvetia, and himself governor of that fortress, exercises ambition and despotic power, wages war on the natives, forces them to work for him, shoots them without formality or the approval of the governor, receives foreigners, no matter whence or how they come, not obliging them to present themselves to the authorities and sometimes not even reporting their arrival, and finally makes seditious threats. With the aid of the Hudson's Bay Company I believe we can remove Sutter from California." [1]

Again he voiced his fears for the safety of California. "Help must come from Mexico. The civil government in unskilled hands has sworn the destruction of the military branch. Military companies must be restored. Abuses of every kind are constantly permitted and relief can come only from the national government, the orders of which are at present despised." [2] In these and other ways Vallejo voiced his fears and also his dislike of his nephew, Governor Alvarado, and their inability to work harmoniously together.

Others, besides the patriotic *comandante*, were writing to their governments at home disparaging reports. The head of the Hudson's Bay Company, Sir George Simpson, visiting California with ulterior motives wrote to his London office: "Nature doing everything and man

1 Bancroft, History of California, IV, p. 238, note 28.
2 Bancroft, History of California, IV, p. 199.

doing nothing—that, in a nutshell, is California. The trade of the whole province is entirely in the hands of foreigners, who are almost exclusively of the English race. Of that race, however, the Americans are more numerous than the British. The foreigners are to the Californians as one to ten, while by their monopoly of trade and their command of resources, to say nothing of their superior energy and intelligence, they already possess vastly more than their numerical proportion of political influence, exciting not a little jealousy.

The population of California has been drawn from the most indolent variety of a most indolent species, being composed of superannuated troops and retired office holders and their descendants." [1] Sir George also warned his countrymen of the potential danger of Sutter's Fort as the center from which the Americans might move to acquire a maritime outlet at the Bay at Monterey, or in the surrounding territory.

About this time a Frenchman, visiting the West Coast, in the capacity of envoy from the French government, observed, "England and the United States flatter themselves alike at the idea of taking California from Mexico. It is more evident that California will belong to whatever nation chooses to send there a man-of-war and two hundred men . . . we should prefer to see it in the hands of the United States rather than in those of England, if it cannot belong to France."

Anticipating the arrival from Yerba Buena of some of these foreign dignitaries at his fort, John took his French uniform from a peg on the wall and shook it carefully to remove every vestige of lint and dust. As he inspected it he saw that the gold stripes Mana had added made it more impressive than before, even if they

[1] Bancroft, Cal. IV, p. 221, *note.*

made its shabby aspect more conspicuous by contrast. Yet he donned the antiquated garment with an air of satisfaction, smiling to himself as he viewed his reflection in a cracked mirror hanging on the wall, for he was in one of his optimist moods. John Sutter, late of Switzerland, now *Comandante* of Fort New Helvetia, he muttered ironically.

With a sense of gratification, he reminded himself that the position he now held was recognized throughout California. Indeed, everywhere men talked in awed tones about John Augustus Sutter and the amazing frontier settlement he was creating in this wilderness. Yet only he knew the difficulty of securing the credit for the materials that went into the Fort together with the six thousand head of livestock pastured nearby. Only he knew with what difficulty he had induced the thirty white men, Germans, Frenchmen, Swiss, English, Canadians, and Americans, to remain there in his employ. Only he knew how difficult it had been to train two hundred indolent Indians to work for him. Troubles. He had his full share of them. He was wise enough, however, to keep them to himself.

After dressing, he left the house and strolled slowly down to the waterfront. He kept his eyes on the river most of the time, watching for a schooner to appear. At intervals he took from his coat pocket a heavy gold watch with his name engraved on it, Nanette's wedding gift.

They're two hours late already. I wonder what's made the boat so late. And why is the American expedition coming to the fort, anyway? he thought.

At that moment he saw a boat round the bend in the river and heard its shrill blast. A schooner flaunting the Stars and Stripes made its way slowly toward the foot

landing. John stepped briskly forward prepared to
meet his guests. As the boat tied up at the *embarcadero,*
a young man leaped ashore.

"Lieutenant Ringgold, of the Wilkes expedition," he
announced, extending a cordial hand.

John welcomed him with his usual courteous bow as
he shook hands. "My fort is at your disposal, sir."

Although outwardly genial, he was inwardly apprehensive at the size of this well-armed United States
force, the first large one to visit the fort.

"We merely stopped to pay our respects," said the
visitor. "Everyone who comes to California wants to
meet Captain Sutter and see his fort. You're the most
famous man here, sir," said the lieutenant. "In fact,
you're famous all over the East."

"Please consider the fort your home for as long as
you like," said John, courteous and affable.

"I regret that we can't accept your offer now," the
traveler replied. "You see, our government sent us west
on a little exploring expedition. We've been in Oregon.
Our commander, Wilkes, is still there. He sent us on
ahead to survey the Sacramento to its source," he said,
indicating with a wave of the hand the men who were
standing at the rail of the ship. "I've Dr. Pickering,
six officers and fifty men with me. Lieutenant Emmons
is on his way down to the Bay from Oregon. He's coming overland."

"Bring your men ashore," said John, "and we'll dine
at the fort."

Lieutenant Ringgold thanked John profusely, but
declined. "We'll be back in a week or so, after we've
explored the Sacramento. Then we'll drop in to see you
again." He shook hands again with a youthful exuberance and clambered aboard.

As John watched them leave a feeling of panic rose
in him. He knew they were only a small part of the
Wilkes expedition sent out from Washington to explore
and map all the territory that lay between the Rocky
Mountains and the Pacific. He asked himself what
ulterior motive they had beyond a survey of the coast.
And why did they intend to map the Sacramento to its
source?

Still speculating on the motives of his visitors, John
walked toward the fort.

Near the main gate he stopped and looked critically
at his fort. Although the outside walls were in place and
presented a formidable front, the interior was far from
finished; and while the cannons pointing through the
outside walls at regular intervals gave the fort an air
of protection, John knew that the impressive façade
was effective only against Indians. It might be well, he
thought, to make friends with the Wilkes men and the
Americans who were just commencing to arrive by way
of the Colorado River, the Mojave desert, Salt Lake,
Walker's Pass, around Cape Horn.

It is more than a coincidence, he thought, that a
prominent Englishman like Sir George Simpson and a
French envoy should be making a tour of the West
Coast at the same time, and were expected almost simultaneously at the fort, and these military men from
Washington, too! John Sutter, lord of New Helvetia,
was the object of considerable comment. He was known
throughout California, that much was understandable;
but to be known in Washington, London, Paris—that
was a disturbing matter.

He wondered idly if Nanette knew about his title and
his fifty thousand acres. He must write to her, he told
himself, if only to inquire about the children. He felt a

pang of regret that he had no money to send them. But he would forward some later. Someday when he was less harassed for funds, he would send for them to come to California. After all, Nanette was still his legal wife. And the children; he would enjoy having them at the fort. The boys would be most helpful; they could one day inherit his vast holdings. They might be rich, once land values in California began to rise. Yes. It was his duty to bring them to the fort, to atone for his past neglect. Some day in the future, perhaps; when he was a rich man. Meanwhile he had Mana and her child, and problems enough of his own to face.

For one thing, there was the matter of the Hudson's Bay Company's new post at Yerba Buena. William Glen Rae, the new agent, had taken the Leese house. That would mean still heavier competition in the fur business he sorely needed for himself, until he could plant grain and raise large herds of cattle. Fur pelts were the only means he had to pay his debts, yet these men were stripping his territory of the best animals. Still dwelling on these unpleasant thoughts, John entered the huge gate, passed its Indian guard, and retired to his own quarters for the night.

A week later John, astride his favorite Pepita, with Mana seated behind him clinging to him with both arms, rode slowly toward the *embarcadero* shortly before dusk. A red sun, sinking rapidly, made its fiery way horizonward. The riders, enervated by the heat, moved listlessly, indifferently.

"The air down by the river may be cooler, Mana," said John, wiping a flushed cheek with the hot sleeve of his shirt. "I'll take you for a ride on the water, if you like."

At the landing they dismounted and climbed into a

small Indian skiff moored to the riverbank. In order to paddle more easily, John removed his moist shirt and tossed it into the bottom of the boat. Mana removed her outer robe and sat relaxed in a simple white undergarment. Thus they rowed out into the river.

It was deserted, except for a few desultory gulls sitting motionless upon the water.

Fatigued by the heat Mana trailed one hand idly in the cool water, as John paddled dextrously. Later, toward evening, mist rising gradually spread a thin cool veil over the water, as they moved slowly downstream for an hour or more toward where the American Fork bending at right angles joins the Sacramento. They had nearly reached there when the sound of singing came indistinctly toward them. The music was soft, melodious, rhythmical. Soon it grew stronger.

> *Mon per' n'avait fille que moi*
> *En cor' sur la mer el m'envoi;*
> *Le marinier qui m'y menait*
> *Il devint amoureux de moi*
> *Ma mignonette, embrassez-moi.*

John leaned forward, listening intently. A look of joy illuminated his face.

"It's French, Mana; someone's singing in French. One of the old *Voyageurs* songs. The kind French-Canadian trappers sing. Heard them often, Mana, at Fort Vancouver years ago."

Around the bend in the river came a barge, manned by Indians. In the stern sat a figure, arms crossed, neatly dressed in a French uniform, singing at the top of his lungs. He was only a few hundred yards away.

John looked in dismay at his own costume, then reached for his shirt.

"Put on your dress, Mana," he said, as he buttoned his own garment. He pushed back his hair and dipped a handful of cold water over his face. "He's someone of importance, I know by the way he's dressed."

The barge moved within hailing distance. The figure rose, bowed formally, and a voice called out in meticulous French,

"Will you direct me, *Monsieur*, to Fort New Helvetia? I have letters to a *Monsieur* Sutter, who lives there." With the barest flicker of light, his eyes swept Mana.

Although somewhat embarrassed by the informality of his setting, John replied,

"I, *Monsieur*, am Captain Sutter, of Fort New Helvetia. I shall be most happy to escort you there."

As the barge followed his lead, John whispered softly to Mana, "That, Mana, is none other than Count Duflot de Mofras, of Paris. Alvarado wrote me that he was at Monterey and would come to see us. I have been expecting him for some time."

After they moored their boats and walked the half mile from the *embarcadero* to the fort, the French traveler and his escort sat down comfortably in the main room of John's as yet unfinished house, and relaxed. Mana directed an Indian squaw to serve them with mugs of *aguardiente*, then Mana slipped silently away, followed by the French count's supercilious glances.

John answered the inquisitive looks on his guest's face by saying coldly, "My housekeeper; I brought her from Honolulu. My wife and children are still in Switzerland. I expect to send for them soon." He thought it advisable to pose as a family man; it lent a becoming stability to his ménage.

The French count gave an amused smile, for John's vagaries were the more pronounced by his obvious attempt at concealment. Had he not called attention to them, Duflot de Mofras would never have given them a second thought. Pioneers are the same the world over, thought the count. An agnostic himself, he accepted the liasons of frontier life with amused tolerance.

Over their drinks, the men grew more confiding. The count, a cultivated, poised traveler, regaled John for hours, telling him at considerable length what was happening in Europe and about the latest foreign books, music, politics. Then the visitor described his trip from Havre to Mexico and up the coast from Acapulco to Monterey.

Listening to the Frenchman's impressions John was amazed at the number of places the count had visited, the prominent men he had seen. "Why, you've visited every settlement, every mission, every town in California, Count de Mofras," he said.

"That's what I was sent for, *Monsieur* Sutter. I am collecting information in order to make a full report on this country for our Minister of Foreign Affairs."

"I was not aware that France had more than a superficial interest in the West Coast."

"In that, *Monsieur*, you are mistaken." Duflot de Mofras was handsome, slender, twenty-five years of age, with a sallow skin and heavy brown eyes, and impressed with his own importance. Gravely diplomatic, he was shrewd enough to realize that Sutter's New Helvetia, young as it was, was the key to California and he intended to win its affable Swiss owner to his side. He looked questioningly around the room.

"You may speak freely, Count de Mofras. We're

quite alone. Whatever you say will be regarded as confidential."

The count leaned slightly forward. "Between ourselves, *Monsieur* Sutter, it might be to your interest to co-operate with the ambitions of *La Belle France*. You already are French in sympathy, *Monsieur* Sutter, are you not? Your attitude, your uniform, which I am told you usually wear, indicate that."

John's face flushed at the count's implied flattery. This, indeed, was an opportunity not to be overlooked. It would be profitable enough too. All those debts . . .

The count eyed him slyly. A keen judge of men, he could read the ambition and pride of his host. He shrugged his shoulders and arched his black eyebrows. It was a typical French gesture, graphic, self-assured. "You would benefit also—just how far I can't say," he added significantly.

"Permit me to explain still further, *Monsieur*," said the French envoy quickly. "France needs to replace the deplorable loss of her colonies—Canada and Louisiana. Already mistress of the Marquesas and Tahiti, she could materially enhance her power by acquiring one of the Sandwich Islands. She would also like to purchase the settlement at Port Bodega and Ross. I understand you yourself are interested in acquiring all the Russian holdings," he added, watching John with an eagle eye.

John nodded. "I am considering it."

"In that case, we might make some agreement that would rebound to our mutual advantage."

"Perhaps so," replied John gravely.

"You see, *Monsieur* Sutter, ownership of these Russian properties would be a preliminary step toward acquiring the entire harbor of San Francisco—the key to the Pacific Ocean. By grouping around the strategic

Bay area the French Canadians of this country, and by opening to our countrymen, who are constantly coming west like yourself to settle, a vast field for colonization, we could establish a new *French America*."

Somewhat aghast John listened to the magnitude of French designs on the coast. Is his conversation to be taken seriously, he asked himself. But the face of the vivacious count was grave and circumspect.

Before he had time to break in upon the conversation, Duflot de Mofras continued, "To accomplish this we should need an agent in California. Someone of importance, like yourself, *Monsieur*. One whom we could depend upon. France is generous and will amply reward those who serve her. Your fort, *Monsieur*," De Mofras let his eyes roam around John's room, "it would make an ideal place...."

"Concisely, what do you propose, Count de Mofras?"

"Until I confer with my government in Paris, I cannot answer," said the Frenchman impressively. "All that I ask now is your promise to support the claims of France."

"The matter is one that requires considerable thought," John replied, although his manner was that of a man about to assent; yet, through his mind came an inner warning, an admonition to be cautious. Now as he sat thinking, he recalled pertinent conversations he had had with agents of the Hudson's Bay Company, who had asked him to help them acquire California. They talked as if they had the government of England behind them. Perhaps ... perhaps England would be a more advantageous ally than France. For one thing, her trappers and traders were already nearby in Oregon Territory. And France ... France was far away.

He looked speculatively at the envoy who was tapping

his fingers somewhat impatiently together. "We may count then on you, *Monsieur* Sutter?"

There was no outward trace of what was in his mind as John replied, "I assure you, Count de Mofras, that I sympathize deeply with the aims and ambitions of France." Again he parried for time. "You have concrete ideas as to how your country might acquire California, I presume?"

"Definitely so," the envoy replied. By nature outspoken and self-assured he did not hesitate to state plainly his viewpoint to one whom he believed to be wholly on his side, and so in his most conciliatory manner he spoke softly to John. "There are ways ... by fomenting a revolution, perhaps. These California politicians will do anything for a bribe." John broke into the conversation long enough to remark, "You understand the Mexican temperament, Count de Mofras ... fortunately."

"Yes, I've had considerable experience with Mexican officials in the past year or so," said de Mofras with the barest hint of a cynical smile, "as I was about to remark, *Monsieur*, the land is on the verge of dissolution as it is, that is what French travelers have been reporting to our Foreign Office. Perhaps you already know, *Monsieur*, all these French ships that put in at ports along the west coast in the past twenty years were actually warships in disguise. They came on official business, you understand, to sound out the country."

"I suspected as much," John replied. "But I doubt if the Mexicans were aware of it. At least not so far as I know." Having thus courteously replied, John lapsed once more into silence.

Again the count lifted his shoulders significantly as he watched John's face.

"You mentioned other ways, Count de Mofras, I believe. ..."

"Another way is to acquire large holdings," said the Count frankly. "I mean by individual purchase of *ranchos* from the Mexicans themselves. We have many French settlers already located here, *Monsieur*."

"Yes, they are among our most prosperous settlers."

"It would not be difficult to send more large colonies of them to the west coast, not difficult at all, *Monsieur* Sutter. Yes, these *mañana* Mexicans, as I believe I heard you call them, could never oppose us, at least not with armed force."

John looked thoughtfully at the complacent count. "Californians are volatile creatures," he said. "Not even God himself knows what goes on in their heads. Many of them, I might add, are wholly under the power and influence of the Mexican-born priests."

"I've known that," said the count, "but I believe we can win them over to our side. The Pope would throw the full weight of his influence to aid us, I believe. The good Fathers have been badly used in California ... their lands and missions confiscated ... they would welcome the protection of France. Moreover I have private information to confirm what I say, *Monsieur* Sutter. Its source I am not at liberty to divulge."

"Is there any danger that the English would oppose you?" inquired John. "You know they now have a post on the Bay. Rae, the son-in-law of one of the Hudson's Bay Company officials, makes his home there."

The count drew himself up haughtily.

"The English are no match for France," he observed with dignity. "Furthermore, most of their trappers and traders are French-Canadians who would be only too glad to migrate to California. They are good Catholics.

They would obey the priests. They, as much as anyone, long to see the colors of France flying over California. Think of it, *Monsieur*. A French flag flying in Yerba Buena. At Fort Ross, at Monterey, Sonoma, Santa Barbara, Los Angeles, San Diego. It would be a pretty sight, *Monsieur* Sutter, a pretty sight."

"And New Helvetia? What about that?"

"For your help, *Monsieur* Sutter, you can name your own price . . . Wealth, power, position . . . lands . . . anything you might ask . . . We might make you commander in chief. Yes, we would go even further than that."

John leaned forward in his chair, his breath coming in quick, eager gasps. His interest in England's advances were overshadowed by the immediacy of the count's offer.

"How far would France go?" he asked.

De Mofras's dark eyes caught the glow of ambition that radiated from John's animated countenance. "Almost anything you want, *Monsieur* Sutter. You have only to name it . . . anything."

John looked the French envoy squarely in the eye. "My price for assisting you," he said . . . "would be . . . would be the governorship of French California."

# CHAPTER XI

# RUSSIAN ARCADIA

GOVERNOR ROTCHEV sat silently with his arm around his wife, Princess Hélène, in their favoiite spot, the summer house on a hill overlooking Fort Ross. They never wearied of the spectacular view over ripening fields and thriving orchards, over the distant pine clad hills. Before them lay the Pacific that separated them from the amenities of civilized life into which they had been born.

He was thinking sadly of his approaching departure from the land he so deeply loved. Less than a month ago he had received an imperial edict from the Czar, commanding him to sell or close Fort Ross and return to St. Petersburg.

He suspected the true reason behind it. The Russian-American Fur Company, with headquarters at Sitka, in which the Czar was part owner, was no longer able to compete against the Hudson's Bay Company. In the event of war, isolated Fort Ross could not defend itself adequately and might fall into British hands. The somber thoughts tempered his delight in the spectacular view he might otherwise enjoy with his wife.

He pressed her shoulder with a firm, affectionate touch.

"Do you mind losing it, Hélène? All that we've built up together? The peace and freedom and joy we've had here?"

"In some ways, yes," she said softly. "Our home. I

shall miss it, of course. And being constantly together. Court life at St. Petersburg was tiresome. Those endless festivities . . . they left little time for the things I really value."

"Such as . . .?"

"Your love. Being with you. Time for books and music. My garden. Fort Ross is a Paradise. God has created few lovelier spots."

"Exquisitely expressed, Hélène. It breaks my heart to think of leaving. But the Czar's orders. Here in my pocket," he said. "They were slow reaching us. More than two years.[1] We have no choice, Hélène. I know this colony has not been a success. God knows I've done my best to make it pay. But it's impossible. The Russian-American Fur can no longer operate this distant outpost profitably. The fur-bearing seals are disappearing. Our wheat crops are not adequate to feed His Excellency's Sitka colony. We can get no friendly co-operation from the Mexican authorities. No, *chère Hélène*, our days at Ross are definitely over."

"Surely you can find someone to purchase it? With all the valuable tools and equipment that go with it. Not to mention the livestock."

"I've tried. None of the wealthy *rancheros* will buy Ross. Not even grasping *Comandante* Vallejo. And the good Governor Alvarado seems to think we should present Ross to the Mexican Government. Both these officials think no one in California is rich enough to buy it and that we'll be forced to abandon it. It's tragic, Hélène."

"I'm sorry you found the Mexicans so unreasonable," said Hélène.

---

[1] The order for the liquidation of Fort Ross was signed at St. Petersburg on April 15, 1839.

"Between ourselves, Hélène, all these local officials are rascals. We Russians are not double-faced. That's why our people find it almost impossible to transact business openly with the authorities at Monterey. California is bribe-ridden from one end to the other, its situation precarious. Mark my word, I predict it will not remain long in Mexican hands. That's another reason why I shall never sell them Ross."

"Would the Czar perhaps consider trying to acquire California?" asked Helene, who had complete faith in the expansive designs of her royal relative.

"No, except for wheat and furs there is nothing on the coast Russia wants, I believe. Besides, it's too far away from the court. We must find someone here to purchase it. Of course you know as well as I do, Hélène, why Ross is being sold."

"Because of competition with the Hudson's Bay Company?"

"Precisely. We haven't the facilities to oppose them. Not with their government behind them. Why, they intend to control all the commerce and land on the west coast of North America. I don't need to tell you what a hold that company already has here. They are expanding all the time. Now they have a commercial house in Honolulu, and are leasing another in Yerba Buena, which are visited regularly by sailing ships, carrying furs, whale oil, tea, spices and merchandise of all kinds."

"If we only had a strong ally out here," said Hélène. "Like France."

"Yes, like France. Young De Mofras agrees with me as to the need for a French colony in California. I had a long talk about it when he was here."

"A thoroughly charming young man," said the princess. "What a joy to meet some one who speaks perfect French."

"And enjoys good wine. Did I tell you, my dear, that he got gloriously drunk the time he visited the Hartnell ranch near Monterey? It seems he was given a room in which the sacrificial wine used by visiting priests is kept. The guest drank it all to the last drop."

"Don't believe all the gossip you hear. You know how these Mexicans like to exaggerate. Besides, the French envoy conducted himself with the utmost decorum all the time he was here."

"That was different," the governor replied. "He came here for a specific purpose, to enlist our aid in the event France decides to acquire California. He was considerably upset when he learned we intended to dispose of Ross. In fact, it was he who thought Sutter might acquire it. He felt it would then be in friendly hands."

"Yes, why not John Sutter?"

"He might consider it, Hélène. But according to Yerba Buena gossip, the Swiss is penniless. I doubt if he could borrow the money to pay for it. His credit is overstrained. He owes bills everywhere. Nathan Spear told me."

"If you made the terms easy enough . . . only a small amount of cash and the balance over a period of years, he might manage. The governor of Sitka could send an agent once a year to collect payments when he buys wheat and cattle for the colony."

"Possibly, Hélène. It's worth considering anyway." He patted her shoulder once more, then rose. "Come, it's close to the dinner hour." Together they walked arm in arm down the hill to their home.

In traditional manner, they dined elaborately by candle light. Bliny—pancakes with caviar and sour cream—was followed by a rich sturgeon soup. Then came local salmon masked in herb-seasoned sauce, planked beef garnished with peas, tomatoes, corn and squash fresh from the governor's garden, green salad, and a rich cheese cake stuffed with fresh fruits drenched in liqueurs. Rotchev lit a Mexican cigarette, took out his reports and began to study them.

Long after Princess Hélène had retired, the governor sat deliberating over the best way to dispose of Fort Ross. His suffering expressed itself in a physical manner. The corners of his mouth stiffened into thin, stern lines that belied his affable nature. The palms of his hands exuded an incessant moisture. Finally he pushed back his chair, and got up.

"It's the best I can do," he mumbled unhappily to himself. "I must induce Captain Sutter to take it. Otherwise it might pass into Vallejo or Alvarado's hands. No worse misfortune could happen to Ross." He went up to the room where his wife lay asleep.

Although he tried not to awaken her as he undressed, she spoke drowsily to him.

"What have you been doing so late, dear?"

"Thinking about selling to Sutter."

Governor Rotchev left the next day for New Helvetia. He was not certain, as he rode on horseback toward Sonoma, where he intended to take a boat up the Sacramento, whether or not he could sell Sutter the Fort. He pondered over it for some time. A shrewd judge of men, he seldom failed in his successful handling of them. I must flatter him, he thought. Any man so conceited has his weak side. I'm suspicious of the man. His pompous manner, his effusive hospitality, his liking for ostentation seem forced. No one here has taken the trouble to find out his past. From all I hear the Captain talks only of his military career with the French army. There's something mysterious about him and his young fort. Rotchev amused himself in speculation as he rode briskly across the countryside. At the Sonoma *embarcadero* he caught a small boat bound for New Helvetia.

Days later, Governor Rotchev stepped ashore at the landing near the fort. He was perturbed by the travel-stained, armed Americans in high spirits who gave a military salute as he passed, and he wondered the reason for their presence.

Two ragged Indian boys escorted him into the fort and to the main house. John welcomed him effusively and with repeated assurances of delight at the honor. He showed the governor his new adobe dwelling built to replace the one destroyed by fire, a two-story affair, whitewashed and roofed with tiles.

The governor was shocked at its lack of neatness. A child's damp breach cloth lay neglected in a corner of the main room. Corn husks littered the unswept floor, dropped apparently by some one making tortillas. There was a keg of *aguardiente* with several filthy mugs atop it.

The two men sat down on uncomfortable wooden chairs. An Indian, dressed only in dirty white trousers, his black locks hanging down his oily brown back, served them. He brought a bottle of French wine, pouring it awkwardly into two stained mugs. At that moment a rat scuttled by.

After a brief conversation on trivial matters, the governor said, "I've come to discuss with you something that will materially enhance your prestige in California, my dear Captain." He stopped speaking long enough to fan himself with his hat. The September heat was exhausting. "You should move to Ross, Captain Sutter. It's cool near the coast."

"I envy you Fort Ross, Your Excellency," replied John in his most gracious manner. "Indeed I do." An inkling of the governor's mission was beginning to come to him. "By all means the finest fort in the west. Those who live there are true aristocrats," he said with a flattering bow.

"I'm delighted to know you think so, Captain Sutter, although I predict the success of your own Helvetia. With your ability, if I may presume to say so, I believe I know how you can make it the leading settlement in California."

"I am afraid I don't understand, Your Excellency, just how might I accomplish this?"

"That is why I am here, Captain," the governor observed with a sigh in his voice. "You may not have heard that Princess Hélène and I are returning to St. Petersburg. We intend to dispose of everything. I should like to see you become the new owner of Ross."

"Then it's true that you intend to leave permanently? I'd heard rumors. I couldn't believe, Your Excellency, they were true. You and the Princess seemed so happy there."

"Czar's orders, not a choice. You are the one man I should like to see acquire my Fort Ross," said the governor in a suave, silky tone of voice. "Wouldn't you care to own it, my dear Captain?" Acquiring Ross would bring prestige, power, perhaps wealth. The offer seemed incredible to John.

"Of course." John spoke rapidly, in an excited tone. "I'm desperately short of everything: lumber, tools, equipment, furniture . . . you have these at Ross."

Rotchev sat erect, trying to ascertain the inner

thoughts of the man beside him. For a moment neither spoke.

It was John who said apologetically, "But the cost, Governor Rotchev. I'm not a rich man. No one in all California has money enough to pay you what it's worth."

Rotchev smiled, "Suppose we discuss the terms, Captain. You may find you can meet them."

"Let me hear them, Your Excellency," said John, making no attempt to conceal his eagerness.

"I will sell Ross to you and everything in it, that is, all except the bare land itself which we do not own, for $30,000."

"Thirty . . . the price is fair enough, but, but . . . I haven't that amount . . . can't raise it." For a moment he rubbed his brow, with the gesture indicative of doubt. Then the self-assurance that was so much a part of his nature asserted itself. "Let me think, thirty thousand . . . no . . . I don't see where I can get it."

"We can arrange suitable terms," said Rotchev. "Don't mistake me, Captain, I would do this for no one but you. Governor Kouprianoff, whom you met in Sitka, admires you tremendously. He wants you to have Ross. He has, in fact, written me in the utmost confidence to destroy everything rather than let any of it fall into Mexican hands."

"What terms would Your Excellency suggest?"

"Let us say an initial payment of two thousand. It could be in gold or goods, as you prefer. The balance to be distributed over three years. For the first two years you might pay us in grain and tallow, needed by our Sitka colony. I am convinced you can easily meet these terms."

"The offer is a generous one." The exceedingly low

price surprised John. "Why have the Russian officials decided to sell?"

"As you know, the Czar is a large stockholder in the Russian-American Fur Company," the governor replied. "To speak frankly, we are too isolated, too far from Sitka, not to mention St. Petersburg, to operate profitably. That's why the Czar has ordered his Company to dispose of Ross."

The governor stopped fanning himself long enough to remove a sheaf of papers from an inner pocket. "Here is a complete list of the properties, everything we own both at Bodega and at Ross. May I be excused to stroll around the fort while you examine it?"

"Certainly, Your Excellency." He accepted the papers. "Dinner will be served in an hour. Suppose we meet here then." He stood up and bowed low as the governor passed from the room.

John began to study Rotchev's reports. Forty buildings; these he could dismantle and use the lumber at the fort. Thirty-five hundred head of livestock. Extremely valuable. A twenty-two ton launch; he needed a boat of his own to ply between New Helvetia and Yerba Buena. Four small boats. Plows, harrows, harnesses, carts, miscellaneous tools. "Excellent, excellent," muttered John. But what of the orchards and vineyards laden with fruit? And the threshing floors and the mills and the outdoor bakeries? To transport all this to New Helvetia was no light task. Was it worth the risk? He read the lists again stopping occasionally to jot down a few figures.

The opportunity to acquire Fort Ross was not to be overlooked. He could not believe that it had actually been offered to him for a mere thirty thousand dollars. After all only two thousand dollars would be required the first year. He must buy it, even though he was already very much in debt. But where could he raise that amount?

For the first payment he might go to Nathan Spear in Yerba Buena for a loan of two thousand dollars secured by a mortgage on New Helvetia. Future installments he could meet from the sale of crops. He began to add a long column of figures. The total amount of debts he owed was staggering. Two thousand dollars more would hardly be felt. As he was about to replace the papers he heard footsteps.

Governor Rotchev entered just as an Indian was ringing the dinner-gong.

Sutter received him smilingly and escorted him to the table in the center of the room. It was covered with a cloth of heavy homespun linen sold by Yankee ships that docked at Monterey. The moment he was seated an Indian with dirty hands set before him a coarse pottery plate piled high with jerked beef, tortillas, frijoles, salmon, and a large piece of watermelon. The foods were lukewarm and unappetizing, made less attractive by being heaped indiscriminately on the plate. Rotchev ate sparingly.

Governor Rotchev observed innumerable signs of feminine occupancy. There were traces of it everywhere: an undergarment dangled from a peg on the wall, a garland of faded flowers lay on the floor. Once the count noticed a slender girl in a strange flowered robe appear for a moment in the doorway, a child in her arms.

He saw John motion surreptitiously to her to go away. All this will amuse Hélène, he thought to himself.

After dinner, the two men settled down to a detailed discussion of the sale.

"It's a pleasure to know that our Russian property in California will pass into your hands, Captain Sutter," said the governor, as the two men were about to retire for the night. "We need only sign the final papers in the presence of legal witnesses, so I suggest that you return with me to the coast tomorrow. My boat is at your disposal."

They made the trip from Sacramento to the coast in three days. Within a week the formal papers were drawn up and signed in the presence of witnesses at Yerba Buena.

From there they journeyed to Fort Ross. In honor of the transfer of Ross a banquet was held on board the Governor's ship *Helena*, anchored off Bodega. Wearing his old French uniform John sat between Governor Rotchev and Princess Hélène, both of whom overwhelmed him with tokens of esteem. The governor insisted personally on filling his glass time and again with champagne.

The rare beverage blended perfectly with the wild duck that had been roasted in imported brandy. "I congratulate you, Your Highness, on the excellence of your dinner," John said in his most pompous manner to his hostess.

"This duck is cooked in the Russian style. We had it often at the court." She was courteous, but reserved. Rotchev had told her about John's Kanaka mistress.

The governor accepted pioneer life with a broader masculine viewpoint. He liked the sturdy Swiss and admired his determination to build a settlement of importance. In fact the more he drank, the more he esteemed his guest.

"Let me see, how long ago was it that you began New Helvetia, Captain?"

"Three years; two and a half, to be exact."

"What? So much in so short a time? Amazing," replied Rotchev. "I predict tremendous success for you," he said, raising his glass. "To the greatest fort in the west. And to John Sutter, its creator. May health, wealth and happiness be his. May his name be immortal. Let us drink to John Augustus Sutter. My friend, and the future Midas of California."

# CHAPTER XII

## FLOODTIME

THE SPRING FOLLOWING the purchase of Fort Ross rains fell incessantly at New Helvetia. Not that they were uncommon in Springtime; in fact they came intermittently from November through May. This year, however, there had been no rain until late March. Then, as if to atone for their belated appearance, all through April rains fell almost daily until the high ground around the fort was a quagmire.

This was only the prelude to the devastation that followed. Spring freshets, roaring down from the Sierras that towered high at a distance, and gathering force from myriad streams in the uplands, changed the usually placid Sacramento into a boiling, seething maelstrom. As they swept from the mountains, they carried in their raging waters a mass of debris: uprooted trees, broken branches, tangled underbrush.

John stood morosely on high ground, watching the rise of the river inch by inch. His face was drawn in his anxiety. He did not know how far it might rise. There was no one at the fort who had lived there long enough to predict what the river might do. No one, that is, except a few Indians. They shook their heads with a reluctant gesture. Some were moving their squaws and babies to higher ground.

There had been no boat from Yerba Buena for a month now. Not even an Indian runner had come through. Nor had he received so much as a line from

161

John Bidwell, the young schoolteacher from the east who had reached New Helvetia soon after the purchase of Fort Ross. He had seemed so steady and dependable that John had sent him to the Russian settlement to take charge of dismantling it and shipping everything that could be moved up the river to New Helvetia: lumber, machinery and livestock from the coast across country to his settlement. John could not help wondering if the land near Ross was under water.

He tried to view the pageantry of the roaring river abstractly, as a spectacular thing apart, not as an avaricious monster bent on destroying crops and livestock, perhaps even New Helvetia itself. Unless he did so, he felt he could not endure the sight of it longer. Moods of hope, that the waters would soon abate, alternated with moods of despair.

To steady himself, he removed from a hip pocket a small flask of *aguardiente*. He drank deeply, tipping back his head until he had drained the contents. With a satisfactory smile he recorked the flask and replaced it in his pocket. Warm and stimulating, the *aguardiente* spread through him.

Metamorphosed by its potent touch, John now viewed the flooding river with less despair. It was rising slowly. There was no need to worry.

It was all part of life, this ebb and flow of the river. And life was made up of contrast. Sickness and health. Plenty and want. Life and death. Darkness and light. Night and day. Good and evil. It was like that the world over. Yes, everywhere. No one could escape it, not in any century, in any place. Not even he, John Augustus Sutter, no matter how hard he tried. It was an elemental force, beyond the ken of mankind.

He could not take his eyes off the swelling river; it

fascinated him. It had come now to have more than a superficial meaning. Viewing it, he felt as if in it the forces of good and evil were fighting for supremacy in the world. These same eternal, immortal forces that endured through time and space.

Good and evil. John knew these same twin forces were embedded in the tissues of his own body, his blood, the brain itself. The good in him was what made him kind to those about him; it was what prompted him to treat the Indians kindly, to befriend the destitute who came to his fort; to treat with courtesy those with whom he came into daily association.

He thought rebelliously of the evil that afflicted him, as insistently as brandy: the urge for women. It was growing worse. Mana no longer attracted him. He desired young squaws. Nor did the vermin that infested them disturb him, if he were under the influence of alcohol. Perhaps it was not wholly his own fault. Just the evil in him. Like the river, human nature, perhaps, must yield before primal instincts.

John recalled his old friend of years before, Charles Weber, discussing it one time in Basle. He had said something about the dual forces in the world. About the Persians. Zoroaster, some six thousand years before Christ. The memory awakened him. Zoroaster. That was it. The Persian. A human sage who was one of the first to recognize the forces of good and evil in everything, one of the first to show his followers how to encourage the one, subdue the other. What was it he called these insistent spirits found everywhere? Suddenly he remembered. *Ahura Mazda,* the supreme good; *Ahriman,* the supreme evil.

Strange that he hadn't thought about it in all these years. It took the Sacramento spilling over its banks to bring it back. Was it because he felt spiritually close to the river that he found in it compensation for something lacking in his own daily life? Was it because he found in it the enduring companionship denied him, one of the penalties of being a pioneer?

Of course there was Nanette and his four children back in Burgdorf. He had been away from them ten years. They were almost unreal. A few letters. That was all. As for Nanette, he could not even recall the color of her hair and eyes.

He desired, he knew, a woman he could idealize; beautiful, cultivated, gracious. . . . He found himself envying Rotchev. No one knew he kept in his desk drawer at the fort a lace handkerchief which had belonged to Princess Hélène. She had left it behind at Ross.

John was so deep in his thoughts that he failed to see that the river was rising . . . rising.

Suddenly aware of it, madness seized him. It was like nothing he had ever experienced, the driving, impelling force that came over him. He looked down in a frenzy at the flood-swept waters. He felt the desire to throw himself in, to let his lifeless body float with it to the sea. He felt the urge to blot out eternally the fears, the debts, the desire for liquor and lustful pleasure that at times controlled him. Perhaps in this way he could find *Ahura Mazda*, the supreme good, light everlasting.

This ineffectual attempt to voice the madness affected him like a hollow mockery. It shamed him with its puerility. He realized suddenly that man's attempt to pit his forces against those of nature could end only in disaster. Was that what the river was trying to teach him by mocking him, by ridiculing him as it lapped closer and closer to his feet? Was it trying to tell him that good and evil would go on eternally throughout time and space in an endless clash, that he, John Augustus Sutter was of no more importance in its scheme of things than a tiny amoeba, that lowest of all forms of life? That he and his fort and his dreams and hopes were of slight consequence in the magnitude of the universe, in a world that had passed from ice age to ice age, from millennium to millennium, from civilization to civilization that had sprung up, thrived, vanished?

The desire to throw himself into the river no longer pressed in upon him. Awareness that the flood had passed its peak brought new life to him. He felt suddenly faint. He walked over to a sycamore tree and leaned his back against its trunk for support. He closed his eyes. Peace and security pervaded his consciousness. Drowsiness swept through him. His head nodded; his body slumped; a moment later he fell asleep.

Mana found him an hour later. She shook him violently.

"Wake up, John. Everyone at the fort has been looking for you everywhere. We were afraid . . . afraid. . . ."

"Of what, Mana *mia?*" asked John, stupidly.

"That you had fallen into the river and been drowned."

"Nonsense," he replied somewhat roughly. "I'm old enough to look after myself."

"No man ever really grows up. Every man needs a woman to look after him."

But even with Mana beside him he was filled with loneliness. He looked quizzically at her. She was still buoyant, full of sunshine and laughter like a happy gurgling child. She was the evil in him, the *Ahriman* in him who dragged him down to taste the dregs of life.

Mana dulled his senses, clogged his ambition; from her, as from liquor, there seemed no escape.

Sunlight playing around her dark hair—adorned as usual with wild flowers—made Mana singularly beautiful that day; yet it was lost upon John.

He walked automatically beside her, scarcely conscious of the footsteps attempting to keep pace with his own.

"Why do you hurry so?" she asked, panting for breath.

"Forgive me, Mana *mia*," he said gently. "I was not aware of it."

She did not speak to him again. She was becoming accustomed to his strange moods. None the less, they frightened her. She knew John was growing away from her; that he spent many nights in the huts of squaws.

John stalked on toward the fort. The hours spent down by the river had been an illuminating experience to him; it was as if he were reborn into a new existence. Thoughts of suicide had made living desirable.

To make his new life more constructive than the past one now became his purpose. He would make his fort the rendezvous for those who came west to build new lives for themselves, to give them the physical and spiritual help they needed. He would try to weave into his life the spirit of good, to cast out evil. This, then, would be his *Ultima Thule*. He would carry this goal forever in his breast until it merged with him into eternity, like a river voiding itself into the sea.

## CHAPTER XIII

# THE MOON IS DOWN

JOHN FOUND THE altruistic resolutions that he had recently made difficult to fulfill. He was always eager to make constructive promises to himself, but slow to circumvent the inevitable obstacles that arose. He often deviated from the things he intended to do. Fate, the pressure of circumstances, ill luck—he grasped readily at these fragile straws to exonerate himself. After each lapse from right conduct, he resolved not to digress again, but he could never seem to keep himself moving steadily forward in the direction he had intended.

John sought escape by the most convenient means: liquor and squaws. He kept kegs of brandy from wild grapes in his rooms at the fort. Night after night he invited congenial friends to join him. More often than not, several of them spent the night at the fort, stretched out on the floor of John's living room, their drunken snores reverberating to the rafters. Even after they had passed into the realm of oblivion, John would continue to drink alone till daylight.

For a time Mana regarded John's lapses from virtue with indulgent pity. As they increased, however, she became annoyed. The rows of men stretched out night after night, not far from where she and the baby slept, changed her pity into sullen fury.

She began to reproach John. Her caustic words tinged, perhaps with jealousy; she had cause to believe that he was trifling with more than one young squaw

167

and as his brazen conduct sickened her beyond endurance, she grew indifferent and careless, leaving her own and the child's soiled garments lying where she had dropped them. It was her way of reproaching him for his neglect of her, for she knew that he liked neatness. After a few ineffectual attempts to curb her slovenly ways, John paid no further attention to her. His indifference hurt her most of all.

One day after dinner, as he held a mug of *aguardiente* clasped in his hand, she came to him, leading their toddling child by the hand.

"I leave," she announced imperiously. "I go back to Kanaka Harry."

John held the mug of brandy, which he was in the act of raising to his lips, in mid-air and smiled cynically at her.

"Go then, Mana. But you must leave the child. He's mine."

"No, no," she cried passionately. "You have many more. Squaw babies," she said scornfully. Swiftly she turned, dragging the bewildered child behind her, and disappeared.

Shrugging his shoulders, John lifted the cup to his lips.

"*Hasta luego*, Mana," he said, gulping it noisily.

She'll come back, he told himself. But do I want her? There are younger and more attractive women. Plenty of them at the fort.

He let his thoughts dwell voluptuously on the graceful young girl his old friend, Chief Anashe, had sold him a few days before for a few strands of gay-colored beads. She was a lovely creature, gay and winsome, and fairly clean for a squaw. She accepted eagerly the silver bracelets of Mexican origin and the fringed, brightly embroidered shawl of Chinese design he gave her.

She exhibited her gifts around the fort, to the envy of the other squaws. No doubt Mana had seen her wearing them. John chuckled to himself. Undoubtedly it had something to do with her abrupt departure. Jealousy turned women into wildcats. As the potency of the brandy began to lull his senses, he lay down on the ground and fell asleep.

He did not awaken till dusk, heavy but sober. He walked slowly into his house and contemplated the dirt and disorder. Mana had taken all her personal belongings, except a few ragged garments she had left lying in disorderly heaps. John kicked them aside. A broken toy he placed with his papers strewn over the table he used as a desk. It reminded him of his and Nanette's children whom he had not seen for ten years.

He recalled that less than a month before a cold letter had arrived from Nanette in Burgdorf, informing him that the children were well and making excellent progress at school. She also said that the eldest son, John's namesake, was eager to come to California. She even hinted broadly that she, herself, would like to join him. He scowled fiercely at the thought, then, moved by some vague sense of responsibility, reproached himself for his neglect. Some day, his conscience told him, he would send for them. When he had funds. But so far he had nothing but debts. They hung over him like lowering storm clouds, ominous, foreboding.

All that evening he refused to touch liquor but sat soberly at his table worrying about his debts. He penned a letter to Nanette. It was even colder than her own. In it he expressed his thanks for news of his family, then went on briefly to describe life at the fort. He stressed the primitive life he led and spoke confidently of his faith in the future. "In a year or so, I'll send the money for your transportation," he wrote, "when the fort is finally completed. You can not be comfortable here at the present time, with everything as rough as it is. Moreover, we have no schools for the children. I want them to have the best of everything; to be a credit to us. They must be educated, if they are to succeed in life." Relieved at this discharge of an obvious duty, he signed and sealed it with heavy wax. He would send it to Yerba Buena the next day to catch the clipper sailing around the Horn for the east coast where it would be relayed to Europe.

Thoughts of Nanette and his growing family made him feel strangely old. There was no escaping the fact that his eldest son must be well into his teens. John shuddered as the dread of age overcame him. He seized the smoking candle and went over to a cracked mirror that hung on the wall. Holding the light so that it shone into it, he inspected his countenance with a critical eye.

What he saw frightened him. The eyes were bloodshot. Beneath them blackish puffs underlined the lashes. Red blotches, as if painted by an impish hand, dotted the sagging face. He recognized these telling evidences of loose-living creeping upon his countenance. Dissipation was already engraven there. It was written there for all the world to see.

For a week he did not drink. Then in self-pity came a veritable orgy of drink. It was only when steeped in *aguardiente* that John could forget the failure of his spring wheat. With this crop he had intended to pay his most pressing creditors and the second installment now overdue on the Russian debt. Liquor made him forget that his fort lacked the evidences of culture and refinement he longed for in his sober moments. It made him forget the squalor around him, the licentious squaws, the bawdy jokes, the crude frontiersmen who swarmed around his fort.

One morning, after a night passed with the panacea of brandy, John dully resumed his duties. He breakfasted on chocolate and tortillas served by a sly-eyed Indian servant, and went out to relax in the warmth of the May sunlight. He crossed the debris-strewn path that led from his house to the gate of the fort, kicking aside the empty kegs, bottles, broken crockery and loose papers that blocked his progress. "*Muchacho, muchacho,*" he called, beckoning to an Indian loitering near the gate.

"Come, clear away this filth," said John, pointing to the rubbish.

"*Sí, Señor Capitán,*" the native replied. He muttered to himself as he worked. He shook his head dubiously as he watched out of the corner of his eye the labored gait of his employer, walking unsteadily ahead. "White man no good. Too much drink. Make trouble with squaws," he said.

When the Indian returned to his settlement near the fort that night he discovered that his own squaw had disappeared. "Where is she?" he asked of the old squaw nearby.

The aged woman, wrinkled and bent, nodded significantly in the direction of the fort.

"*El Señor Capitán?*"

A quick jerk of her head gave him all the information

he needed. He slunk away. His face burned with shame and disgrace. He ran on past the native village and into the adjoining forest. He flung himself face downward on the matted undergrowth.

He imagined himself kicking the lifeless body of Sutter aside and rolling it into a muddy ditch. The more he thought about it, the more the urge to kill obsessed him. At intervals he gave out low, bitter words that came from the depths of the misery within.

Late at night he went to the *temescal*, the Indian sweathouse frequented only by men. He found assembled a few younger braves and the usual group of village elders, who decided all important matters pertaining to the settlement. In their midst, sat the chief. He was unarmed but many of the younger men, who lay naked in the stifling heat, had their bows and arrows beside them.

The intruder greeted them with the deference expected from young men. For several moments there was a communal silence, while the chief waited for the visitor to speak. "What is it?" asked one of the elders curiously.

"Speak out, my son," admonished the chief.

The young native launched into a tirade against the Captain, against all white men at Sutter's Fort.

"They've taken my squaw," he said passionately. "She's gone."

"And mine."

"And mine."

"And mine."

Three men rose quickly out of the shadows; as they spoke they advanced toward the chief.

The chief turned and talked in an undertone to the village elders surrounding him about the white men's

PORTSMOUTH SQUARE

viciousness. Then he raised his hand and spoke slowly but in a loud voice so that all could hear.

"Tomorrow night . . . the moon is down . . . it will be dark . . . the white men are evil . . . they try to destroy us . . . they must die. . . ."

# CHAPTER XIV

# NIGHT OF TERROR

As THE INDIAN guards swung open the fort gates very early the following day, Chief Anashe slunk silently through, and on to John's house. He tapped on the heavy oak door. Ever since the day three years before when he first guided John and his ten Kanakas up the Sacramento he had shown a paternal interest in the welfare of the young colony.

John roused himself, "Who's there?"

"It's Anashe, *Señor Capitán*, your friend."

John was alarmed. He slipped a worn coat across his shoulders and stepped barefoot to the door. He unbolted the heavy latch that held the door in place. "Come in, my friend," he said.

As he entered Anashe peered cautiously on all sides.

"What brings you so early, *amigo mio?*" John inquired.

"Bad news, *Señor, muy malo*. Indians," he whispered. "Make war tonight."

"Many warriors?"

"The Cosumnes. All of them," said the chief. "They had a council of war last night. They intend, *Señor ...*" he paused, being reluctant to impart the unpleasant news.

John bowed his head. "I understand, Anashe. They plan to attack the fort."

"*Si, Señor*," replied the chief. "*Hombres muy malos*."

"Who told you?"

174

"*Un amigo.*" Anashe closed his lips in a cryptic silence and started away.

"*Gracias, amigo mio,*" John called after him.

For several moments John gazed into space. A sense of frustration left him weak; he felt powerless to move. His mind refused to function, to direct his muscles. "What to do? *Dios,*" he repeated. "*Valgame Dios.*" A feeling of suffocation suffused him like a drowning man.

He needed time to decide what to do, and men and guns, if he were to save the fort. From the wall he removed a brace of pistols, an old rifle, a sword, and placed them near by on the bed. Painfully, with the labored, awkward touch of a sick man, he began to dress.

Knowing that he had only a few hours to prepare for the attack, John called every white man at the fort into his room and secretly explained to them the danger they were in. Each was provided with a gun and ammunition and had a post assigned him. John knew that the Indians counted on surprising them unarmed. Gunfire, he well knew, they bitterly feared. To them evil spirits, the devils of the universe, lurked in the strange black barrels that spewed forth fire. Even the arrows of their most indomitable warriors were powerless. Cold logic told him that the odds were on his side. Realization of it somewhat eased the tension.

By noon every man was prepared for the attack, expected shortly after dusk. To avoid arousing suspicion, which might precipitate a premature outbreak, John told them to go quietly about their daily tasks as usual. They obeyed implicitly. To all outward appearances at least, the day was a normal one at New Helvetia.

At five o'clock, the men, some forty in all, dined as

they always did at the long oak table in the main room of John's house. They were unusually silent, however, gulping their food hastily and washing it down with more than twice the usual amount of *aguardiente*. John, inwardly so nervous he could scarcely eat, sat stiffly at the head of the table. He kept an eye on the open door through which he could see the main gate of the fort, guarded as usual, by four ex-mission Indians he could trust.

Supper over, a few of the men pretended to play cards. Most of them, however, merely puffed at their pipes and grimly watched the sun go down.

By eight o'clock it was pitch dark outside. John peered out through the door. All was quiet. "Man your posts, my friends," he said sharply. "No talking. Not even a whisper." He held the door half open as his men, guns cocked and knives dangling from their belts, filed noiselessly by. The four Indians guarding the main gate, which was closed as usual at dusk, watched them with curious eyes.

John walked over to them and spoke in a scarcely audible voice. "The Cosumnes are expected to attack tonight. Listen closely for every sound. Report at once if you hear the slightest noise. I'll be in the left corner watch-tower."

The four guards saluted respectfully.

Before John could take up his vantage post two dogs that had been sniffing at the gate began barking furiously.

A moment later one of the guards ran over to John mumbling excitedly, "*Señor*, Indians outside. I heard."

John ran as quietly as he could over to his comrades who were massed in front of his house. Dark as it was, they could see his warning hand white against the black sleeve of his coat. "Don't fire until I tell you," he whispered. He went to the men stationed at the cannon mounted at the loopholes. He repeated the same words to them.

He returned to the first group and whispered to them to follow. Guns cocked, they moved silently until they were massed twenty feet behind the entrance. He knew that the Indians were counting on a surprise attack. He surmised that they intended to scale the gate by climbing on one another's shoulders. All day long he had anticipated their movements. He was grateful now for his years of experience with Indians. He gave a last swift glance around. Everyone was ready.

He tiptoed over to his Indian guards and said softly, "Give me time to get back to my men and get the dogs away. Then at the right moment throw open the gates as wide as you can. Run for your lives and hide behind the house."

They waited tensely until they saw John take his place near his comrades. They pulled the massive fort doors open. An instant later they disappeared.

John raised his rifle and roared at the top of his lungs: "Fire!" Instantly the intense quiet became a blazing inferno as guns belched forth a murderous barrage. Hundreds of Indians massed in confusion. Oaths and throaty words resounded as the white men attacked. The cries and groans of wounded natives told them they had struck their targets.

Through the intermittent flashes of light made by belching cannons, some indication of the damage inflicted on the enemy was apparent. The crouching, seething masses of Indians were growing smaller; many were stretched upon the ground. The groans of the injured reached John. Those not wounded fought valiantly, sending volleys of arrows at their white foes. Most of the missiles went wild, however, for the white men, dressed in dark garments, were not so readily discernible in the night as the gaudily painted natives.

John maneuvered his men closer to the gate. Their position was now more vulnerable. Several of his best marksmen were hit. They swore loudly as they extracted arrows from arms, legs and other parts of their bodies. A few fell moaning to the ground. John yelled for volunteers to remove them to safety. Four young men rushed out and dragged the sufferers behind the line. During a brief lull in the fighting John saw that a few of his own men were dropping back.

"Stand your ground," he called sharply, "*por el amor de Dios*. We need every man we've got."

Again oaths and shrieks and vituperations mingled with the whir of speeding arrows, the rattle of gunfire; the spit and roar of cannons being fired made the night hideous. Although they had fought less than a half hour, to John it seemed much longer. Determined to bring it to a swift conclusion, he urged his men to end the battle.

As they closed in on the Indians, John saw three of them drop with pitiful wails in pools of blood. A fourth, shot in the groin, fainted, hit the ground, rolled over and suddenly stiffened. Two more turned and tried to escape; a bullet caught one in the spinal cord, the other in the neck. Both fell over, writhing in death agonies, dying out to sad wails. The pile of dusky bodies near the gate was rapidly increasing, hampering the ablebodied. The native fighters began a retreat. The rifles, having the advantage of closer aim, seldom missed their targets.

"It's almost over, men," John shouted to encourage them. "A few more bullets and they'll disappear."

He was mistaken, however. As he was about to fire again, the dark, shadowy figure of a tall Indian stepped forward and raised his right hand. "*Amigo*," he called out. "*Dios va con Usted.*"

He spoke indistinctly with a pronounced native accent. None the less it was clear enough for John to understand.

"Don't fire, men," John called out, as he advanced cautiously toward the dignified native who moved his gaudily painted body, topped by a swaying feather headdress, majestically toward the master of Sutter's Fort.

Ten feet in front of John, the warrior placed his bow and quiver, in which only one arrow remained, significantly on the ground. The meaning of the gesture was not lost upon John. He called to one of his men to bring a lighted torch. The man snatched an Indian fagot from the ground that had been thrown at the white men and was still burning, and held it between the two leaders.

"*Amigo,*" said John, throwing his gun aside and advancing with outstretched hand.

The chief shook it gravely. "*Dios va con Usted,*" he repeated in halting Spanish.

"Let us make peace and be friends," said John.

The Indian grunted and bowed to the ground. Then he raised his head and began to speak rapidly in his native dialect.

Baffled, John shook his head. "I don't understand," he replied. Then he turned to a grizzled frontiersman who was standing a few paces away. "Find our Indian guards to interpret for us. They're hiding somewhere. They can't be far away."

Presently the man returned with the ex-mission natives, who understood enough of the Cosumnes dialect to translate it into Spanish.

"Tell me what the chief is trying to say," demanded John.

There followed a low-voiced conversation between the chieftain and the fort guards. Then one of them explained in plausible Spanish, "He wants to be your brother. He wants peace. He wants to make friends with the white men at the fort. He wants to exchange pelts for coats and hats and shoes like the white men wear. He wants . . ." The speaker's voice dropped off timidly, as if reluctant to continue.

"What? Speak out," said John, a note of impatience in his voice.

"Indian chief say . . . You leave squaws alone. White men spoil them. No more any good. Braves want them for themselves. Then no more fight."

A faint smile crossed John's face. Quickly he stifled it and turned a solemn countenance toward the dark figure before him.

"Tell him I agree," he said. "Let us be friends. Let his men come and work for us here at the fort. I will pay them with food and good garments. Also, we promise not to take his squaws away. Is it agreed?"

The interpreter relayed John's words to the warrior. A pleased expression brightened his countenance. "*Bueno homo, bueno homo*," he replied.

John extended his hand once more.

The chief squeezed it in his own, with a pathetic, clinging gesture, "*Bueno homo*"—you are a good man —he repeated three times.

The chief and his braves, carrying their dead and wounded, departed into the night.

"It's all over, my friend," John called out in a jubilant voice. "Now let's bind up these men with arrow wounds. I doubt if they're serious. Then we'll go back to my house and celebrate." Laughing and talking noisily, the men stacked their arms and went indoors.

"*Aguardiente, aguardiente, muchacho,*" John called out to a barefooted Indian servant who appeared from a closet where he had been hiding.

Tension eased as the heat of the local brew filtered through their tired bodies. A few burst into song, singing off pitch the familiar melodies of Stephen Foster but they quickly resorted to bawdy lyrics.

Time moved swiftly by.

A guard on his tour of the Fort called hourly: "All's well. All's well."

# CHAPTER XV

# HALCYON RETREAT

EVEN JOHN WAS surprised to find how constantly Sutter's Fort was in the limelight these days. It was both famous and infamous. It was known far and wide. Travelers considered it more important than Monterey itself.

This notoriety was a source of inestimable satisfaction to its Swiss founder. To his delight New Helvetia was sufficiently significant to make Alvarado turn jealously away from Sutter, his former stanch ally. It was of enough magnitude to cause *Comandante* Vallejo, aroused by its potential danger as a foreign rendezvous, to write scathing letters to the highest officials in Mexico City about Sutter and his notorious fort. In fact, Vallejo even sent a special envoy, Victor Prudon, all the way to the Mexican city to stress the urgency of his report. "The Swiss upstart," he wrote, "intends to make a second Texas out of California, and, even worse, to make himself lord and master of all California. We need men and guns to protect ourselves and we need them desperately."

Aid arrived, indeed, but in a way that surprised and infuriated *El Comandante*. For there was appointed to succeed him a new *Comandante del Norte*, a handsome young general named Manuel Micheltorena, who was given the combined rank of military and civil governor of Alta California, thus supplanting Vallejo and Alvarado, who were relegated to minor positions under him.

The news caused uneasiness the length and breadth of California. Firm friends of Vallejo and Alvarado muttered insidious threats. Some even plotted to revolt the day the new appointee arrived.

Down in Mexico City, Manuel Micheltorena somewhat superciliously ignored the disturbing rumors that reached his ears. He was slim, aristocratic, poised, with a firm jaw and an iron will. His slender Greek-like nose, high forehead and wavy hair, worn brushed back from his face and falling in clusters around his neck, gave him more the aspect of a scholar than a soldier. Nonetheless he handled dexterously his army of five hundred men, a motley gang of bandits, thieves, robbers and fugitives from Justice, taken from the prisons of Mexico City. He had no choice but to make soldiers out of these law-breakers. A rigid disciplinarian, he sailed north from Mazatlan with his nefarious army determined to control the bickering Californians at any price.

At the fort John received word of the new governor's arrival in Los Angeles with satisfaction, because it afforded him a new opportunity to insinuate himself into the gubernatorial favor as he had done, four years before, with Juan Alvarado. He saw in the appointment of Micheltorena another opportunity to exercise that diplomacy for which he was already famous up and down the coast.

He gave considerable thought as to the best way to approach the new arrival, who was residing temporarily in Los Angeles. It would be a friendly gesture to send him a letter by special messenger, offering his services. He believed the new governor might need him, especially now that several foreign warships were reported to be hovering mysteriously off the coast; a French fleet, some English ships, and an American gunboat; the latter in command of Thomas A. C. Jones, was expected to put in any day at Monterey.

Furthermore, with so many strange ships in Pacific waters, John felt the need of some protection for his fort in the event their goal was New Helvetia. He suspected, although he did not actually know, that Micheltorena might have some erroneous ideas about him, after all the letters Vallejo had written to Mexico City. If so, it was vital to bring himself, at once, into the new leader's good graces.

That was why he called William Flügge into his room for a confidential talk one day. The German lawyer was an old friend, one whom John felt he could trust implicitly. As they sat across the table from one another, he remarked in his most ingratiating way, "I have an important mission for you, Flügge. It's a thing I would entrust to no one else."

The German cast a quizzical glance at John. "My services are at your disposal."

John smiled warmly at him. He reached into his pocket and brought out a neatly inscribed envelope. "Here is a letter. I want you to take it to His Excellency, Governor Micheltorena."

"But His Excellency is not even in Monterey yet, Captain," he replied.

"So much the better."

"Well then, where shall I deliver it?" asked Flügge doubtfully.

"In Los Angeles. I want Micheltorena to know before he reaches the capital that I am his friend."

"I can see no reason for such haste," said the German.

"It's a long trip to make. No particular reason I can see."

"Let me make myself clear," said John a shade of impatience in his voice. "Perhaps you are not aware, Flügge, to what extent evil tongues have been maligning me."

"I've heard rumors, of course, plenty of them."

"And so has everyone else. All this nonsense about my acquiring California and making myself governor."

"Perhaps you're right," admitted Flügge, with German slowness. "You usually are, John."

"I'm sure of it, Flügge. I must ingratiate myself with Micheltorena without delay. That is the purpose of this letter. You might add a few words on my behalf. Assure him I have no evil intentions. Assure him I am loyal to the Mexican government. You might tell him that I resent the conduct of Vallejo who tries to prevent me from communicating with my source of supply at Yerba Buena. You might even add that *El Comandante* tried to stop me from bringing men and cattle overland from Fort Ross to my fort."

The trace of a smile flickered around the German lawyer's lips, then quickly vanished. It was the outward indication of his inner thoughts about John; how quick he was to attach himself to those whose friendship might bear fruit.

"I'll leave at dawn, Captain Sutter," he replied with suave decorum. "If you will excuse me now, I must pack. You should have been a diplomat, Captain," he called over his shoulder as he left the room.

As John hoped, the letter elicited the co-operation of Micheltorena. He replied and invited John to visit him sometime at Monterey. "Call on me if you need assistance," he had told Flügge as he was about to leave

Los Angeles on the return trip to Sutter's Fort. "I am
told that your settlement is the goal of travelers everywhere, English, French, German and Italian. I'm told
they prefer it to Monterey. And Captain Sutter, I
understand, is extremely kind to those in distress."

William Flügge reached the fort just as a wagonload
of emigrants pulled in at the gates. The conveyance
was piled high with household effects. Two sick children,
so weak they could not lift their heads, lay on top of a
feather mattress. Near them, fanning the flies away
from her hot face, crouched an old woman. An equally
aged man sat in the driver's seat. Three emaciated men
and a young woman rode on lean mules close behind.

The feminine rider hailed Flügge. "Where's Captain
Sutter?" she asked.

"I can't say, lady," he retorted, "somewhere around
the fort, I suppose. Just ask inside." He galloped on
ahead, his horse's heels kicking up a blinding dust
cloud.

John welcomed the lone traveler at the door of the
main house with shouts of delight. "I can't wait to hear
what Micheltorena's reaction was to my letter," he said.

The German sniffed the brandy breath of his friend
with a frown of disapproval. Drinking far too much
these days, he thought, as he contemplated his friend's
suspiciously jovial face.

"Tell me, Flügge, what did old Micheltorena say?"

"His Excellency is not old, Captain, far from it;
he's spruce and young and well-mannered, I can assure
you."

"Never mind," said John, impatiently. "That's not
what I want to hear."

"You may count on his support and friendship, I
believe," said Flügge, with deliberation, "in the event of

trouble. By the way, Captain, I've considerable gossip to report. You may not have heard the talk that's going the rounds everywhere, in the south, particularly, that Vallejo and Alvarado intend to foment a revolution. They have secretly armed a large army of Californians. The situation looks black indeed. We may be drawn into it here at the fort."

"I'll take my chances," said John with the debonair air of the confirmed inebriate.

Their conversation was interrupted by the arrival of the emigrant wagon. "Another," sighed John. "Probably sick and penniless like most of them. I need colonists desperately, of course, but I hadn't planned to turn my fort into a place for the sick and indigent." Forcing a hospitable smile to his face, he walked over to the newcomers and offered his services.

Flügge smiled to himself. The most generous man in the world and the most improvident, he thought. Everyone plays on his feelings. Just look at him pick up that sick child.

"This baby needs milk," he heard John say to the old woman. "Come, I have plenty in my house." John led them indoors where dinner was just being placed upon the table.

That night John moved uneasily about on his hard bed revolving the emigrant problem in his mind. "It's becoming a menace," he groaned. "The steady stream of Americans coming in all the time. I need men of all kinds if the fort is to pull me out of debt. More than half the emigrants are worthless. And those women and children. All they want is for me to feed and clothe them. At least so far. But if these Americans keep on I can't say what the outcome will be."

Suspicions of the blackest sort dominated. The Manifest Destiny of America the newcomers talked so much about tormented him with incessant fear. He had heard it from hundreds. It was the manifest destiny of America to absorb the entire west coast. If this plan were realized, what could prevent New Helvetia from falling to the United States?

John tried to forget. But it was firmly ingrained in his subconscious. It clung like a leech, refusing to be displaced. If, in some nefarious way *Los Americanos*, those wagonloads of determined *gringos* who braved Indians, famine and the deadly snows of the Sierras to reach his fort, acquired Mexican California, what would be his fate?

He felt an overpowering sense of loneliness, of frustration. In the solitude of night he began to lose confidence in the guiding hand of fate that had led him through each peril of his precarious position. He fell at last into a tormented sleep.

During the daytime, the outward mask of ease and prosperity deceived everyone at the fort. It was the shield behind which he concealed his anxiety aggravated by the mass of unpaid bills, the accrued interest owed the Russians, the fear of Indian raids, suspicions of every foreigner, including *Los Americanos*. The last perturbed him most.

A subtle change was forcing its impress. To blot out despair he began to drink. Until far into the night he retired to the solitude of his own quarters where he could drink undisturbed. There he consumed *aguardiente* until he fell in a stupor onto the floor.

Corpulency was beginning to show in him; the back of his neck became fat, and his waist spread. He walked with less agility, and he found trips on horseback fatiguing.

Loss of physical endurance was counterbalanced, however, by an added courtliness. Grandeur now became an affectation. He enjoyed nothing so much as imagining himself *le grand seigneur* of Sutter's Fort, the ruler of a small principality. He surrounded himself with Indian serfs he bought at will. He dressed and trained them as a colorful bodyguard to impress visitors. Distinguished guests found amusement often when the staggering Sutter wove through his marching columns.

He prepared a bulwark for himself against the slowly mounting tide of foreign ingress from all sides. He was wise enough to know that since the slow surge of peoples toward the west was inescapable, all he could hope to do was to turn it somehow to his own interest.

He made it his habit to visit frequently the older pioneers, developing land grants he had given them along the Sacramento, American and Feather rivers. Invariably he directed the talk to the future of his fort. There was considerable divergence of opinion among them. Slow-moving Nicholas Allgeier, who was planting his acres of wheat on Bear Creek, was indifferent to the suspicions John tried to arouse.

"*Himmel*, Captain," he told John, "isn't there enough vacant land out here in this wilderness for every Yankee in the States? Let them come, let them come. I would like to see more of them. A few good-looking women, too. I'm sick of squaws." He jerked a fat thumb toward a bedraggled old hag cooking bear meat over a smoky fire.

John soon discovered that his neighbors sought better living. He tried to convince John Sinclair who lived at *Rancho El Paso* on the opposite side of the American River, or Theodore Cordua, who had settled himself at Mecklenburg at the junction of the Feather and Yuba rivers, or Sebastian Keyser, or Pablo Gutierez, or the two Frenchmen who occupied the *Nemshas Rancho* on the Cosumnes, who had difficulty working their land grants with inadequate Indian labor, that American emigrant labor was imperative. "We need men," he said. "All we can get. That's the only way to develop this country. It will make our land valuable, make all of us rich. That's what we all want, isn't it?"

"Yes, that's true," they would reply. "But suppose *Los Americanos* want to take over our land?"

John Bidwell, who managed the country place called Hock Farm, where John raised fruits and vegetables, was also apprehensive about the number of Americans coming to California.

Sutter adopted the policy at this time, however, of giving generous grants of land to all immigrants whom he sought to make his friends. He organized them secretly into a defense battalion whose task was to defend his fort, should such a contingency arise. He let them believe that the military drill was in case of Indian raids. Sutter's Company, the men called themselves and submitted reluctantly to military maneuvers once a week, for they preferred to spend idle hours over drinks and cards.

John had not been unduly alarmed until the day when two horsemen wearing Scotch caps rode up to the gate of the fort. They saluted formally. "Captain Sutter, I assume."

"Yes, sir," John replied pompously, thinking the men were merely Hudson's Bay Company trappers passing by. "And your names, sirs?"

"John Fremont and Kit Carson."

Before John could reply the former began to speak rudely, as a superior addressing one of lesser rank.

"We've come west on a government mission, Captain. We're exploring the country west of the Rockies for the U. S. Topographical Bureau at Washington."

"Come in, come in," said John with his customary hospitality. "Dinner, I am certain, is ready."

The men accepted with alacrity. The hospitality of the Fort was theirs. They remained for two weeks, living on what he supplied. At the end of that time, outfitted with new garments and provided with Indian guides and fresh food and horses, they departed.

John looked ruefully at the orders of the United States government in Washington which Fremont left with him in payment for supplies. He had strained himself to provide generously for his guests.

"I wonder when or where or how I can collect," he thought. "I need every cent of it to apply against that old Russian debt."

## CHAPTER XVI

# WHEELS OF FATE

A MONTH OR SO LATER, John heard a knock on his door. He laid down the flagon of brandy. On the threshold was an Indian, hot and travel-stained, holding a large official document in his grimy hand.

"*Buenos dias, amigo,*" said the native handing Sutter the missive. "*El Gobernador.*"

The captain regarded it for a moment; with a flourish of the hunting knife from his belt, he slit it open.

"So he wants me to be his guest at Monterey?" he asked the Indian bearer.

"*Sí, Señor,*" replied the native, apparently aware of the contents of the document. He grinned in a friendly manner.

John studied the communication reflectively, attempting to deduce the true motive behind it. That *El Gobernador* had in mind something he had not thought fit to disclose in the message, was probable. He considered the flattering invitation and its hidden implications. If he declined Micheltorena would probably resent it. Acceptance, however, would be tantamount to an open admission that he espoused the newcomer's cause. He hesitated to do so openly, although he was secretly in favor of this man who had the full support of the Mexican government. The revolt under Alvarado and Vallejo were widespread now throughout California. There was always the cloying dread in his mind that *Los Indepen-dientes,* as they called themselves, might attack New

192

Helvetia. Yet, to stand high in the governor's favor he dared not overlook.

He flung the Indian a heavy silver coin with an eagle on it, a useless gift John Fremont had given him.

"*Bueno*," he said, "ride fast to Monterey. Tell His Excellency I accept." "*Con mucho gusto*," he added.

His conscience again assailed him. After all, Alvarado had befriended him when he had come to California, a penniless stranger and he had treated him with kindness and generosity. He owed all his land to Alvarado. The pang of conscience lasted only a brief time, however; John shook it off and went indoors to prepare for the trip to Monterey.

He left at dawn, accompanied by John Bidwell. They were escorted by ten native soldiers as bodyguard. The guards were not needed, but John felt that it was incumbent upon him to impress the governor with his importance upon their first meeting.

They traveled southwest past the John Marsh *rancho*, *Los Meganos*, and stopped for a day at San Jose, to visit the British vice-consul, John Alexander Forbes. Forbes took John into his confidence, as he was anxious to enlist the captain's sympathy on behalf of the British cause in California.

The Britisher dropped his usual reticence and talked openly: "All these happenings at Monterey give me considerable concern, Sutter. You know, of course, what they are?"

"Not entirely." John attempted to be non-committal. "We've had lots of rumors at the fort."

"Patriotic Californians, sir, resent this appointment of a new governor from Mexico City. They want a local man, I am sure. Someone who knows local conditions and understands the people." With studied indifference, John said, "So I've heard. You may be right."

Forbes was eager to unburden his thought. "Micheltorena himself is capable enough, I feel certain, but that vagabond army of his. Every citizen in Monterey is worried. A gang of ex-bandits. No wonder they, the Monterey people, are concerned. Who would want to trust their futures to such a motley crew?"

"I agree," said John.

The vice-consul placed his hands on his knees. "I think I should tell you, Captain, something of what is going on. You have the right to know. After all you have your own life and property to protect."

John became too interested even to drink the wine before him.

"Revolution," whispered Forbes. "Led by Castro and Alvarado. They intend to run Micheltorena back to Mexico, along with all his desperados. They've even hired a ship; it's waiting in a cove below."

Feigned surprise clouded John's face. "Against Micheltorena. Umm, that's serious."

"It will purge California of an unwelcome leader," Forbes replied. "After all, he's not the man for us."

John did not answer. He could not decide. It was clear that Forbes was not aware of his support of Micheltorena. He had mentioned only casually that he was going to the capital on business, letting Forbes assume that he was buying supplies.

John's silence mystified the speaker. "I assume of course, that you side with the Californians," Forbes said finally, "and favor the cause of Alvarado. We may need you to help us. Castro and Alvarado are out now scouring the back country getting men to enlist.

They're bound to succeed. Micheltorena's doomed. No doubt in my mind."

Forbes did not observe John's failure to acquiesce. He assumed that Sutter, having acquired his land from Alvarado, would naturally support him. He was unaware of the jealous rivalry between Alvarado and Sutter.

The next day, without disclosing his attitude, John rode on to Monterey. As he traveled along this well-worn road he could not shake off the doubt that perturbed him. Forbes' talk had distressed him deeply. If the revolution went against the new ruler, how would it affect him and New Helvetia? So far he knew Micheltorena only from his letters. Would he be disappointed in the man himself?

The next afternoon he met the new governor in the garden behind Spence's house on Alvarado street, where he always stayed. A *merienda* was in progress. John was instantly charmed by Micheltorena's dapper graciousness. The governor was alert, courteous, and full of energy and initiative. He welcomed John effusively. "Captain Sutter, *amigo mio*," he said, kissing him on both cheeks.

They were soon fast friends. John liked him and listened attentively to his plans to bring about reforms in the politically-corrupt province. They talked about world events: the French menace in Mexico, England's growing interest in the west coast, the latest news from the United States. "The Yankees have flocked to California," the governor told John, "ever since Oliver Larkin took up his duties as United States consul here at Monterey last spring."

"I saw the *U.S.S. Savannah* here in the bay," John

replied. "I was surprised to find a warship. What is it, business or pleasure?"

"Who knows?" retorted Micheltorena gloomily.

As the guests, including all the prominent citizens of Monterey, sat together at one of the long wooden tables in the Spence garden, they could hear from across the blue waters of the bay, the sound of music coming from the *Savannah*.

"That's Yankee Doodle," said the American consul Larkin.

The brass band, having delivered itself of the gay little air, paused briefly. Then it began to play more solemnly. Larkin rose in dignity, hat in hand, and bowed his head:

> *"My country 'tis of thee,*
> *Sweet land of liberty,"*

he sang softly, but so distinctly that all the guests could hear.

"*La Libertad*," John whispered to Micheltorena. "He sings of *La Libertad*."

"*Independencia. Sí, Capitán. Los Americanos.* They think of nothing else. It runs in their blood."

"You like music?" John inquired.

Micheltorena lifted soulful brown eyes to John's face. "*Siempre la musica. Siempre con los Españoles, Señor Sutter. Es aquí,*" he said, indicating the region of his heart. "*Musica simpática. La Paloma, viene del corazón.*"

"Ah, the dove. Yes, I know it," John replied, proud of his knowledge of the popular Spanish song.

They stopped speaking. From the deck of the *Savannah*, in loud unison, the band played with a kind of glorious acclaim: "*Hail, Columbia, happy land.*" This time, Larkin did not rise, but sang *Hail Columbia* with the exuberance of a happy schoolboy.

With the background of music unwittingly afforded by the *Savannah*, the *merienda* assumed new life. An incipient vivacity could be felt, spreading through the guests.

As suddenly as it had begun, the repertoire of the *Savannah's* musicians terminated. With its ending, ennui crept over the guests, one or two yawned openly, making no attempt to conceal their weariness. A few indulged in brief siestas, their heads nodding languidly against the backs of their chairs, while the table was being cleared of the remains of the feast.

For a moment John, who had eaten sparingly of the heavy Mexican repast, watched the colorful assemblage with unconcealed delight. Then, in a sudden mood of decision, he turned to Micheltorena.

"Could I have a few words with you in private, Your Excellency?"

"*Con mucho gusto,*" the dignitary replied.

They went into the cool white *sala* which was used by David Spence as both drawing room and place of business. It was sparsely yet quite comfortably furnished. A few pieces of fine old Spanish brocades gave the room color. The two men sat for a moment without speaking, a tacit indication of the bond of sympathy between them and the rare prerogative of friends.

"I have news of the utmost importance, Your Excellency."

Micheltorena flashed him a friendly smile of encouragement. "I presume it concerns your fort, *Mi Capitán?*"

"Perhaps. But that's not what I came here to discuss."

"Oh?"

"The revolution. It's under way."

"What?" exclaimed Micheltorena, a startled look on his face. "You say revolution, Captain?" A shudder traced his slender frame; his teeth chattered involuntarily. Then he quickly brought himself under control. "Where, Captain?"

"Here. At Monterey."

The governor stared in bewilderment. His voice strained. "Who's behind it? Who are these enemies?"

"Your predecessor, Your Excellency. Juan Alvarado and you might know, his bosom friend, José Castro."

The governor drew a long breath and expelled it in a labored sigh. "I'm not surprised," he said. "I know. The Californians don't like me. They've made it plain enough from the moment I set foot in Monterey. I have almost no friend here, *Señor* Sutter."

"I shall esteem it an honor, Your Excellency, to aid you in any way. The resources of New Helvetia are yours."

"My dear Captain Sutter, I need you desperately." Intense appreciation was in his voice. "But how can I ever repay you, *amigo mio?* Name your own price. Anything for your support."

"You intend to fight?"

Micheltorena lifted his head proudly. "*Sí, Mi Capitán*, I do. I came here to stop graft. I intend to stamp out evil of all kinds, revolution included."

"Suppose we make an agreement," John replied slowly. "I will aid you to the very extent of my resources: men, horses, cattle, grain, guns, ammunition. Anything else you need. All I ask in return is more land for my rapidly growing colony. Let's say another land grant." [1]

"Little enough," Micheltorena replied. As he rose he did not reveal to John his dread uncertainty over the future. A revolution was not what he had expected of Californians—*Valgame Dios, los rebeldos,* Castro and Alvarado, and after they welcomed me with open arms the day I reached Monterey, he thought to himself. The scoundrels.

After taking leave of Spence, his host, he walked gloomily up the hill behind the town to the house he occupied, the gubernatorial mansion built by Alvarado, cursing under his breath as he went.

The following evening leading Montereyans met again, this time at the official banquet Governor Micheltorena gave, in an effort to make friends. Troubled by the lack of support he had expected to receive as Governor, he dreaded the occasion, and admitted so to John. It was a relief to have someone into whose sympathetic ears he could voice his suspicions and fears of Castro and Alvarado.

To his surprise, the banquet was a success. There were no signs of animosity on the part of the two ex-governors. Castro and Alvarado laughed and shook hands amicably with Sutter and Micheltorena, as if they were all bosom friends.

The climax came after dinner. The governor had brought a red toy balloon, from a sailor on the *Savannah,* which was blown up and sent skyward, to the delight of the guests. As he watched it soar buoyantly overhead, John noticed Castro and Alvarado whispering together. He felt a premonition of disaster. With a few

[1] The general agreement was signed at Monterey on Dec. 23, 1844.

words of apology he left his host and returned to his quarters.

At daybreak he boarded a small boat for Yerba Buena where his own schooner was waiting to take him up the Sacramento to New Helvetia. For the next three months he drilled white men and Indians with feverish haste. War preparations were not popular at New Helvetia, especially among the white settlers as they disliked becoming involved in Mexican politics.

"Unless we support Micheltorena, we lose all," he warned them sharply. "He's promised us more land if we aid him. You want more land, don't you?"

John won his point and the settlers joined in the clumsy military maneuvers that were held daily.

The events kindled swiftly to flame. At the turn of the year John received marching orders. Days of haste and confusion followed at the fort. Finally Sutter's Army passed through the gates of New Helvetia. Bugles resounded gaily as they rode, flags held stiffly before them. The sharp click of newly-shod hoofs striking the hard ground echoed with rhythmic clatter.

Several hundred men, neighbors, settlers, Indians, and deserters from the Californian forces followed John south. Never a good rider, *El Comandante* sat on his horse with obvious effort, his old French uniform, now frayed and shabby, stretched tightly across his portly body. It was the only impressive garment in the entire army for most of the military costumes were ragged, ill-fitting and antiquated.

Notwithstanding, the men were in high spirits. They whistled and sang vile lyrics as they rode, as if bent on a joyous holiday of debauchery.

John, however, rode morosely, his hat pulled far down over his ears as if to shut out the tumult of his men.

It was his first war. Fear and doubt possessed him. Even the exalted title of Commander in Chief of the forces of the Sacramento Valley bestowed on him by Micheltorena failed to compensate for his pathetic ignorance of war. He alone knew that the aura of his past military experience which had spread around him at the fort was a colossal chimera.

Guns and warfare were thoroughly distasteful to him. Heartsick and uneasy he rode glumly ahead. How it would end? Had he gambled on the right side?

About fifty miles from the fort he met a breathless rider who reported that Micheltorena had been besieged by Castro and Alvarado's armies at Monterey. The message implored Sutter to come at top speed.

Before John had time to reach the capital, however, the attackers had been repulsed and had fled south. At the Salinas River, near Monterey, Micheltorena and his men joined forces with the army from New Helvetia. The combined armies followed on the heels of the fleeing revolutionists in their flight to reach Los Angeles, where they expected to receive aid from their friends, and to make a final stand against the pursuers. Progress for both sides was slow, for cold weather, rains and roads churned into rivers of mud made riding precarious. By raiding towns, ranches and even the missions along the way, they secured fresh food and occasionally, on wet nights, a dry roof. After leaving Salinas John suffered from a bad cold and a mild fever, brought on by hardships and bad food, and Micheltorena was so ill by the time the army reached Santa Barbara that he could travel only in a litter borne by Indians.

He was taken to the mission in a drenching rain and there was made as comfortable as possible. His illness threw John into despair, for he had relied on the Gov-

ernor's military knowledge to direct the troops in the
event of combat. He stayed near him, hoping to hasten
his recovery. He was deeply troubled. If Micheltorena
were to die? If he did . . . what would happen to all that
land the Mexican governor had guaranteed him for his
military services? It was for land, for land alone that
he had joined this mad campaign. Heart-sick and
weary, he trudged from the cloistered promenade out
into the rainy night and climbed the short flight of steps
that led into the church, the only dry place he could
find.

He shook off the surplus water from his greatcoat
and sat heavily down upon one of the hard benches
toward the rear of the high-peaked sanctuary. A few
meager candles burned with a weary lassitude upon the
main altar. John was exhausted in body and spirit. As
the lights waned, he went into the priest's cell where
Micheltorena lay half asleep on a hard cot covered by
a heavy woolen serape.

The general, ill as he was, could not fail to read the
panic and despair on the countenance of his military
associate. A wan smile spread over his pallid face.

"Don't worry," he said with a pretense of cheerful-
ness, "the war's scarcely begun. Just give me a day
or two here at Santa Barbara, and I'll be a new man. I
promise you I have no intention of dying yet."

They talked in low voices about trivial things, for
vital as the matter was to him, John felt a hesitancy
about leading up to what was foremost in his mind.
Finally he observed in a casual tone of voice, "Since we
have a few quiet hours to ourselves perhaps we should
conclude the business we began at Monterey."

"We discussed many things," Micheltorena replied.
"To what do you refer, *Mi Capitán?*"

"If it does not tire you too much," began John, hesitating slightly, "I should like to bring up the matter of the land grant you agreed to give me for my services in this campaign."

Micheltorena sighed so faintly that it almost escaped John's ears. "Perhaps we should, *amigo mio*. You are one of the few who has treated me like a friend. I appreciate it; indeed I do."

"You see," said John, now more confidently, "I have already spent out of my own pocket eight thousand pesos on this campaign."

"I know," Micheltorena replied. "Horses, food, guns and war supplies are costly. I'm almost bankrupt myself."

"Could you not ... could you not ... make over to me now land to reimburse me for it?" John put the question timidly, for he was half ashamed of his request.

Micheltorena did not reply. His closed eyelids merely fluttered ever so slightly; otherwise he gave no indication of having heard.

Softly, John whispered into his ear the request. The governor's eyes half opened. "*Sí, sí, sí,*" he said. "Thirty-three square leagues.[1] That was our agreement, wasn't it?"

He raised a weak head from the straw-filled pillow. "Bring me pencil and paper, *amigo mio*, and I'll make the land over to you now ... tonight."

Under clearing skies and with spirits revived by food and rest, the two generals and their armies left the mission the next day, for Mission San Buena Ventura some thirty miles south, where scouts reported the

---

[1] 229 square miles.

enemy had pitched camp. Although Micheltorena was forced to lie on a straw mat in a wagon as they traveled, the crisis of his illness appeared to have passed.

At Buena Ventura, where they passed the night, they found the utmost confusion and disorder everywhere. The enemy had left only a few hours before, after several days of dancing and merry-making, leaving a few drunken revelers behind. Reports of the Bacchanalian orgies convinced John that demoralization was rampant in the Castro-Alvarado camp. After a brief consultation with Micheltorena, the next day John led the army south in pursuit of the enemy.

In high spirits he galloped ahead, enjoying to the full the crisp fresh morning air. The country was rich and luxuriant after the early rains. It was a region of rolling hills, dotted with oak and sycamore, with snow-capped mountains faintly visible toward the south. Behind trailed his army, dirty and ragged and weary.

Upon rounding a bend in the road, John came upon a small ranch house looming up ahead. At the door he reined in his horse and dismounted. A young woman opened the door. Noting how pretty she was, John removed his hat with more than his usual flourish and spoke deferentially to her. She smiled coyly at him as did the small boy who clung timidly to her skirts, a small bundle clutched in one hand.

The woman pushed the boy toward John. "Speak to the gentleman, Nino," she said.

He walked soberly toward the traveler and extended the bundle toward him.

"*Gracias, muchas gracias, hijo mio,*" said John, patting the boy on the head.

He accepted the gift with one of his ingratiating

smiles. He was about to hand the package to his Indian servant when he observed the lad's crestfallen face. Intuitively, he opened it. Within were twelve tortillas, obviously freshly baked. On top lay an unsealed letter. John opened it curiously and ran his eyes rapidly down the page:

"If you and your men will abandon Governor Micheltorena and come over to our side, it will be well worth your while.

José Castro and Juan B. Alvarado."

The enemy must be in desperate straits, he muttered to himself.

He shoved it indignantly into his pockets, dropped the tortillas on the ground, and with a frigid bow to the *Señora*, climbed into his saddle and galloped away.

## CHAPTER XVII

# CANNONS ROAR

THE ROAD OVER which John was traveling was the old mission trail blazed by the early priests and *conquistadores* connecting San Buena Ventura with San Fernando. As he reached the open valley north of the latter mission, a sand storm was blowing with such force as to blot out visibility. Scouts reported that the enemy was not far away.

As it moved south, Sutter's army would hardly have satisfied the critical eye of a professional soldier. But to Sutter, as he rode along, buttoned tightly in his old French uniform with the frayed gold braid, it did not seem to make such a bad showing. At least, it presented a more martial appearance than Micheltorena's gang of ruffians, which at this moment was straggling somewhere in the rear, if, indeed, it had been able as yet to tear itself away from the petty looting and pilfering of the previous night's halt at Buena Ventura.

So far, Sutter's military prowess had been strictly a matter of boastful talk. Like his bogus rank of Captain, it was a pure fantasy that had sprung straight from the brandy keg. Now, unexpectedly, his warlike pretensions were going to be put to the test.

As soon as Alvarado's rebellion had started and Sutter had decided to throw his weight on the side of the new Governor, he had suddenly found himself being consulted and deferred to as an ex-officer of considerable military experience. Everybody, from the Governor himself downwards, was anxious to follow *El Gran Capitán* into the fray, trusting in his superior knowledge to direct operations with all the skill of an old campaigner. As for Sutter's own men, he had taught the Indians at the fort as much drill as he could remember having seen in his youth in Europe, and not much else. As soldiers they knew how to stand at attention, shoulder arms, and march more or less in step. Beyond that they knew next to nothing. A few of them could shoot fairly well, it was true, but Sutter had not been too eager to teach his Indians how to defend themselves with the white man's weapons. For the actual fighting he would have to depend on his Americans, hardened colonists, most of them, who had crossed the plains and had learned to depend on firearms for their food and their lives.

Sutter took heart. As the head of his column began to enter the San Fernando Valley neither of the two parties of Indian scouts which he had sent well ahead of the main body had reported, as yet, any signs of the enemy. Perhaps there would be no battle. Perhaps, hearing that the lord of New Helvetia was descending upon them in his might, Alvarado and his rebellious Californians had decided to submit to the new Governor without a fight. Had not Napoleon quelled whole countries by the mere threat of marching upon them with his invincible army? Sutter pulled to the side of the trail where he could watch his artillery, consisting of five small cannons from the fort mounted on farm wagons, rumbling past.

Instinctively, as he reined in his horse, he thrust his free hand between the brass buttons of his uniform, his head bent forward, and a Napoleonic scowl spread over his features.

A thud of fast approaching hoofs brought an Indian scout, his horse in a lather. He said that the enemy had been sighted retiring in the direction of the Los Angeles River. Sutter thought a moment. Across the valley a heavy dust storm was getting up. Soon it would be impossible to see more than a short distance ahead. Sutter decided to take advantage of this and to press forward under cover of the screen of dust. After having given the order to continue the march across the valley, he could not repress the thought that perhaps he really *was* a military genius after all.

That night camp was made near one of the mission adobes called Cahuenga. Scouts reported that the enemy was making camp not far away on the other side of the Los Angeles River. Sutter wondered if, perhaps, he had advanced too far. Secretly he felt glad that a river, even if it was only an almost dry one, lay between him and the enemy. He wished he had a real soldier to advise him instead of having to keep up this pretense of being a real soldier himself. Alvarado evidently did not intend to retreat or he would have gone on through the Cahuenga Pass before dark. No, there would be a battle in the morning. But should he attack first, or wait where he was for the enemy to attack him, or what? An Indian brought him a bowl of hot soup, the first hot food he had tasted in a week. The soup was full of dust and grit but he drank it down. Evidently, his followers were not disturbed by the presence of the enemy. They were making fires and cooking food and preparing to settle down for the night, quite unperturbed. Sentries had been posted and Sutter warned everyone to expect an attack at dawn. Long after dark, Micheltorena and his ragged band streamed into camp and they also settled down comfortably for the night.

Sutter felt drowsy and heavy from his cold and the brandy he had been drinking to ward it off, but he dared not take a nap, for fear something might happen. He sat alone, wrapped in a blanket, peering out of the door of his tent, sipping brandy and trying to keep awake.

Suddenly, Sutter was aroused by a loud, splintering crash followed by several shouts. He realized that he must have dozed because it was daylight. Throwing off the blanket and seizing a musket he hurried in the direction of the sound. A group of Indians were gazing at a wagon. The side of the wagon was splintered and one of the large sacks of cornmeal with which it was loaded had burst and poured its contents on the ground. So the battle had started and the first of Alvarado's cannon balls had made a hit! It was pure chance, of course, for the enemy were too far away to do anything more than fire in the general direction of Sutter's forces.

Sutter immediately sprang into action. His Indian groom came running, leading Sutter's old white mare, and helped him to mount.

"Pring op de gannon," he shouted, his German accent getting the better of him, in his excitement. The old mare, feeling Sutter's spurs dig into her in an unaccustomed manner, suddenly broke into a fast gallop. Sutter arrived in the midst of his Indian foot soldiers, lined up in the best parade ground style, clinging ignominiously to the mane of his mare. But he made up for this slight lapse of dignity by the energy and loudness of his commands.

"Advance both companies to the edge of the river

and fire two volleys," he roared. "Sergeant Ignacio, station the ammunition wagons behind that clump of trees. Keep the enemy in sight. I will bring up the artillery in support."

Soon a regular fusillade started. Micheltorena's men, on the left, had been firing intermittently since dawn. Now everybody was firing, the enemy as well. The enemy were evidently out of range as no bullets seemed to be coming from their direction. In fact the only danger, so far, since the early morning cannon ball, was the wild firing of Micheltorena's men who seemed to be letting off their muskets in every direction. In the midst of the general firing, Sutter heard the two volleys he had ordered; but judging by the constantly increasing noise, his Indians, once having fired their muskets, had got a taste for it and had decided to keep on.

Sutter was leading his home-made artillery to a forward position where a slight rise in the ground gave a view of the enemy's position on the other side of the river when two horsemen rode up. He recognized them as Jim McCoy and his son, American colonists to whom he had given some land up the Feather River.

"Better stop 'em, Cap'n," said the elder McCoy, jerking his thumb in the direction of Sutter's now wildly firing Indians. "The ammunition won't last the day through if they keep that up. And me and Jacky here, and the rest of us'd like to get a couple o' shots at them monkeys when they get near enough."

"Get near enough! *Donnerwetter!* When I have the artillery in position they'll not dare to cross the river. We'll advance, Mr. McCoy, we'll advance."

The McCoys turned back to rejoin the contingent of Americans who had taken up a position behind some low bushes on the right flank of Sutter's little army. Then the boy turned back.

"My dad says it's all right if us kids goes ahead into the riverbed to see if we can get some shots. Is that all right with you, Sir?"

But Sutter wasn't listening.

"*Himmelcreutz!* Get near enough! What do these Yankees think they're doing, shooting quail, or something?"

When the farm wagons and their guns had been maneuvered into place and loaded, a fine martial din started with the distant hills echoing to the brave sound of cannon fire. As the day went on, the enemy seemed to have brought up some cannon from somewhere and they, too, started firing. On the hillsides by Cahuenga Pass, Sutter could see the crowds of spectators who had come out from the little town of Los Angeles to watch the fun.

Braving the stray bullets which had not hit anybody so far, with the exception of one loose horse which had strayed into the riverbed between the two armies, Sutter rode over to Micheltorena who was in charge of the right flank. Sutter found him examining the enemy lines attentively through a spy glass.

"Ah, my *valiente amigo! Que tal?* You are the very man I want to see! Take a look through this glass! It seems to me that your artillery has put two of their guns out of action. They seem to be making a general movement to retire, but look yourself. You, with all your military experience will be able to interpret what is going on far better than I." He handed Sutter the spy glass.

Yes, Sutter could see that things were going on behind the enemy lines but what was the meaning of it?

He could see a small body of horsemen detach itself from the main body and move away. Two of the guns had stopped firing and some wagons that looked like ammunition wagons were going back through the pass. It must be a retreat! This was the moment to act!

"*Señor Gobernador*, the enemy is in retreat. We must advance at once. If you will drive them with your force toward the pass, I will block their escape on the right. We must act at once."

Smilingly the Mexican-Spaniard and the Swiss-Mexican shook hands. Sutter mounted and rode to his headquarters.

As soon as he got back, he dispatched Indian runners in every direction with the order to all troops to advance and to acknowledge receipt of the order immediately. After a while the runners returned. The Indians of Sutter's Regiment were ready to advance but reported that they had no more ammunition. The gunners said they could not advance because, owing to the continued firing, the wagon wheels were immovably stuck in the ground.

On all sides men were beginning to waver. John gave the order to charge. Not a man responded. Treachery was in the air. He rushed over to one of his lieutenants, a huge backwoodsman by the name of Gantt. His men, John found, were lolling idly, their guns stacked in a pile near by. "*Gott im Himmel*. What does this mean, Gantt?" he cried.

The lieutenant who was chewing a small stick of wood shrugged his shoulders indifferently. "They won't fight, captain. I can't make them. They've been casting ballots to see who wants to stay with me and who wants to desert to the other side."

"*Himmel*," groaned John.

Even as he watched, a group of *Americanos* from the enemy ranks sauntered over and shook hands with Gantt's men. Sensing the futility of further argument, John leaped into his saddle and rode swiftly away in search of Micheltorena known to be somewhere behind the lines.

As he stood lost in thought a pale-faced orderly rushed up, saluted, and said apologetically, "The men are taking a vote, *Señor*."

"A what?" roared John. "What ... do ... you ... mean? Tell 'em to fight, not vote, or I'll hang every damned one of them." John paced back and forth angrily, hands behind his back as he talked.

The orderly disappeared. A moment later he came back. "They refuse, *Señor*."

"Why? It's outrageous. I don't believe it."

"Our men say they recognize some of their old friends on the other side; men who came across the plains with them. They're afraid of killing them."

"*Diable*," yelled John, now so angry he could scarcely control himself. He was about to go over and talk with the soldiers himself when he saw about thirty unarmed men, the foremost carrying the Castro-Alvarado flag coming slowly toward him. "A delegation from the enemy, I see. *Americanos*, to a man," he muttered under his breath. "Some of those who didn't turn tail and run, like most of the *Mexicanos*," he added. He waited until they were some ten feet away. "Well, what is it?" he asked. He glanced furtively around to see if his men were rallying to his support, but they had thrown their weapons on the ground and the *Americanos* were waving to their old comrades among the opposing forces.

"We do not intend to fight friends from back home," said the spokesman, a tall, gaunt man who spoke with a curiously soft, drawling voice. "I'm from Kintuck . . . and so's Jim over there." He indicated with a quick jerk of his thumb an equally lean figure who stood in the foreground of the Americans clustered behind their leader.

"This is ridiculous, utterly ridiculous," John retorted, bitterness and chagrin in his voice. He was powerless, however, to stop the determined Yankees who had joined the Castro-Alvarado army only because the two leaders had promised to supply them with large land grants in return for their support. And so they went over and shook hands apologetically with their old friends with the comment, "Didn't know there were any *Americanos* with Sutter and Micheltorena or we'd never have signed up. The instant we heard about it, we stopped fighting at once." Soon they were all chatting amicably together.

John raged. With all the self-control he could muster, he reached into his hip pocket and drew out his flask of *aguardiente*. He emptied it in a few swift gulps. "*Diable*," he gasped, revived. As his mind resumed its normal functioning, he began hazily to realize that he was caught in an inextricable dilemma. He was about to join Micheltorena who had been standing speechless with surprise a short distance away when the thirty Californians, upon a sign by the man from Kintuck, formed a circle around him.

"Hands up, Captain," shrilled a voice, obviously that of the leader. John recognized the man as Antonio Castro.

Castro spoke, "You're our prisoner, I'm afraid." Then beckoning to a vaquero, he ordered, "Find Alvarado and bring him here. Meanwhile, captain, wouldn't you like to rest?" He thrust his fat thumb in the direction of a sycamore tree.

Red-faced, humiliated and apprehensive, John walked over to the spot indicated and sat down. Embarrassed by the eyes watching him, he removed his hat and fanned himself nervously.

"*Cigaretto, Capitán?*" asked one of his guards.

Although he did not like the Mexican brand, John accepted it, not knowing what else to do. The pound of hoofs came up the road. Presently a flushed and dusty rider dismounted near where John sat. The captive looked up into the flashing brown eyes of ex-governor Juan B. Alvarado. He tried to avoid them, but without success.

"*Capitán Sutter, amigo mio,*" said Alvarado, throwing his arms effusively around his old friend, in the impetuous Mexican manner. "*Viejo amigo mio.*"

Several minutes later, John found himself seated between the enemy leaders. They treated him in a friendly manner, plying him with *aguardiente.*

"My sincere apologies, *amigo mio,*" said Alvarado. "I regret I must confine an old friend. But unfortunately war is war. You are our prisoner. I must place you in confinement."

The governor's unforeseen gesture, his warm-hearted reference to their former friendly relationship, hurt John far more than had he hurled at him sharp words. Magnanimity, he knew, he did not deserve. He turned his head away, too ashamed to speak.

The governor looked pityingly at the crestfallen man before him. "Vaquero," he called, "bring *aguardiente;* it's in my saddle bag."

The two men drank in silence together. "Let us be friends, friends as we were when you first came to Monterey," said the governor. "You remember those days, don't you?"

Subdued and contrite, John nodded assent. "To the victor," he mumbled, raising his newly-filled glass in a shaking hand.

Presently Alvarado and his escort of soldiers took John to a small adobe at Cahuenga where they placed him under guard. As the governor departed he laid John's old French rifle ostentatiously outside the barred door. The news of the capture of Captain John Sutter spread like wildfire. For hours curious crowds of men, women, and children pressed around the solitary grilled window that let light and air into John's dark cell, viewing him with apparent relish. The heat of their perspiring bodies, the cries of the babies, the low-muttered words, derogatory and jeering, the hordes of gnats and flies in his musty room nauseated him. In desperation he stretched out on a hard wooden bench, face to the wall, and closed his eyes.

In Los Angeles, where they moved him the next day, he was quartered in the home of a prominent Yankee merchant, Abel Stearns. It was a delightful adobe overlooking the main plaza, glowing with colorful flowers; in fact it was the largest mansion in *La Ciudad*. Abel Stearns himself proved a gracious host. He kept John informed of what was going on in the city: that all the women had left; that Micheltorena and his troops had been captured; that Castro and Alvarado and all *La Ciudad's* notables had celebrated the victory at Cahuenga by an elaborate banquet. He even consoled him when Micheltorena was sent home to Mexico under armed guard. He was also instrumental in having John released, his horse and a small bodyguard supplied, and allowed to go home.

As he headed north toward his fort with the disgruntled and disheveled remnants of his army, John thought ruefully that he had cast his lot with the losing side. He harbored a feeling of rancor within him that fate, one of whose favorites he considered himself to be, had basely deserted him. True, the enemy had treated him magnanimously enough, releasing him upon his promise to support Castro and Alvarado and the Californians in the new government they intended to set up in Monterey. They had acted with equal generosity toward the defeated Micheltorena, whom they placed aboard a ship bound for Mexico.

He reproached himself bitterly for allowing himself to become embroiled in local politics. Worst of all, he was more heavily in debt than he had even been before and there was no certainty that the new land grant Micheltorena had given him at Santa Barbara was valid. And for it he had spent the princely sum of eight thousand dollars.

As he rode into the fort with John Bidwell beside him, he observed ironically that it was the first day of April, April Fool's Day. A most appropriate day upon which to return. He felt foolish, humiliated. He took little pride in his new title, *Comandante de las Fronteras del Norte y Encargado de la Justicia.*

The months following John's return from the southern campaign were so full of momentous events that he had little time to brood. Indians were stealing horses and cattle which he could ill afford to lose. The possibility of war between Mexico and the United States disturbed him deeply. Furthermore, the new governor, Pio Pico, had even sent a proclamation, or *banda* to New Helvetia, closing all immigration from the United

States into California and at the same time notifying John to forbid all travelers to enter his fort.

Late that same fall, the governor sent a delegation to New Helvetia with an offer to purchase it. They told John they wanted it for two reasons: because it was the key to California and because it was the rendezvous for American settlers on the west coast.

For a time John could not decide what reply to make. Desperately as he needed the money, to meet the ever-increasing flood of unpaid bills, he felt morally bound to protect the settlers living in and near the fort. Their protests, their pleas to him not to abandon them to the mercies of the Mexican officials, were what made him decide not to sell. Even when Governor Pio Pico's representatives came back a second time offering him in addition to the $100,000 they had originally said they would pay, all the lands and cattle belonging to Mission San Jose, John still refused.

For he knew he could never bring himself to part with the fort at any price; it was his own creation carved almost single-handed out of the wilderness. Now it stood there solitary, substantial, immense—the mecca of overland travelers. Furthermore, John could not deny that he liked the role of master of Sutter's Fort.

He did not have the courage to turn any of the poor starving people away, despite Governor Pico's proclamation which, indeed, was never actually enforced.

There were times, however, when John regretted he had not sold the fort, especially when bands of outlaws began to infiltrate the West Coast. They came late that spring, shortly after the formal declaration of war between Mexico and the United States. It ushered in an era of "no laws." He liked to meet and extend hospitality to the endless stream of travelers, to hear them address

him as *Comandante Militar de las Fronteras*. Yes. Here
at New Helvetia he was monarch of all he surveyed. At
last he had achieved what he had dreamed of as a boy.
He was uncrowned monarch of the Far West. Thou-
sands were moving into his principality. Despite Pio
Pico's edict, emigrants kept on arriving at the fort.
They poured in daily by wagon, on horseback, by foot.
They were usually short of funds. John had to feed
them, clothe them and act as physician and counselor.
In so far as he could, he gave them work.

Even John C. Frémont, secret agent of the American
government, who appeared suddenly at the fort with
his old scout-guide, Kit Carson, and demanded animals
and supplies that John was unable to supply, was courteously treated at the fort, although his presence, with
a large number of armed soldiers, disturbed John.

"I wonder what he wants?" he asked young Bidwell

"I don't actually know. But I have my suspicions,"
replied the young clerk.

"What are they? I believe he's a government agent.
I suspect the United States has designs on the West
Coast."

"You mean they intend to take it away from
Mexico?" asked Bidwell. "That doesn't surprise me in
the least."

It was not long after that a rider galloped into
Sutter's Fort one hot afternoon in mid-June. Jumping
off his panting horse, he went over to where John sat
on his front porch.

"We've raised the Bear Flag at Sonoma," he shouted
gleefully. "We've captured Vallejo. Hurrah for the
Republic of California."

Astounded, John looked at the American perspiring

profusely, but exuberantly happy. "California . . . a republic. . . ." He could not believe his ears.

"Come in, my friend," he said with the unfailing courtesy characteristic of him even in times of stress. "Tell me all about it."

The American described in vivid language the raising of the Bear Flag. "We made it from an old shirt," he smiled. "An American woman cut out the figure of a black bear and sewed it on for us. It made a fine flag."

"I knew the Americans were discontented with the Mexican régime, but I didn't think they would revolt so soon."

"We kept it a secret," the American replied. "We've been deceived and repressed and mistreated here in California long enough. No red-blooded man could be expected to stand such treatment. We want California for ourselves. Now we have it. We intend to make John C. Frémont our first governor. Meanwhile we're under martial law. I've come to ask you to co-operate with us, *Señor Comandante*," he said respectfully to John.

Conflicting thoughts moved swiftly through John's brain. What would happen to his lands and fort if he joined the American cause? What if the Californians gathered together an army and whipped the Yankee revolutionists? What would happen then? Which side would ultimately win? California, with Mexico behind it? Or the United States? And what would happen to all these American emigrants living in the Sacramento Valley? They made the fort seem more like an American stronghold than a cosmopolitan center as he had intended. Confusion overwhelmed him.

"May I give you an answer at a later date?" he said, by way of evading a direct reply.

Thanking him, the traveler excused himself, saying

he wished to convey the news of the Bear Flag Republic
to every settler in the Valley.

Three weeks passed by. Then came rumors of more
exciting events connected with the Bear Flag Revolt.
In early July, Frémont assumed command of the new
republic with headquarters at Sonoma. The California
Battalion of 250 men patrolled the country and kept
order. For a time martial law was enforced.

Then from Monterey came stirring news that overshadowed in importance the Sonoma revolt. Commodore
Sloat, sent out from the east coast on the *S.S. Savannah* to assume charge of California after the war with
Mexico, had gone ashore at Monterey and hoisted the
American flag over the custom house.[1] That means the
end of Mexican rule, John thought as he sat disconso-
late in his room at the fort, uncertain as to his own
future. The following day he also learned that the
United States flag had been raised in the Yerba Buena
plaza; that Lieutenant Joseph Warren Revere had replaced the Bear Flag at Sonoma with the Stars and
Stripes. Anxiously, John waited to see if the same thing
would take place at the fort.

He was not surprised when an American sailor appeared at his door, carrying an American flag, neatly
wrapped under his arm. "I'm William Scott, sir," he
announced. "Lieutenant Revere sent me to request you
to place our flag over your fort. The Americans, sir,
are now in full possession of California."

He saluted respectfully, placed his bundle at John's
feet and returned at once to the waiting schooner that
had brought him up the river from Sonoma.

John felt alternately the desire to laugh and cry.
Controlling his emotions with some difficulty, he went

[1] On July 7, 1846.

out into the courtyard, where he discussed with his majordomo plans for holding a celebration the next day. Then he went into his own room, there to indulge in an orgy of drinking that lasted far into the night.

At sunrise, every inmate of the fort, with the exception of the prisoners, summoned by the bugle, stood at attention. Slowly, impressively, and with all the dignity he could muster, John walked over to the flagpole that stood in the center of the fort. He untied the ropes and hauled down the battered Swiss flag that hung limply to it. As he did so, a tear rolled down his cheek. Then he fastened in place the Stars and Stripes. It began to flutter in the morning breeze.

"Fire the cannon," he called huskily, breaking under the strain of the emotion within him.

"Gentlemen," he said, turning to face the hundreds of men standing, hats in hand, who were watching him. "We are under the protection of a new flag, a very great flag, the American flag. Today Sutter's Fort passes out of existence. It has now become Fort Sacramento. The fort, you and I, and everyone living in California are from this time on under a new master. From this moment we shall take orders only from Washington. Let us salute the American flag. Let us love, honor and obey it, and defend it with our lives."

# CHAPTER XVIII

# OVERLAND SAGA

THE THOUGHT CAME moodily to John one morning, as he dressed, that he was no longer master of Sutter's Fort. It had passed into the control of the United States. It was now Fort Sacramento; men in neat uniforms had replaced the tattered Indian army he had trained. New rules and regulations were expected out from Washington any day; new laws by which he must abide. Worst of all, a young lieutenant called Edward M. Kern, a member of Frémont's party, was in command of this new United States post. And he, *Comandante* of New Helvetia, was obliged to serve under him at the paltry stipend of fifty dollars a month. Fifty dollars a month! He threw back his head and laughed, a shrill, ironic laugh.

He threw on his clothes as quickly as he could. Then he rang sharply for a servant. "*Aguardiente, muchacho,*" he snapped. The Indian slipped silently away, returning moments later with bottle and mug.

John poured himself a generous portion, downing it with the speed of long habit; then another. For the next two hours he sat in his bedroom, drinking in solitude. Then, reeling and stumbling, he clapped his broad-brimmed hat far down over his curly blond locks, thinly streaked with gray, twisted into tight curls the ends of his waxed side whiskers, took his gold-headed cane and, leaving the fort with a stiff salute to the American soldier on guard as he passed through the gate, sauntered off to the Indian village in search of his current favorite, Mary.

Autumn came unseasonably early to the Sacramento Valley that year. Rains began falling intermittently in September; by October storms blew in off the Pacific almost daily, attaining the proportions of cloudbursts. The lofty Sierras between the sandy desert wastes and the lush lands of California were blanketed deep with snow. The trail leading from the fort across the mountains and on east, usually passable in winter was closed to travel because of ice. Pioneers and Indians, long accustomed to rigid winters shook their heads. So far as they could recall, they had never seen one like it before.

Despite the storms, overland travelers arrived that fall in ever-increasing numbers, pushing ahead to cross the mountains and reach the fort before winter set in. The migration was by far the largest contingent John had ever seen: men, women and children, with their wagons and household goods, packed the courtyard.

Each day as he wandered about, John looked dubiously at the crowds of Americans glutting the fort. "Where can we ever house them all?" he said, one morning to his clerk, John Bidwell. At the moment they were standing at the entrance gate watching a dilapidated wagon, whose canvas cover was half gone and which was dragged by two emaciated mules, pull in.

The dapper clerk shrugged his shoulders diffidently. "I was thinking the same thing. More sick babies, too, I see." He indicated with a wave of his hand a weazened infant clasped in the gaunt arms of its weary mother sitting on the front seat of the creaking vehicle lumbering by.

"Anyway, there are a few husky men among them," observed John philosophically. "And we need all of them we can get. On the whole they're far more ambitious and dependable than these lazy Mexicans you find all over California."

Bidwell shook his head doubtfully. "But we don't want women and sickly children, Captain. It's a shame, I tell you, to drag them across the plains."

"Well, let the United States look after them," John replied, relief in his voice as if events were moving so swiftly that he was glad no longer to face the responsibility of newcomers at the fort.

"If we wait for help to come from Washington they'll all die of starvation," Bidwell replied.

"I suppose that's true. I'll see what we can do." He went over to greet the newcomers. The driver, a bronze-faced young man, climbed out and grasped the hand John held out to him.

"Captain Sutter, I presume?" he inquired courteously.

"Yes. I'm Commander Sutter," John replied with his usual impressive manner. "I'm glad you got here before the pass was blocked with snow. Another week and you might have been forced to camp for the winter on the other side of the divide."

"Yes, thank God, we made it. But there's another large party behind. The Donner party. We met them at the rendezvous at Fort Hall several weeks ago. Eighty-seven in all. They were talking of taking a new route across the desert. Hastings Cut-Off, they called it."

"Who's in charge of the party?"

"Uncle George Donner. He's sixty-two, but spry as a colt. He's a rich farmer from Springfield, Illinois. Mrs. Tamsen Donner who is with him is his third wife. They have five children. And no end of baggage. In fact

old Uncle George has enough milk cows and beef cattle
to supply an army. And his wife! You never saw such
a collection of silks and laces and books and gewgaws
as Tamsen Donner has in her bags. And the choice
household goods she brought along! They were the envy
of every emigrant crossing the prairies."

John listened with attentive interest. Wealthy settlers
were direly needed at the fort, and as he thought of the
renegades and loafers whom he was forced to support,
he said, "We'll be glad to have them settle here in or
near our fort. When do you think they will arrive?"

"They planned to reach the fort in September or
early October at the latest, but many of the wagons
broke down. Then several women fell ill. Two died."

"Of cholera?"

"No. Childbirth, I believe."

John led the travelers into his own house where he
provided them with hot food and a comfortable place
to sleep.

The man thanked John effusively. The woman gave
him a wan smile, invoking God's blessing for his generosity. Her gratitude, the spiritual look on her face,
touched John to the core. Watching her with her sick
child in her arms made John think of his own children
back in Switzerland. And the thought came to him that
what was lacking at the fort were devoted loyal women.
They alone would prevent the fort from becoming the
stronghold of idlers and desperados.

Meanwhile, as the days passed, new events crowded
out of John's mind the non-arrival of the Donner party.
He had much to occupy his thoughts these days. For
one thing, Mana had quarreled with Kanaka Harry
and then with one of the white pioneers who had offered
her the protection of his roof. She now came almost

daily to the fort, for she was trying to win back John's affection by exhibiting the precocity of their child.

"I want him to be an American citizen," she said proudly. "Just like Lieutenant Kern and his men."

John half suspected that she came not so much to extract from him the money he always gave her for the child, as to flirt with the newcomers, especially those in uniform. He tacitly ignored her all too obvious feminine deceptions, however, while keeping her at arms' length. He was also careful to see that she did not meet his Indian squaw, Mary, not daring to risk another one of those screaming, hair-pulling feuds that not infrequently disgraced the fort. For Mary, sweet and gentle as she appeared to be, had been known to display upon occasion tantrums worthy of a white minx. Moreover, he was anxious to sever as many as possible of his mesalliances, in anticipation of the time when his wife and family would reach the fort.

He had less leisure now for feminine companionship, with travelers coming in from all over the United States. They arrived in sizable units, coming by land and by sea. One ship even brought a contingent of Mormons, led by Samuel Brannan. The leader was nonplussed to find waving over the fort that "damned American flag" he had hoped, by coming west, to escape.

However, the Mormon elder had no alternative but to form his men into a battalion of their own, *Los Independientes,* pledged to serve under the Stars and Stripes.

John did not welcome the arrival of these professed bigamists. He was afraid of them and their ways. Marriageable women were scarce enough as it was and the idea of one man having two wives, or nine, like the head of the church, Brigham Young in Salt Lake City, he found thoroughly distasteful. Worst of all, he discovered that the newcomers, despite their spiritual qualities, were materialistic to the core. They proved to be shrewd and hard-headed business men; they injected many sharp practices into the rather lax and casual business methods John employed at the fort. He ignored these in so far as he could, inwardly praying that the thousand reputed to be on their way west would not be like the Brannan crowd.

Late that fall, as John was riding from the fort to the *embarcadero* to meet the weekly schooner from Yerba Buena, he met two bedraggled men, walking toward him. They were so close to starvation they could scarcely speak. He leaped from his horse.

"You look ill, my friends. Do you need any help?"

The taller of the two skeleton figures tried to lift his right arm to remove his hat, but it dropped limply back to his side. "My . . . name's Reed, Sir . . . I'm from . . ." Dizziness overcame him and he dropped in a heap at John's feet.

His comrade stooped over him in alarm.

"What is it?" John inquired.

"We're starving, Sir," he gasped, and slumped beside his prostrate companion.

Swiftly John removed from his hip pocket the flask of *aguardiente* he always carried with him and poured a few drops down each man's throat. It was stimulating enough to revive them immediately. The tall one whispered faintly, "Where, Sir, is Sutter's Fort? And Captain Sutter? We must see him at once."

"I am Captain Sutter," John replied.

The men were unable to walk, so John called for some Indians. They carried them into the fort and put them to bed with hot bricks at their feet. Mana herself brought them a light but nourishing soup. They were too exhausted to sip more than a few spoonfuls.

After they had rested, John urged them to talk.

"We're part of the Donner Party. We were caught in the early snows in Emigrant Gap," Reed said. "Our leaders lost their heads. Oxen and cattle were buried under the snowdrifts. We had no way to rescue them. At first we slept in our wagons. Then we decided to build shelters of pine logs near a lake. We realized we might have to spend the winter near Emigrant Gap. That's where we left the rest of our party."

"How much food have they?" asked John.

"Practically nothing. They're starving. Most of them are walking skeletons. Some can't even get out of bed. The children are so weak they don't even cry. If we don't get food to them . . ."

"We'll find a way. With Indians, perhaps. They have remarkable powers of endurance," said John.

"We'll give you everything we have, if you'll save them," the younger man said feebly.

"Don't think of that. I'm only too glad to assist. This fort is at your disposal. But now you must rest. It will take us a day or more to collect meat and flour. And, too, I must find responsible men." He left them with faint smiles on their faces, the first in many weeks.

He lit his pipe that evening and prepared to glance through a sheaf of papers Lieutenant Kern had left with him to sign. He was fatigued by the strain of being forced to take orders from young Kern, rather than giving them himself. It was the first quiet moment he had had all day. The peace he had once enjoyed in the wilderness of the Sacramento Valley had disappeared. Notwithstanding its rules and regulations, to him the

United States army seemed all bustle and confusion by contrast.

Then there were all those poor starving people, the Donner Party, marooned in the Sierras. He dared not let his thoughts dwell too much on them. But he wondered what had happened to all of Tamsen Donner's furbelows. Despite the reassurance he had given Reed and his companion, he had not told them what was actually in his mind; that the chances of saving them all were slight. He knew it would be difficult to find anyone to make the trip, no matter what reward was offered. Worst of all was the large amount of food needed to feed even meagerly some ninety people. John tried to blot out from his mind these unhappy pictures as he sat reading Kern's report.

But he could not concentrate. He pushed the papers aside with an impatient gesture and started out to see if he could find someone who would attempt the rescue. He went briskly to the various quarters occupied by those employed at the fort pleading the cause of the marooned Donner party.

In some rooms men were playing cards, in others eating, drinking and telling stories, and a few had already retired for the night. But wherever he went he met only violent objections.

"Are you crazy, Captain?" most of them asked. "Man, it's sheer madness. Only an imbecile would attempt it. They'll probably survive anyway, the poor fools. Come, Captain, join us in a game of cards. Or a drink."

The more refusals he met, the more John was determined to find a way to rescue the stranded travelers. But no white man would entertain for one moment the thought of crossing the frozen sierra. Only Indians would attempt it. The situation was unprecedented. Californians everywhere were aroused by the Donners' tragic plight. The newspapers were full of it and published appeals for funds for the rescue work.

The following morning John called two sturdy intelligent Indian boys aside.

"I want you to take seven mules loaded with provisions to some starving people camping in the mountains," he said.

"*Si, Señor*," they replied enthusiastically, liking the prospects of a trip.

"I will pay you in gold," he went on. "Real gold, U.S. dollars. The kind the American soldiers use at the fort."

The Indians looked at him in surprise. The pay the Captain was offering seemed suspiciously high.

"You may be gone some time," John added. "The trip may be a hard one. You will have to travel through snow, deep snow."

He looked sadly at them. They were his favorite Indian boys, still slim and youthful. "Take plenty of warm clothes and blankets," John cautioned them with a paternal air. "And be ready to leave two days from now."

On the appointed day John apprehensively watched them set forth. "Pray God they'll make it," sighed John Bidwell who was standing by his side. Sadly he watched the train of mules tied together by ropes carrying panniers of jerked beef and beans and hard bread, file past the fort gate. One Indian rode on the first mule; the other on the last of the cavalcade.

"The odds are a hundred to one against it," the Captain presently replied. Then cupping his hands around his lips he called out with an attempt at levity, "*Dios va con Usted. Hasta luego, amigos, hasta luego.*"

That same evening, while John was having supper with his friends, a soldier in a United States uniform arrived from Monterey. He strode directly into the dining room, over to John, and handed him a sealed letter.

"From Colonel Frémont, Sir," he said lifting his hand in a military salute.

As he slit it open with his dinner knife, John said, "I wonder why the colonel's writing me and not young Kern." An instant later his face became distorted with an anxious frown as he read:

"Serious trouble has broken out in the south. The Californians have revolted against United States rule. Near San Pedro they met 400 hundred men off the *U.S. Savannah* and drove them back. They have recaptured Los Angeles and Santa Barbara. Rush every available man to our assistance."

# CHAPTER XIX

# STRANGE PROPHECY

AT THE FORT no one talked of anything but war. There was interminable confusion everywhere; messengers came and went; U.S. recruits were being enlisted with feverish haste, untrained volunteers culled from young emigrants who had not the slightest idea about the basic principles of warfare. Most of them were country lads who had come west from the emigrant rendezvous at Independence, Missouri. Short of funds, they chose this means of livelihood.

Companies of these hastily-assembled men under captains of little or no experience streamed out of the fort day and night and rode south to join the hard-pressed Americans near Los Angeles. But the conflict was of short duration. For with the arrival from the east of General Kearny and his Army of the West, the fate of the revolting Mexican-Californians was sealed. A series of minor skirmishes took place.[1] Then, in January the war came to an abrupt end.

John was grateful when the war was over and life returned to normal. The arrogant ways of Lieutenant-Colonel Frémont and his executive officer, young Kern, galled him almost beyond endurance; Frémont's unbridled temper, which he often unleashed against his prisoner, Mariano Vallejo, lacked all consideration for

[1] The Treaty of Cahuenga was signed on January 13, 1847, on the outskirt of Los Angeles.

the amenities which he had striven to inject into life at
the fort.

On more than one occasion John remonstrated with
Frémont about it. One day he said boldly to him, "I
understand Commodore Stockton has orders from
Washington for Vallejo's release."

The American officer gave John a chilling look but
did not reply.

"Just why should Vallejo be held any longer?" John
persisted. "Epecially now that the war is over?"

"I did not know you and *El Comandante* were such
cronies," said Frémont, his voice brittle with sarcasm.

John's candid blue eyes twinkled with repressed delight. "We're not," he retorted. "But I hate to see even
an enemy of mine suffer needlessly. Furthermore, Vallejo cannot endure confinement."

"Few men can," snapped Frémont.

"He's been held too many months already. He's aged
greatly. He's a sick man, anyone can see. Shouldn't he
be released?"

But Frémont evaded the issue. How could he tell
John that Vallejo was merely being held so that his
cattle and horses and crops could be pilfered until little
or anything was left.

"I intend to write to Washington myself and inter-
cede," John observed with quiet conviction.

"Don't do that, I beg of you, Captain Sutter," said
Frémont with belated courtesy. "In fact, I'm considering releasing old Vallejo tomorrow morning."

Whether the threat of writing to Washington was a
contributing cause John never knew, but Frémont kept
his word. For purely selfish reasons, John was glad to
see Vallejo leave the fort, primarily because his pitiful
presence was a painful reminder of past differences.

The fort was in the throes of a trying transition, brought on by readjustment to the idea that California now belonged to the United States. The military crisis was over, and tangible evidence of the new master was prevalent on every hand. Some phases of the transition were extremely irksome; others John found highly agreeable.

He enjoyed the officers who came to the fort. They were jolly, enthusiastic young men, of fine physical presence, in striking contrast to the lackadaisical ways of the Mexican-Californians. Gradually, because of his superior knowledge of pioneer conditions, they came to look upon John as the true master of the fort and the United States government as a kind of remote overlord in the east. He felt a new zest in the role. The long, weary years he had spent establishing the fort were now forgotten. The fort became again a living, vital community.

In these days as he walked around its neat and orderly court, John felt satisfaction over what he had accomplished. He was glad now he had not sold it outright during the war to the United States, and retired to his country place, Hock Farm. He had been strongly tempted to do so, for he had heard that Leidesdorff might attach the fort as payment against the Russian debt.

He thought happily of the outburst of post-war prosperity apparent on every hand. The influx of newcomers was incredible. Yet only eight years before the Sacramento Valley had been a wilderness.

At the government's request, John took a census of the settlers living in and near the fort. To his surprise, there were some three hundred whites who had erected among them sixty houses, and five hundred tame In-

dians, not to mention uncivilized natives roughly esti-
mated at twenty thousand. Every day more and more
white men were taking up land along the Feather and
American forks.

Contemplating this budding prosperity of his valley
brought elation such as he had felt but few times in his
life before. There was, he also sensed, something almost
fantastic about it, as if it were ephemeral, unreal, a
thing that might somehow suddenly escape. Would he,
as he sometimes believed and often heard men say, become the richest man on the Pacific Coast?

His lands were increasing tremendously in value.
Each year he planted more and more acres to wheat,
until now he harvested forty thousand bushels annually.
Livestock multiplied at an amazing rate. In fact he had
so many thousand head that he had lost count of them.
He owned six flour mills, and a tannery. His looms were
never idle; from them came blankets and miscellaneous
fabrics. Indians, painstakingly taught by overseers,
produced creditable leather articles: high boots, hats,
saddles, spurs, bridles, belts and decorated jackets
trimmed with cut work, which he sold to *rancheros* living around the Bay. For the first time there was an
undercurrent of feverish activity noticeable at the fort.

Caught in its spirit of progress, John found himself
planning new and important ventures. He improved
conditions at the fort, for bettering the lot of those
around him was uppermost in his mind. He envisioned
Fort Sacramento as a thriving center, teeming with
industry, the hub of California. Many things were essential before this could be accomplished: doctors, medi-
cines, teachers, schools, better food, adequate housing,
a closer contact with the government at Washington.

He began to make plans for granaries, threshing

floors, a large bakeshop. He even thought of erecting a sawmill and gristmill up the river.

One day one of his most dependable mechanics, a Scotsman called John Marshall, whom he had known for a long time, approached John's office. Tall, lean and stoop-shouldered, Marshall was carelessly dressed in a buckskin shirt and trousers and carried a Mexican serape on his left shoulder. His outward appearance gave no inkling, however, of his sober character, nor of the fact that he was known to be a spiritualist which led many of his associates at the fort to consider him queer.

John accosted him with his usual friendly manner. "Come right into my office, Marshall. I have some plans I'd like to talk over with you."

The moody, dreamy-eyed man viewed the speaker somewhat uncertainly. The Swiss Captain's invitation might mean nothing more than that he wanted someone with whom to have a drink. To Marshall hard liquor was anathema. He paused uncertainly. "Is it important, Captain?" he finally asked.

"Extremely so."

Marshall entered the office and for some time the two men talked about the possibility of building a sawmill in the mountains, where there was plenty of timber. They decided on a place called Culluma or Coloma, some forty-five miles away in the mountains, a beautiful valley, on the south fork of the American River.

"I'll tell you what I'll do, Marshall," said John. "I'll pay all your expenses and give you an interest in the mill if you'll take charge of erecting it. We can employ some of these Mormon friends of Sam Brannan; they're industrious and reliable."

"Fair enough, Captain," Marshall replied. They shook hands by way of binding the agreement.

Nothing was done about it immediately; John's thoughts were wholly absorbed by the tragic plight of the Donner Party slowly dying of cold and hunger, snowbound in the high Sierras. Three separate relief parties had been sent out to rescue them and got through. They started back with a few of the more hardy, who preferred to risk the chance of reaching the fort despite the snow, to almost certain death in their camp. Luis and Salvador made their way for some distance through the deep drifts with a handful of half-sick emigrants, but most of them, including the two Indians were frozen to death. The second and third groups fared somewhat better; more than half lived to reach the fort.[1]

At first John refused to believe their incredible tales of babies perishing of cold, and being eaten, or women scraping leather to make soup, of starved men becoming raving maniacs, and staggering away to die in the snow. He refused to believe that men would eat the flesh and suck the bones of their lifeless relatives.

But finally their reiterated tales left little room in his mind for doubt. They were, indeed, made even more vivid by the ghoulish figures of the forty-eight survivors who dragged themselves through the melting snows that spring to the haven of John's fort. He could scarcely contain his emotions as he watched them arrive: little children parentless, women without husbands, men who had lost family, possessions, health. The mountain tragedy aroused John to a realization of human suffering such as he had never known before.

---

[1] Out of the eighty-seven members of the Donner party, forty-eight lived to reach the fort.

Late spring found John so exhausted by the strain
and horror of the Donner tragedy that he began to lose
weight. His usually good appetite deserted him and his
sleep was broken into by hideous nightmares that he was
freezing to death in the snow. To distract his mind
from the daily problems that now seemed irksome, he
decided late in June to make one of his rare trips to
the Bay.

It proved to be an exciting journey. John traveled
on the new river steamer, The *Sacramento*, which was
in command of the infamous Louis Keseberg, the last
survivor of the Donner group to leave camp and
against whom charges of the grossest inhumanity had
been made. Although officially cleared of all cannabalis-
tic accusations—he was believed to have saved his own
life by living on the flesh of those who had died—a certain stigma was still attached to the husky German
which he could not escape. Whispering passengers eyed
him suspiciously; the more fastidious refused to take
their meals at the same table.

More important to John than dissecting Keseberg's
character, however, were the superlative appointments
of the swift-moving *S.S. Sacramento*, which made the
trip in half the time it took the old schooners. Many
Americans, newly arrived in California were aboard
her, bound on their first trip to the Bay. Their high-
pitched ejaculations of wonder and amazement as the
countryside swept by, made them conspicuous among
the more seasoned travelers.

Keseberg, meanwhile, had been keeping to himself
to avoid the curious glances and suspicious looks cast
in his direction. Despite his huge Germanic frame, he
was touchy and sensitive and steadfastly refused to
exchange a single word with any of the passengers.

He amused himself by slyly watching his famous passenger, Captain Sutter, observing his courtly manner, engaging smile, the twinkle in his blue eyes, his neatly curled side whiskers and his silky mustache. The way John's blond hair curled back from his temples and stood up in a ring of curls as the wind ruffled it, intrigued Keseberg more than anything else. It suggested a kindly way about him, a humanness, a friendliness that the ostracized captain of the riverboat found definitely appealing.

Captain Keseberg was elated when John joined him one morning on the bridge of the steamer and shook hands with him in his most cordial manner. They visited amicably together for some time, their talk centering on the changes taking place at the Bay.

"You'll hardly recognize it, Captain Sutter," Keseberg volunteered. "It's growing tremendously."

"So I've heard. Yerba Buena will be a city some day."

"San Francisco, you mean."

"What?"

"Yes, the name's been officially changed. The new Yankee alcalde, Washington A. Bartlett, saw to that. He published a proclamation. San Francisco's in the grip of a land boom. People are actually paying cash for small lots on the waterfront. As much as twenty-five dollars, I've been told."

"Trust a Yankee to turn mud flats into dollars," replied John with the barest suggestion of contempt.

"Yes. They're good business men," Keseberg retorted. "Especially at auctions. They can sell anything and at the most ridiculous prices. Why, the new gazette is filled with notices of goods to be sold. Much of it is utterly worthless, too."

"I understand *The California Star* in doing well," John replied. In fact the stories they printed helped us collect the funds and supplies we needed to go to the relief of you and your comrades."

The allusion was a distasteful one to Keseberg. He looked coldly at John, then became suddenly pre-occupied with the compass near by. Belatedly aware of his comrade's embarrassment, John diverted the talk to more agreeable channels. "I hear a public meeting was held not long ago in the plaza, in protest against the governor."

"Yes. Frémont's appointment was a bad mistake. Few of us out here on the coast like or trust that man. They're all trying to get him out."

"I can readily understand why," said John remembering his relations with him at the fort.

John disembarked the following day at the wharf and engaged a *carreta* to drive him to the City Hotel, built the previous year by his friend Leidesdorff, and now run by John H. Brown. The two-wheeled cart creaked noisily as it bumped along, throwing considerable dust over John's neatly-brushed coat. They were scarcely under way when a gun boomed overhead. Simultaneously crowds of men and women in the streets waved their hats and cheered.

"A fiesta?" John inquired of his Mexican driver.

"*Sí, Señor*, fiesta *Americana*," the man replied with a hiccough, induced by over-imbibing in *tequila*. He lashed his mule to an awkward trot. The cart heaved forward with an uncomfortable lunge, moved swiftly up Clay Street, and, crossing Powell, Stockton and Dupont Streets soon reached Kearny, which opened into the plaza, where the celebration was taking place.

The driver squeezed the *carreta* into a small space

near the wooden platform on which sat, somewhat primly, a scholarly-looking American with a sheet of paper in his hand. "Who is he?" John inquired.

The driver draw himself up importantly, proud of his ability to impart imformation to the visitor. "*El Señor Doctor* Robert Semple. *Hombre muy grande. Muy inteligencia. Muy rico. Sí, Señor...*" A large hiccough interrupted his loquacious comments. "*Sí, Señor, El Señor Doctor* Robert Semple *es el hombre mas alto en todo California. Mas que cinco—mas que seis—lo que digo es verdad, Senor.*"

He paused, as if to stress the importance of what he was about to impart.

"*Sí, es verdad, El Señor* Semple *es siete pies, mas o menos, alto. Es el hombre mas alto in California.*"

"You lie," said John. "I've never known a man that tall. Almost seven feet! It's utterly ridiculous. You've been drinking too much *tequila*, my good friend."

"*No, no, Señor.*" The driver looked reproachfully at John. "*Por todos los santos, lo que digo es verdad.*" John recognized Semple as the man who had established the first newspaper in Monterey, *The Californian.* He watched with keen interest as *El Doctor* lifted his huge frame, adjusted his spectacles, arranged his tie, blew his nose, and finally after the cheering had subsided, began to read from the paper in his hand.

His speech proved to be a eulogy on San Francisco. He extolled its situation, its climate, its superlative bay, its fertile back country, its future possibilities. Then he rambled on in a dreary monotone that made listening difficult. John was beginning to yawn and stretch when Robert Semple's voice unexpectedly rose to a swift crescendo as he cried out: "San Francisco, with its population of five hundred people is destined

to be a second Liverpool or New York; it is destined
to be the great commercial emporium of the Pacific
Coast; it is destined to be one of the largest, finest,
richest, most aristocratic cities in the United States."
Then, exhausted by the force of his own eloquence, he
sat down.

Thoughts of a most unpleasant nature made John
writhe in his seat. He looked around at the squalid, dusty,
ill-kept plaza, littered with old papers, empty liquor
bottles and trash of all kinds. Could this shabby village
ever grow into the magnificent metropolis Semple pre-
dicted? As great as Liverpool or New York? It was
unthinkable. Yet if it did, it would rank ahead of his
own fort. Jealousy swept over him; a sickening, depressing feeling that he could not shake. He realized
at that moment how much his whole life was wrapped
up in the prosperity of his fort. It meant more to
him than anything in life, more than his family back
in Switzerland, more than Mana or any of the Indian
squaws he kept in his own private quarters; nothing,
indeed, could replace it.

He dismissed the driver with a handful of silver
coins and, bag in hand, entered the City Hotel, an
adobe structure of no architectural pretensions.

"You seem tired, Captain Sutter," remarked the
proprietor, John Brown, as he showed him to his room.
"By the way, what did you think of Old Beanpole
Semple's speech? I'm thinking of adding a wing to
this hotel to take care of some of these newcomers he
talks about. But I'm afraid it will be some time before
we're as large as Liverpool or New York." He chattered
on in the airy manner of hotel managers the world over
without waiting for John to reply. At the end of a

long passage he opened a  door, placed John's luggage on the bed and withdrew.

Although he had not dined, John did not feel hungry. Instead, he removed from his bag a large bottle and poured himself a glass of brandy. He sat for an hour, drinking steadily. A haze stole over his senses, dulling them until his mind became almost devoid of feeling. Nothing, now, seemed vital. His head drooped and fell forward. A saccharine smile spread across his reddened face. From his lips came a low mumbling, almost incoherent, as they sought vainly to form the words: great commercial metropolis of the Pacific Coast.

## CHAPTER XX

# RICH RIVER

LOWERING CLOUDS rolled across the heavens with ominous portent. Standing by the office of his fort John watched them pile up in dark masses toward the east. Raindrops spattered sharply against the window; more followed. They quickly merged into a heavy rain. The way it's coming down it may last several days, thought John as he drew the curtains together, lit the lamp, and slipped off his boots, exchanging them for his more comfortable fur-lined moccasins. He sat down in his arm chair and began slowly to fill his pipe from a beaded Indian pouch he always carried.

It was pleasant to sit quietly in his room, to realize that the sawmill and gristmill were almost completed, and that so much business was pouring into the fort that soon all his debts would be paid. It was pleasant to think of the day when his children would come from Europe to be with him in California. He felt a fresh satisfaction in being a substantial family man. It lent weight and importance, backbone and substance to existence. He had been away from his three sons and his daughter far too long. Tonight even the thought of reunion with Nanette lost some of its terror. Perhaps time had mellowed the acerbity of her tongue. He had not heard from any of them in a long time. Undoubtedly the fault was his own. He had always found writing to them difficult. He must make amends.

From his table he took a sheet of paper and a quill and began to write:

*Meine Liebchen*:

The intimate mode of greeting would please Nanette, even though it conveyed sentiments he did not feel. He glanced down at the sentimental salutation, and scowled. *Meine Liebchen.* There was something ironical about it. Yes. Writing Nanette was always a sordid business. He dipped his quill into a jar of ink and regarded it contemplatively. *Meine Liebchen.* Now that they were written, the words seemed irrevocable. He began to write. He asked first about the children, their health, their progress in school, their personal appearance; he thought of them still as little ones, and found it difficult to realize that they had grown up. He wrote laboriously, stopping frequently to rest. Then he told her of his plans for the future, of the effort he was making to clear off the Russian debt. "I expect to send for you all to come to California. It will be soon, I hope. Meanwhile I am building a fine country place where you will live. I call it Hock Farm, because the Hock Indians live near by." Relieved now that the abhorred task was finished he signed himself with an elegant flourish, in the classic German manner

*Dich liebender Gatte.*

Without rereading it, he sealed and stamped the missive; then addressed it. *"Gott sei Dank"* he breathed half-aloud, "that's over." Within his breast rose that half-stifled feeling, that sense of resignation, of frustration, of desuetude that invariably arose when he thought of life with Nanette. He had often tried to analyze it to his own satisfaction, but without success. No other woman had ever affected him in this singular manner; certainly not Mana or Mary or any of the numbers of young Indian squaws who had shared his bed. Why was it?

Unexpectedly it came over him like a flash. Nanette's diabolical possessiveness, that was it! Her eternal feminine demands, her so-called rights upon which she insisted, her right to order his life as she desired, to tell him when and what to eat, what clothes to select, what books to read, how to conduct his business. It was as if he had no mind, no will, no thoughts of his own. Away from her he was a totally different man. But back in Burgdorf, he had not been able to call his soul his own. Yes. That was it. Possessiveness! Strange that he had never recognized it before. It took a rainy night, years of separation, and the Atlantic between to reveal Nanette to him in her true light.

But still she was his wife, the mother of his children. That responsibility he could not evade. Memories of his almost forgotten past flitted through his mind: his youthful days in Berne, with his lust for freedom, wealth, power. All these he now had almost within his grasp. A few more turns of the wheel of Fate and he would be independent for life. A few more fine crops, a few more thousand head of cattle, a rise in the value of his miles upon miles of fertile land. Any one of these would make him the Midas of the West. He smiled happily.

He could well afford to smile now. He could even smile sardonically at his impetuous, unhappy youth. He could smile at his vanity, his ambition, his love of pomp and circumstance, at his youthful rebellion against the constricting mores of his homeland, its neat traditions, its smug, stifling contentment that had so galled him. Well, he had broken away from all that. He was a free man now. He could defy the constricting laws and petty regulations that had hampered him back in Switzerland. He chuckled. He found himself wondering whether the old order for his arrest was still a matter of concern with the Chief of Police at Basle. With the Atlantic and the American Continent between, he felt secure out on the Pacific Coast. Many of his cronies had left unsavory records behind them when they came west. Such things were regarded lightly at the fort. A police record, indeed, gave a man a certain prestige among his associates. It was all water over the dam; all his miserable, unhappy past would soon be forgotten.

He had, in truth, everything to be grateful for. His fort, his enormous land holdings, perhaps the largest in the west, his complete freedom from restraint, his daily life which was to direct as he alone chose. What more, after all, could a man desire? Yes, he mused, the years had dealt kindly with him. Only one thing more could he hope to accomplish: to see his fort become the controlling influence on the Pacific Coast.

A sharp knock at the door startled him with a jolt. "Captain Sutter," called a low voice, "let me in. I must see you immediately. It's Marshall."

John strode over to the door and flung it wide open. "Why, Marshall, what brings you out on a night like this?" Water oozed from the man's thick mudcaked boots, from his buckskin jacket; it dripped, too, from the brim of his felt hat, which he twisted nervously in his hands.

"Sit down, Marshall, and have a drink. There's nothing like a good swig of brandy on a night like this."

The visitor dropped wearily into the hard seat. "Are we alone?" he asked. He tapped the floor nervously with one foot; there was an air of repressed excitement about him which John could not fathom. Panic came over him. Had some calamity happened to the sawmill? Or were the Indians stealing and killing again?

"Are we alone?" Marshall repeated.

"Come into my bedroom," said John. "There we shall not be disturbed."

They walked into John's private quarters.

Marshall spoke rapidly. "I want two bowls of water, and a pair of scales. Quick."

John looked at his friend as though he were out of his mind. To humor him he went over to the door, unlocked it, and called to an Indian servant to bring the articles. When they had arrived, John bolted the door securely.

Marshall set the articles on the table in front of him. Then he dug into his trousers pocket with fumbling fingers and drew out a dirty white cloth rolled up and securely tied in a knot.

"I have a surprise for you, Captain," he said excitedly.

John poured himself a stiff drink of brandy and swallowed it. Meanwhile he kept his eyes on Marshall as he unrolled slowly, carefully, and with maddening deliberation his knotted bundle. This he now held out to John. "Look here," he said.

John looked closely at it. Within lay a pile of small particles of glistening yellow; some were flakes, others were round grains that varied in size from small pebbles to almost microscopic particles. A puzzled look came to his face.

"What is it, Marshall?"

A frenzied excitement shook Marshall's huge frame. His dark eyes, weary and bloodshot from loss of sleep, appeared to double in size. "Don't you know, Captain?"

"No. What is it?" He looked superciliously at the dirty bundle and its glittering contents.

"It's gold, Captain," Marshall blurted out. "Pure, unadulterated gold!"

"Gold? I don't believe it," gasped John. "What kind of a joke it this, anyway? Stop teasing me, Marshall."

"You must believe me, you must. It's virgin gold. I know it is. I have tested it." His voice rose excitedly. "And there's more, much more, where this came from."

"Where did you get it?"

"Near the new sawmill, Captain; we were cleaning out the . . ."

Quickly John interrupted. "On the American River. Gold! I can't believe it, Marshall. It's not true."

"But it is, Captain. I'll prove it. Give me the bowls. And the scales. And two silver dollars, please."

John watched in fascination.

Marshall weighed out equal quantities of gold and silver and placed them in two bowls of water, then laid them carefully on the balance.

Neither man spoke. But they did not take their eyes off the scales as they began slowly to move. Both held their breath as the bowl containing gold dropped lower and lower.

"Do you believe me now, Captain?" asked Marshall. There was an ecstasy, an exultation in his voice which he made no effort to hide. "Look. Look."

John stood spellbound, staring with fascinated eyes at what he saw. "Gold," he cried like a man in a daze. "It must be gold."

"I know I'm right." Marshall cried vehemently.

"We made every test we could at the sawmill. We pounded it until it was thin as tissue paper. We tested it with *agua fortis*. We bit it with our teeth. Why, we even held a piece in red hot flames; it came out untarnished. In fact we dropped it in boiling lye."

"*Gott im Himmel.*" John clasped his hand against his forehead, with a gesture of mixed joy and despair. "I can't believe it, Marshall."

Outside the rain still poured. John walked over to the window and peered out. The storm had reached flood proportions and showed no signs of abating.

"What a night," he said. "What a night to discover gold. It's fantastic. It's unreal. Am I dreaming? No, it can't be true." He stood gazing with unseeing eyes at the stormy night, his brain in a whirl. Then he turned and faced his friend. "You'd better get into some dry clothes, Marshall, and have something to eat"

"No. I'm starting back to the sawmill at once, Captain. I want you to come, too."

"What? In all this rain?" John felt too exhausted physically and emotionally by the news Marshall had just brought to do more than drop limply into a chair.

"But you must. It's of the utmost importance. I want to show you the spot where we found the gold at Coloma. It may not be raining forty miles away."

"But it's late and dark. Besides I've not had my dinner yet. Tomorrow will be time enough."

"As you please, Captain," Marshall replied, disappointment obvious in his voice. "But I'm leaving right now."

He lifted the soiled rag containing the remainder of the gold dust with the utmost tenderness and replaced it in his pocket. Then, after downing the brandy the captain handed him with one large gulp, he went out into the stormy night.

John ordered his supper served in his own room that evening, and as he sat down to it in solitude he could not take his mind off the gold Marshall had just shown him. There was something ephemeral, even mysterious about it which he could not fathom. "Gold," he muttered over and over to himself.

He began to mull over in his mind the insistent rumors that had come to him during the past few years about the presence of gold in California. Many believed the mission Fathers had known about it for some time, but would not let the Indians divulge where it was, and not so very long ago a Mexican called Lopez had located some particles of gold dust in Placerita Canyon near Los Angeles, which had, however, caused only a mild ripple of excitement·in the south. What was it that the minerologist attached to Lieutenant Wilkes expedition had told him three or four years ago when he stopped for a few days at the fort? He remembered that the man had said he believed there was gold in the vicinity of Mt. Shasta. More recently the Swedish naturalist, old Dr. Sandels, passing through the fort, had discussed at some length his views about gold. He had observed that it would be found in considerable amounts throughout the Sierras. "Pray God," breathed John, "the Swede is right." Then he remembered the words of his old servant, Pablo Gutierrez, who had said he was positive there was gold on Bear Creek. John was sorry now that he had laughed so rudely in the old man's face.

With an impatient gesture he pushed to one side his plate of jerked beef and beans. His usually good appetite had deserted him. Rising from the table, he rang for his *muchacho* to remove his untouched dinner. Then, fully dressed, he flung himself down on his bed, intending to start at dawn for the sawmill.

He tossed most of the night, sometimes elated over the possibility of new-found wealth, at other times apprehensive over the disastrous effect it might have on his fort. That gold, if found in large deposits, would revolutionize life at the fort was all too apparent to him, but would the good outweigh the evil? That was what troubled him.

At long last dawn broke upon his fitful rest. He washed hastily, gulped down a light breakfast and, accompanied by two Indian servants, he left shortly after sunrise for the sawmill at Coloma, almost forty miles away. The trail, muddy and slippery after the rain the night before, made traveling hazardous. He had gone about half way when he saw Marshall riding toward him. When he was within hailing distance, John called out, "I thought you were in Coloma by this time, Marshall. Didn't you leave last night, after all?"

"Of course I did. I got there safely, slept a few hours, and then decided to come back and meet you on the road." He turned his horse around and rode off at a brisk gallop at John's side. They headed toward the mountains.

By now the air was crisp and clear and sunny with the invigorating quality about it that comes after a heavy rain. That, combined with the feeling of exhilaration both men experienced at the prospects of immediate wealth, made them so animated that they could scarcely sit tranquilly in their saddles. At intervals John swished the rump of his white mare with a small stick, as he urged the panting creature to move faster. Burning impatience gripped him as he neared his goal. Although he had made the trip to Coloma innumerable times while the sawmill was in process of construction, the journey had never seemed so long as today.

They crossed the pine-covered foothills that rose behind the rocky banks of the South Fork of the American River along which they had been traveling for some time. Then Marshall called out, "We're almost there, Captain, ride as fast as you can."

John whipped his mare's flanks brutally. Marshall dug his spurs into the sides of his mount. Together they rode on as if devils were nipping at their horses' heels toward the long wooden shed that housed the new sawmill up ahead.

At the door they jumped down and handed the reins to the two Indians who had been following. Then they ran over toward a group of workmen who stood waiting for Captain Sutter to arrive.

"Wait till Old Cap sees all the gold we've been saving for him in the bottom of the millrace and he'll treat us to a few bottles of brandy," one of them whispered to the man next to him.

His comrade snickered. "He'll never know we collected it up and down the riverbed and salted it there. Yes, put it in one spot for a joke."

"Well, it's the only way I know to make Old Cap cough up a few drinks. I, myself, haven't had one for a month."

"Nor I." The speaker nudged his friend under the ribs with a sharp elbow. "Watch Old Cap now. We're in for some fun."

John, meanwhile, had hurried down into the riverbed at the point where a side stream had been diverted to test out the sawmill. Suddenly he leaned over to inspect a yellow pocket formed by several small rocks. His eyes bulged. His hands trembled. His stomach indulged in strange gyrations; he thought he was about to vomit. Perspiration drenched his face and dampened the stiff curls of his waxed moustache. "*Gott im Himmel,*" he gasped.

His unwonted loss of self-composure delighted the workmen, who were by this time peering furtively over his shoulder. They had never seen him drop his mask of fine manners before. "Old Cap's only human like the rest of us," mumbled one of them, sotto voce.

"Gold," said John, taking it up in his cupped hands. "Pure virgin gold. *Gott sei Dank.* Look, Marshall. I found almost a handful in this one spot alone. It's worth a small fortune."

Marshall looked at it critically. "I don't understand, Captain. It wasn't there when I left. It's hardly a fortune, but I believe there's enough in it for a large ring. And more, too."

"Come. Let's celebrate, boys. We'll have a few bottles of brandy. I have some in my saddle bags. Bring the *aguardiente, muchacho,*" he called to the Indian standing at his horse's head.

Appreciative grins spread over the faces of the men clustering around him. "We'll relish it, Captain," said one of them. "Brandy's scarce in these parts."

They tossed their hats high in the air and cheered noisily while Marshall poured the drinks into their tin cups.

John soon learned of the mischievous prank perpetrated upon him. He took it good-naturedly, however; salting the tailrace did not affect the amount of gold found in deposits along the riverbank, and there was a growing belief that quantities of gold might be found elsewhere. Only the magnitude of the discovery worried him. He wanted to keep this area and the regions near by unexploited until he could arrange to mine it himself. Moreover, the new sawmill would not be ready to operate for another six weeks and there was a grave danger that it might have to be entirely abandoned if the men left and began hunting for gold. After considerable discussion and by dint of promising them claims of their own to work, he was able to persuade the workmen at Coloma to keep the discovery of gold a secret for a period of six weeks.

Confident that his men would keep their word, John returned to the fort the next day to make the necessary arrangements to mine for gold around Coloma. Less than a week later, he sent one of his teamsters, a Swiss called Jacob Wittmer, to the sawmill with supplies. He was about to start back to the fort when one of the workmen's children, a grubby lad six years of age came up to his wagon. He held his hands tightly clasped behind his back.

"Guess what I have here?" said the lad.

"I can't guess. You'll have to tell me," Wittmer replied.

"It's gold. I found it near the sawmill." He exhibited a small handful of yellow dust, which he held in his smutty hands. "Captain Sutter found lots of it, too," he added. "But he said not to tell anyone. You won't tell, will you?"

The teamster looked quizzically at his small informant. "I don't believe it," he scoffed. "Run away, lad, and play."

"You can have it," the boy said generously. "If you'll give me some candy."

Wittmer tossed the boy some gumdrops he had in

his pocket. "It's a trade, son," he said. He thrust the gold dust the child gave him carelessly into an old envelope and placed it in his pocket. "Good-by, son," he called out, waving his hand as he slapped the reins and shouted to his mules. They moved slowly away in the direction of the fort. The more he thought about it, the more he was positive that the child had spoken the truth. He was convinced finally that what he had was gold.

When he reached the fort he was tired and thirsty after the long trip. He drew up in front of the popular fort store run by the two Mormons, Brannan and Smith, leading members of the Latter-Day Saints, who traded merchandise for hides and tallow and grain. The merchants were not popular at the fort; one of the grievances the local citizens had against them was the fact that they would not sell liquor on credit. The teamster flung down his envelope of gold dust on the counter and asked for brandy.

"You know you can't have it, Wittmer, without paying cash," said squint-eyed Brother Smith.

"But I have cash. Or rather gold. Same thing." He opened the envelope and shook the contents out on the counter.

"Don't try to fool me," Smith said sharply, brushing it aside. "I don't want any of this queer yellow stuff."

"You don't want gold?"

"Certainly. Give it to me."

"There it is," replied the teamster, pointing to the scattered particles strewn on the counter. "Real, virgin gold, Brother Smith."

"Stop insulting me, Wittmer," roared the irate proprietor. "You scoundrel, you."

"It's gold. You can go over to the Captain's room

and ask him, if you won't take my word for it. You'll believe him, won't you, Brother Smith?"

The teamster waited somewhat impatiently while Smith ran over to Sutter's quarters close by. Breathless, the Mormon accosted the Swiss. "One of your teamsters is trying to slip me some yellow stuff for a bottle of brandy. He claims it's gold. But I know he's lying. Am I right?"

Hesitantly, John cleared his throat. He needed time to think. He did not know whether to try to deny what Wittmer had said, or to tell the truth. Obviously someone had let the secret leak out at Coloma. If so, the news would soon go the rounds of the fort. Further concealment seemed futile. He looked Brother Smith squarely in the eye. "Yes, George, it's gold," he replied.

Without a word, the Mormon turned and rushed out of the room. Within fifteen minutes a crowd of excited men were pushing and shoving to get close to John in his office to question him.

"What's this about gold? Tell us where to find it. We're leaving for the sawmill tonight."

They tried to extract all the information they could. Hearing it, they laughed and screamed with delight. They sang at the top of their lungs. They swore volubly in loud-pitched voices until the room reverberated with their foul oaths. "Gold," they shouted deliriously. "We want gold. Gold. We want gold!"

## CHAPTER XXI

# GOLDEN SCOURGE

THE NEXT MORNING as John was about to pass the blacksmith's shop, he heard a commotion inside. Through a crack in the door came the sound of men shouting and whistling, laughing, singing and yodeling hilariously. He went inside. Cries of joy greeted him.

"Come on Cap, and help celebrate," yelled a round little man, who was dancing madly about the room, a lead spoon held tenderly in his cupped hands. He thrust it under John's nose. "See! Pure, unadulterated gold, Cap. Three cheers, boys, for the gold!"

Quietly John examined the yellow flakes in the spoon. "Where did this come from?" he asked.

"Coloma, Cap. One of your workmen brought it in late last night. He showed it to us while we were playing faro. At first we all thought it was a joke, didn't we, boys?"

Their excited flushed faces shone with delight. The men were now pushing and shoving to get close to John to hear what he had to say.

"So we wanted to find out," the little man continued. "We got the smithy here, old Fifield, out of bed," he jerked a blackened thumb over his shoulder in the direction of his friend, "and made him test it for us. Didn't we boys?"

"Yes. Yes. That's right," several voices replied.

"What test did you make?" John inquired.

"First we heated a black lead spoon until it turned snow white. Then Fifield pounded the largest yellow flakes with his hammer and put it in the spoon. It expanded, as gold should. Correct, boys?"

Absorbed in the reiteration of their crude test, they acquiesced with affirmative nods of their heads. "We'd just finished and were celebrating, when you came in, Cap."

"I had intended to keep it a secret for a time, boys, for reasons I can't explain, but the secret's out. Yes. It's true. Marshall found traces of gold at Coloma. But how much more we'll find, I can't say." By thus adopting a casual attitude toward it John hoped to minimize its importance. He deceived no one, however.

The men began to leap and dance and shout and sing louder than before. Some seized partners and whirled dizzily around the room as if demented. Others, seizing the blacksmith's tools, began to pound rhythmically on the anvil as if it were a drum, singing over and over: "We've found gold, gold. We'll be rich, rich, rich, rich as Croesus, rich as Croesus."

John watched them apprehensively. He could not believe his eyes. Am I delirious? Drunk? Or asleep? For the first time there flashed into his mind the potentialities of the gold discovery, and its widespread implications, its latent dangers, unpredictable—perhaps widespread. Would the discovery be a blessing in disguise? Or would it prove to be a curse which would bring havoc on his cherished fort? Solemnly John stepped out of the smithy and, abandoning the business he had intended to transact, returned to his own quarters.

The danger of a widespread knowledge of the Coloma gold was clear to him. Aware that it would soon be

CAPTAIN SUTTER'S ACCOUNT OF THE FIRST DISCOVERY OF GOLD

public property he felt the urgency of protecting himself. There was only one thing: to secure for himself at once a lease on the land near by. He had not done so earlier, because he believed he could keep the men at Coloma from talking. He did not wish to have others competing against him for the privilege of leasing mineral rights, which he intended to acquire without arousing suspicion anywhere. But such a course was no longer possible. He must lose no time.

He told his Indian squaw, Mary, to pack his leather saddle bags. "Coloma?" she asked with the intuition inbred in her race.

"Yes, yes," John replied. He was so accustomed to Mary's facility for deducing what he intended to do that he seldom bothered to mention his plans to her any more.

"*Oro?*" she asked tersely.

John indicated by a brief nod of assent that her guess was correct.

"I'm going, too," she announced with an emphasis quite foreign to her usual placid ways. "*Sí, Señor*. I go to Coloma."

"But you can't go, Mary," John retorted crossly. "I'm going on extremely important business."

"I know. You may need help. I go get fast horse." She ran from the room.

"No, Mary, no," he called sharply after her.

She continued to run swiftly ahead, as if she had not heard.

Presently, when he climbed into his saddle and rode through the front gate of the fort on his way to Coloma, he discovered she was following at a safe distance behind. Not caring to waste further time in futile argument with his stubborn Indian mistress, John ignored her and galloped rapidly down the road.

The forty odd miles to Coloma, by now so familiar to John, were covered in less than six hours. Without stopping at the sawmill, however, John went on up a side trail that led to a native settlement two miles beyond. There he alighted at the hut of the chief. Being on friendly terms with the old warrior, John was cordially received and invited inside.

After some moments of desultory conversation carried on slowly and deliberately as befitted the chief's scant knowledge of Spanish, John was able to convey to the native leader his desire to lease their ancestral lands from the local tribe.

"*Es posible*," however, was the only reply he could elicit from the chief. Unable to make further progress with the noncommital Indian, John was about to leave when he saw Mary peering in through the open door. "*Gott im Himmel*, so you followed me all the way. Well, now that you are here, come in," he added ungraciously.

She glided in and sat demurely at the chieftain's feet.

John looked at her. "Perhaps you can interpret for me, Mary. The chief doesn't seem to understand my Spanish very well."

"What shall I say?"

"Tell him I want a three years' lease on twelve square miles of his land, including the country around Coloma. Tell him I'm looking for minerals. Tell him I'll pay for it with enough hats and shirts and leggings and flour and sugar and tobacco and *aguardiente* for his entire tribe. Find out how many there are."

Mary talked at some length with the chief using all her persuasive arts. Finally she turned to John. "He agrees to make his mark on your paper in return for food and garments for his people. There are sixty-nine in his colony."

John took from his pocket a piece of note paper and wrote briefly upon it the essential legal phraseology of a lease. This he handed to the Indian who laboriously and stiffly made a curious native mark at the place John indicated. "*Bueno, amigo,*" said John, extracting from his hip pocket a small bottle of brandy. "*Salud y pesetas,*" he added, offering it to the chief.

The Indian drained more than half its contents, then, wiping the bottle on his long, matted hair, handed it back to his guest. "*Salud ... y ... pesetas,*" he repeated, pronouncing the unfamiliar Mexican phrase with some difficulty.

They parted with all the formality, the bows, the grunts of goodwill and the final handclasps the occasion required. John followed by Mary left the hut and rode over to Coloma, where they spent the night. He talked briefly with Marshall about the new lease. Both men agreed that it should be rushed at once to Monterey for the signature of Governor Mason, the official representative of the United States while the Treaty of Guadalupe Hidalgo was being drawn up and prepared for the signature of the American and Mexican governments.

"I suppose you know, Marshall, our secret leaked out," said John.

"No," said Marshall, "but I was afraid it might."

"Yes, the whole fort knows we've found gold at Coloma."

"I'll be damned," muttered Marshall.

"I'll try to keep my men with me at the fort, at least until this lease is signed and the wheat cut and stacked.

But I make no promises, Marshall," said John as he got on his horse.

Back at the fort, John found a Mormon named Bennett, whom he believed to be honest and trustworthy. He gave him the paper to be delivered to Governor Mason for signature.

"Keep quiet about the gold," said John, "not a word. Remember. Your mission is confidential. Take the first boat leaving for San Francisco—there's one this afternoon, I believe—then beg a ride in a *carreta* to Monterey. Or travel on horseback. Go anyway you like. Good luck, Bennett."

John found the weeks that followed Bennett's departure extremely busy ones. Work piled up. His desk was littered with unanswered letters, bills and requests from all over California for information about the gold. Every day strangers wanting to hear all about it stopped in to see him; because of these interruptions he had practically no time for his own affairs. The callers ate his food and drank quantities of his wines and brandies, for John was too hospitable to turn anyone away, instinctively extending to them the courtesies of the fort. At the end of each day he was often so exhausted, so overfed, so full of intoxicating drinks that he could do little more than stagger to bed.

Drunkenness was again becoming habitual with him. And while he resolved at least twice a week not to touch liquor again, he could never withstand the temptation to have just one more brandy. It became axiomatic at the fort that a stranger could get almost anything he wanted from old Cap Sutter if he knew the proper approach. The two sure avenues to John's favor were flattery and drink.

John could never resist the smooth-tongued words of

hypocritical travelers who, even at the first meeting, praised him without restraint. And if they said to him: "You are the best-known man in the whole United States today, Captain; you are famous everywhere for your generosity, your kindness to those in distress," he would accept the words at their face value and ply his new-found admirers with his finest French brandies.

After he had stumbled or been dragged away to his room by his majordomo and put to bed, his flatterers would laugh merrily together. "Dissolute old fool," they would say. "Why, the man's a wreck at forty-five, and all because of too much liquor, too many squaws, too little common sense. What opportunities he has wasted. Yet what an empire he controls. However, the man's almost bankrupt, so everyone says." They spoke with malice and envy and began to plot how to get some of his property for themselves.

It was inevitable that John's power and importance were of such magnitude as to command the attention of men all over the United States. John Sutter, of Sutter's Fort—the old name still clung to it rather than the newer one of Fort Sacramento —was the one person whom every overland traveler had heard of and longed to meet. To many he was the epitome of pioneer life in the Far West. He was the man who had carved an empire for himself out of the wilderness; as such he was the idol of ambitious emigrants everywhere. As the man whose fort was the hub of California, he was looked up to not only by politicians, traders and business men of all kinds, but by visiting Europeans who felt more welcome because he spoke foreign languages.

John gloried in this notoriety, growing pompous and self-satisfied under it. At this time he looked older than he actually was. His blond hair, streaked with gray, receded from his forehead, giving him the appearance of old age. His face was finely wrinkled; heavy puffs of loose flesh formed dark half moons under his eyes, which had turned to a faded blue. His nose suffered likewise from over-indulgence in brandy; it had become bulbous and thickly veined and inclined to be red. At the corners of his mouth deep lines had carved permanent furrows in his soft flesh. He seldom left his room nowadays without his cane; his reliance on it was the outward symbol of his inner weakness.

Beneath an air of grandiloquence and simulated prosperity, he tried to hide these signs of dissipation, but its grip he could not shake. Many knew of his chronic drinking; few knew of his nocturnal ways, his habit of meeting Indian women in little-frequented spots in the forest, and indulging in sexual orgies. Comely squaws were seldom free from his advances; if they protested, he found ways of forcing them to submit. His conduct caused muttered threats against him on the part of young braves who bitterly resented the Captain's high-handed appropriation of their lawful wives. Several surreptitious attempts were made against his life.

John preferred the young Indian girls of eleven, twelve, thirteen years of age. He enticed them into the forest or lured them to his room under false pretenses. They were usually girls from distant tribes whom he bought for this purpose; in this way he avoided having to cope with irate relatives. To his chagrin, most of these girls proved to be too young and too lacking in strength to survive the demands of his ardent nature; one by one they fell ill or died. Several, terrified by the experiences of their young friends, managed to escape.

John suspected that Mary, his acknowledged Indian

mistress, was responsible for their mysterious disappearances. She denied his accusations vehemently. But he condoned it in her because she concealed from the outside world his subversive peccadillos, his flights of prolonged debauchery and nursed him through them. John called her his *Madrecita*, his Black Madonna, and found in her the consolation he craved.

Under the strain of overwork, late hours and squaws, John began to drink more than he ever had before. He was drunk one or two nights each week and the strain of it brought on a serious liver ailment. The fort physician, Dr. Bates, warned him sharply to reform. John smiled, promised, then sinned again.

He was recovering from a prolonged spree that had lasted a week and was sitting up in bed one day drinking hot tea mildly laced with brandy, when an Indian boy brought in a note from John Bidwell, asking to see him. "He came in on the steamer from San Francisco," said the boy, "and seems very anxious to see you."

"Of course, of course," said John, who harbored a deep-seated affection for his former clerk. "Bring Bidwell in at once."

The two men greeted one another with effusive handshakes.

"There's no one I'd rather see," said John. "Sit down, Bidwell; sit down."

The guest slid into the chair Mary moved toward him near the side of John's bed. "You've been ill, Captain?" he inquired sympathetically.

"Only a mild cold. It's left my stomach weak. Dr. Bates ordered me to stay in bed and drink nothing but tea. Mary," he said, beckoning to her, "bring *Señor* Bidwell some brandy."

She complied, pouring a glassful for the guest.

"A sip for me, too, Mary," pleaded John.

She gave him a withering look, "No, *Señor*," she replied gently but firmly. "Perhaps tomorrow. I'll have to ask Dr. Bates." She departed, bottle in hand.

As the door closed behind her, Bidwell remarked, "It's good to be back at the fort. San Francisco's growing too big for my taste. Buildings and houses are rising everywhere. And the prices they ask for land. Ridiculous. By the way, have you seen the latest copy of our San Francisco newspaper *The Californian?*"

"Which one?"

"March fifteenth," he said, drawing a folded paper from his pocket. "It carries an account of the discovery of gold. It's the first mention of gold I've seen."

"Do you mind reading it to me?" John replied.

Bidwell turned to the second page of *The Californian.* A brief item at the bottom of the third column caught his eye.

"Gold Mine Found—In the newly made raceway of the Saw Mill recently erected by Captain Sutter on the American Fork, gold has been found in considerable quantities. One person brought thirty dollars worth to New Helvetia, gathered there in a short time. California, no doubt, is rich in mineral wealth. Great chances here for scientific capitalists. Gold has been found in almost every part of the country."

"It's accurate enough," observed John.

"What I came to see you about, John, was to find out from you how true the article is. No one in San Francisco seems to take it seriously. All they do is joke about it, that is, all except Semple, editor of *The Cali-*

*fornian.* I understand he's gone to Coloma to find out for himself."

"Confidentially, Bidwell, California may have mineral deposits of the utmost importance. It's too soon to say how much gold these mountains may hold. I've tried to keep quiet about it. I've stayed away from Coloma myself, waiting for Governor Mason to validate my lease. I sent Bennett to Monterey with the papers some time ago."

"Charles Bennett? That rascal? Why, I met him on the streets of San Francisco only a few days ago. That's where I first heard about the gold. He's been telling everyone from Benicia all the way to the Bay about the gold discovery."

"What? The liar! He swore he wouldn't tell a soul about it. Are you positive, Bidwell?"

"Absolutely. Bennett can't be trusted after he's had a few drinks. On the trip down from Sacramento everyone on board bought him *aguardiente* because he said he was carrying an important message from Captain Sutter to the governor at Monterey that would bring fabulous wealth to California and they wanted to find out what it was. They carried your messenger off the boat at San Francisco so drunk that all he could babble was: gold, gold, gold. But when anyone asked him where you found it he said he couldn't remember, but he thought it was near a river. . . ."

"*Gott sei Dank.* So Bennett couldn't remember where it was? That's the only thing in the devil's favor."

With the comfortable familiarity of old friends they talked together for several hours, discussing the discovery of gold and its probable consequences. At midnight Bidwell departed in high spirits over the epochal news. He walked toward a storeroom that had been recently converted into a rooming house. Before it he saw a small group of men scanning copies of *The Californian*, that had just arrived on the *S.S. Sacramento*. Several were reading aloud the account of the gold discovery. Bidwell stopped and asked, "Are you surprised, boys?"

"No. We've known it for a long time."

"Then why haven't you left for the mines?"

"We're waiting until Old Cap tells us where to go. He's promised us leases if we'll wait until the crops are in and he can spare us from the fort. He's guaranteed to make us rich."

"That's right, boys," said Bidwell loudly. "Follow Captain Sutter's advice."

As he moved on he muttered to himself, "It's the lull before the storm."

# CHAPTER XXII

# MAD NEMESIS

LATE THAT SPRING, Charles Bennett returned from Monterey. He handed John a letter in which Governor Mason refused to sign the mineral rights' lease. John was totally unprepared for the blow, for he had confidently expected to retain under his personal control all the country in and around Coloma. He was forced to concede the justice in the refusal, realizing that until the treaty pending with Mexico was actually concluded, the United States had no right to dispose of rights or properties not yet belonging to them in California.

Now that his plan had miscarried, he was at a loss to know what to do. Once the news from Monterey was out, he had no doubt that a stampede to the gold regions would begin. After thinking it over for a day, John reached the conclusion that he had only two alternatives; either to remain at the fort and conserve what he had devoted so much effort to accomplish, or to abandon it and hope to make a quick fortune panning gold.

Before he could decide, however, Bennett had told everyone at the fort the results of his trip to Monterey. "You or I can mine gold now. Old Cap can't stop us."

A general exodus began that same day. Men tanning leather left vats half-filled with skins and after spending every dollar they had for food and equipment, started for Coloma. Blacksmiths, carpenters, weavers, agriculturists and miscellaneous workers immediately followed. The first groups left quietly, stealing off by twos and threes. Then larger groups began to form, selecting leaders who bought supplies in large quantities, intending to set up separate camps beyond Coloma. John found long lines of deserting employees waiting outside his office door each morning, demanding their pay.

"Just stay until the wheat is sent to the Bay," he begged some of his more responsible men.

He did not tell them how desperately he needed the crop to reduce his Russian debt, two years in arrears, or how dangerously short he was of ready cash. "Don't leave me quite yet, boys," he pleaded. Within the week he realized the futility of trying to check the wave of gold hysteria that was mounting daily. The fort began to take on the aspect of an abandoned village: mounds of refuse hastily dumped out, lay in scattered confusion around the court. John tried to find men to clean out the debris, but there was not one to be found. The Indians had left in a body, and what few white men remained demanded outrageous prices John could not afford.

Wages and prices of food and supplies of all kinds reached absurd levels. They were rising daily, conforming to the basic law: the scarcer the article, the higher the price. Contemplating the high cost of living made John heartsick, for his expenses increased while his revenue diminished. It was a maelstrom into which he had innocently been drawn. With misty eyes he stared at his great abandoned vats, his deserted looms, his grain stacked but with no hope of shipment, his livestock suffering from privation. This fort of his creation, this small universe which he had made a living, vital thing, was disintegrating before his very eyes. He shud-

dered for its future. Only a miracle could save it. Again
he found his only solace in brandy.

Reports circulated constantly around the fort, often
exaggerated but with enough verisimilitude to lend
credence to them. At first John tried to discount them
or to ignore them. Finally he accepted as true the tale
about the fort storekeeper, Sam Brannan, rushing
through the streets of San Francisco, waving a bottle
of gold dust urging all brother Mormons to abandon
work and head for the mines. "And don't forget Our
Lord's rightful tithe," he had cried. Brannan started
a gold rush of spectacular proportions. Every pious
Mormon in the town followed the enthusiastic leader
to the diggings where they amassed thousands of dollars
daily at Mormon Island.

Hundreds of rich placer mines were being discovered
far beyond Coloma. Gold was being panned along the
banks of hundreds of sidestreams and abandoned river
bottoms in the foothills of the Sierras. Gold dust worth
fifty thousand dollars was said to be removed each day.
Enormous amounts were sent back to the fort in heavy
cowhide bags for safe-keeping, or buried in bottles
beneath marked trees, or recklessly gambled away.

John remained for a time indecisively at the fort,
renting rooms to miners. Then the desire to prospect
seized him. "I intend to form a mining company of my
own, Mary," he said one night, as they were preparing
for bed.

"No, Señor, no," she warned, as she gave a solemn
wag of disapproval with her dark head. Intuition cautioned her of its danger. She knew John was not a good
business man, that his forte lay in being host at New
Helvetia where he could display his self-esteem and importance by posing as the gracious, generous master,

the friend to those in distress. She knew that John's fastidious nature was unsuited to the rough life of a miner. She did her best to dissuade him. Indeed she even hinted that she knew three attractive young Indian girls that could be bought cheap. "They can live in the inside room next to ours," she told him. "No one need know they are there."

John smiled indulgently at her, aware of this feminine subterfuge. "No," he said with finality. "I must make a fortune quick. I want to send for my family back in Switzerland. In fact, I believe my son is already on his way here. For several years he has been saving what he earned to pay for his passage to California."

Mary's face became ominously red. Sullen rage blazed in her dark eyes. "*Su familia,*" she stormed, "*Es malo, muy malo.*" She turned rebelliously toward John. "Hell," she cried, "hell." The inflection in her voice, her language were so obviously those of the miners at the fort, as to startle John. "*Madre de Dios,*" she added, as she glided angrily from the room.

The business, Sutter's Mining Company, was organized that same week. It began operations at rich diggings beyond Coloma, on the American Fork, where one hundred Indians and half as many white miners worked diligently from dawn until dusk, washing gold in crude home-made sieves, called cradles. In the first few days so much gold was panned that every miner for miles around moved in. They staked out claims of their own and overcrowded the location so that no one could work advantageously. Every night three saloons that had opened up in tents, resounded with noisy customers who drank, gambled and fought over cards until dawn.

The camp became a center where his men were becoming rapidly corrupted; they did less and less work.

John was temporarily sobered by it. He moved his mining company to a new claim he had staked out at a place he named Sutter's Creek. Ten grog shops followed him, and again his men spent all their gold drinking and gambling until they were too tired or ill to handle a pick or a shovel. Although sacks of gold dust had been sent back to the fort, John, with the excessive rectitude of the belated reformer, did not believe future prospects justified remaining at a place so demoralizing to his crew. Furthermore, he knew the miners were robbing him of his share, for which he had advanced them supplies. He also suspected that they secreted the largest nuggets they found in their boots and belts, keeping them for themselves. He did not argue the point with them, for fear of their guns. Miners brooked no insulting questions; a man bold enough to voice a complaint was apt to pay for it with his life.

Then, too, coarse food, hard beds, lack of even the simplest amenities of life were hard for a man of his years. He yearned for the more civilized atmosphere of his fort. Worst of all, the rough calculations he made in his head led him to suspect Sutter's Mining Company was operating at a loss. Although fortunes were being made on every hand by miners, speculators and merchants, John now decided to open a General Merchandise store at Coloma. His partner was Lansford Hastings, a prominent overland traveler, reputed to be a good business man. Like the mining ventures, this ended disastrously and yet the gold rush was gaining momentum and the demand for mining supplies of all kinds was enormous. Beaten and bewildered by this savage rivalry, John returned to the fort.

By late spring, everybody at the fort was bound for the mines. Schools and churches were closed, places of business were boarded up. Penciled signs reading: "Off to the placers," were nailed to the doors.

In San Francisco Bay, ships were abandoned, officers and sailors alike having joined in the gold rush. At least three-fourths of the Bay city's male population participated in the hectic exodus to the Sierras. Building came to a standstill; land prices dropped spectacularly. Monterey was similarly depleted of its masculine population, as were the smaller towns and *ranchos* up and down the coast. Roads everywhere were jammed with travelers riding horses, mules, donkeys, or traveling in antiquated Mexican-made *carretas* that lumbered slowly along. Those unable to find transportation trudged wearily along on foot, pots and pans and rifles loaded on their backs.

As a swarm of locusts denudes a field of its grain, so the mad migration stripped the entire west coast of its manpower, leaving only the young, the weak, the aged, behind.

After his return from the mines, John watched the prospectors stream through his fort. Since it lay on the most direct route to the placers, it was there that the prospective miners rested for the night, renting every spare room he had. At the store he had opened at the fort they bought quantities of food and liquor. His profits were amazing. He had never before seen so many Spanish pesetas or American dollars. He had extra locks put on the iron chests in which he stored his money. Once a week he counted his profits, making a notation of the amount in a small book. He hoped to have enough saved by fall to clear off the old Russian debt, which constantly lay heavy on his conscience.

Late one night, as he sat counting the coins by candlelight, he heard a slight commotion in the court-

THE MINERS

yard outside and the sound of horses neighing. There followed a sharp knock at his door.

"Let me in, Cap," called a voice which John failed to recognize. "There's a sick man outside. We must have help, or he'll die."

Without taking time to lock his boxes, John unbolted the door. The black muzzle of a gun was pointed at his face; it was held by a man wearing a black mask. Several shadowy figures hovered in the background.

"Hand over that gold, Cap," said the bandit. "No words and no delay; we're in a hurry."

John did not move.

"Hell! So you won't, eh?" The man moved his gun inches nearer John's face. "Well, boys," he called over his shoulder, "Cap needs your help. Tie his hands, boys. Now a rag. Blindfold him. Gag him. Move fast. We don't want him to recognize any of his old friends; he might be surprised."

They hauled him into a chair and fastened him securely with a small rope. John heard the clink of coins as they rifled his boxes of the heavy canvas sacks that held his treasure.

"*Muchas gracias, Señor,*" said the leader, as the men tiptoed out of the door. "*Hasta luego.*"

They galloped away under a full moon through the main gate of the fort, past the open fields where hundreds of mounds of wheat stood in huge piles left by the workmen when they headed for the placers. "Drop a light in one of them," called the leader, "just for fun to see it burn."

They lit one of the largest piles that soon sent smoke and flame skyward. The spectacular sight delighted the marauders. From stack to stack they rode swiftly, dropping lighted fagots in them. Then they galloped up

the road, turning occasionally in their saddles to watch
the lurid columns of smoke and fire.

With sickening haste John freed himself and rang
the bell for help. No one answered.

"*Gott im Himmel!* Where is that devil of a servant?"

He found the courtyard deserted except for a few
drunken figures lying on the ground outside one of the
grog shops. He recognized the familiar faces of two of
his former clerks who had come in from the mines that
morning with several bags of gold dust. He was about
to step into one of the canteens in search of assistance
when the glare of fire in the fields beyond caught his eye.

"*Gott im Himmel.* It's my wheat. It's on fire. The
wheat I saved for Leidesdorff."

He clasped his hands over his eyes to blot out the
tragic sight, then turned and staggered with faltering
steps back to his own quarters. There he stared for a
few moments at his rifled strong boxes. Then he sank
down on his bed. He drew a full bottle of whisky from
beneath his pillow and drank until the last drop was
gone. Soon intoxicated, John began to laugh uproar-
ously, his sides shaking with mirth.

"What a joke on the Russians," he hiccoughed. "And
old Leidesdorff. He'll be here soon, perhaps tomorrow.
What a joke. What a funny, funny joke."

His lids began to droop over his bloodshot eyes; his
head drooped lower and lower until he fell asleep; he
gave a few wheezes, then he began to snore.

In another month it was mid-summer in the Sacramento Valley, with its heat, its drought, its dust. Over
the countryside, withered and parched, a strange quiet
settled; over the fort, a pall of sickness and death.
Dysentery and cholera, contracted by miners working
long hours with inadequate food, and often hip-deep

in water, stalked throughout the fort. Sick miners were daily brought by their comrades into Sutter's Fort in search of medical assistance.

John's rooms were inadequate to hold them; he was obliged to move all his merchandise out of two of his largest storerooms and convert them temporarily into hospitals. Old Dr. Bates, with only a few decrepit Indian women to assist him, worked day and night over the sufferers, administering purges, applying cold packs, brushing away flies and insects, and forcing broth down the throats of those able to swallow. The more hardy recovered; those who did not were hastily removed and buried in a common grave, for there were no carpenters to make coffins.

Without thought of remuneration John gave freely of his supplies while the epidemic lasted, desperately as he needed all his resources for himself. It seemed like the intervention of Fate that the cholera did not spread beyond a fifty mile radius of the mines and the fort, and that the more distant Monterey and the Bay area were spared. As the men recovered, however, they lost no time returning to their favorite digging to scramble for gold: to Coyote Diggings, to Whiskey Flat, to Mormon Bar, to Milkpunch, to Rich Gulch, Humbug Canyon, Rattlesnake Bar, and Graveyard.

The fort was again deserted. John walked listlessly around the courtyard. It was a desolate clutter of old wagon wheels and discarded harness, of broken boxes and whisky kegs with nauseating odor. There were the remains of the spectacular display of fireworks shot off on the Fourth of July celebration held in honor of Governor Mason who had come from Monterey to talk over the mining situation with John; scattered about were broken chairs, torn shoes, miners' clothes, all filthy and caked with mud.

"Find some squaws and clean out all this rubbish," John said to Mary. "It's all we can do when there isn't a man around. I've a mind to take a trip to the mines myself," he added. "After listening to these convalescents talk about their claims, I'm curious to see if what they say is true. I need a holiday. I'll start tomorrow morning. I'll visit the new mines along the Mother Lode."

Two days after he left, the *S.S. Sacramento* pulled up at the *embarcadero*, vigorously tooting her horn. Passengers crowded her decks. Boxes and kegs and bales of goods were stacked near the exit. Commotion and activity attended her safe docking. As the last rope was made taut to the wharf, the gangplank was set in place. Travelers swarmed gaily down it, luggage in hand.

Among them was a quiet slim youth some twenty years old, carrying a foreign-made bag. He carried himself with a self-consciousness, military bearing, and seemed ill at ease in his obviously European clothes. At the *embarcadero* he paused and looked around.

"Expecting someone, son?" asked an old man loitering near the riverfront.

"I'm looking for Captain Sutter. Can you tell me where to find him?"

"Old Cap left for the mines two days ago."

"Do you know when he'll be back?"

"Nope. Can't say." The old man inspected the foreigner from head to toe. "Ain't been long in this country, has ye, son?"

"*Nein*, I've just arrived from Europe. I'm Captain Sutter's son."

# CHAPTER XXIII

# SHATTERED IDOLS

OBLIVIOUS TO THE mid-summer heat, Augustus Sutter walked in bewilderment up the dusty road that led from the boat landing toward the fort. The conflicting rumors circulating about his father confused him. Some said that he was the richest man in the west. Some said that he was so careless with money that he was on the verge of bankruptcy. Others claimed that he was the most generous man on the coast, and that everyone respected him. Still others insinuated that he was a physical wreck, and morally and financially a scoundrel of the lowest order. Out of these disconcerting thoughts, Augustus could formulate only the vaguest picture of the man he had not seen for fifteen years.

All the pleasure of his trip to California and reunion with his father vanished. His youthful exuberation faded into cold dread. What if all these scandalous tales were true? What if his father were a chronic drunkard? What, then, of his own patrimony and that of his sister and brothers, waiting so eagerly to come to America? Who would provide their passage money?

To Augustus, trudging sadly along, the two-mile trip to the fort was one of the longest he had ever traveled in his life before. Colored by his dismal thoughts, everything he saw took on a somber aspect. The rutty, ill-kept road filled him with vexation. The untilled fields showed unmistakable signs of neglect.

Weighed down by these depressing thoughts, young

Sutter's shoulders began to droop. The bag he carried seemed to weigh more than it ever had. He gazed with painful misgivings at the walls of the fort looming ahead. For years back in Switzerland, he had dreamed of this glorious citadel in California. He had invested it with a halo of romantic fancy until it became as miraculous as Mohammed's paradise.

A cold lump of misery clogged his throat. He blinked his eyes rapidly in an effort to blot out the sickening illusion. He was so anguished by his own turbulent emotions that he did not hear the thud of limping footsteps behind.

"Hey, son," called a voice.

Young Sutter turned. Directly behind him was the old man he had seen loitering near the wharf.

"Hey, son. I clean forgot my manners. I was that flabbergasted t'larn old Cap had a white son. Yer old man 'ud nar forgive me, if I'd let ye walk t' the fort all by yerself. Spik a liddle Englis, don't yer? So yer just here from Europe, be ye? Well, son, that's quite a trip." He continued to ramble on, in the loquacious, somewhat incoherent manner of very old men, until they reached the fort.

The main gates, half torn from their supports and propped up by heavy timbers leaned precariously backward, as if about to fall. Only a few drowsy old Indians, seated against the wall with serapes draped over their heads were in evidence.

Glancing curiously at their squat figures and fat faces, Augustus went past them and on to the large white house that stood quite by itself a short distance beyond the gate. Intuition told him this was what he was seeking. At that moment the old man pointed a shaking, withered forefinger directly at it.

"Old Cap's house be that white mansion yonder, son. Go in and make yerself to hum. I rek'n no one's thar, 'cept Mary."

"Mary? Who's that?"

He looked around, but his decrepit escort was limping rapidly back along the road. The boy entered the house. The filth, the disorder, the aspect of flagrant neglect filled him with disgust. *Gott*, why did I come here? he thought. He picked his way through the litter of old bottles and faded newspapers. Dust and cobwebs clung to the ceiling, the walls, the floor and the crude, Russian-made furniture. Decaying filth left by rats and mice strewed the floor.

Piled carelessly on a table were several books. He glanced idly at the titles. Some were in French, some in German. Rousseau's *Emile*; Goethe's *Werther*; Scott's *Waverly*, in French; two volumes of Voltaire; one on Napoleonic Wars. Near by in a Swiss frame was a faded daguerrotype, showing his mother with four small children grouped in strained attitudes around her. On it was written *Johann und Nanette*. There was also a smaller picture showing the square in Burgdorf. Home-sickness overpowered Augustus. He felt a little ill. Through a door that was slightly ajar, he saw something move. He went over and opened it wider. An Indian squaw rose from a disheveled bed and with eyes flashing angrily faced him.

"I'm John Sutter, Jr.," he said sternly. "Who are you? And what right have you to be here in my father's bed?"

"*Hijo, hijo, hijo*," she screamed. "I'll kill you." She lunged in a mad frenzy toward him, her scrawny fingers outstretched. "Go away, or Mary'll kill you."

Young Augustus faced her in glacial silence.

His unexpected composure was disconcerting. Accustomed to frontier brawls, she could not understand his failure to respond. A short distance away from him she dropped her arms, tense and immobile. "I kill you," she said quietly, "some day."

Augustus ignored her threats. "What are you doing in my father's bed?" he repeated.

"*Yo son* Mary, I sleep . . . here . . . with *El Capitán* . . ." She spoke with difficulty in broken English, but the meaning of her words was plain.

"Now, I go away, far away. Never come back." She snatched a few feminine garments from a peg on the wall.

Bits of the unsavory gossip he had heard all the way from Panama to the Golden Gate came overwhelmingly back to him. *Gott,* he groaned, and stalked out of the room.

In one of the almost deserted bars, he found some of his fellow-passengers off the *S.S. Sacramento* drinking convivially together. Seasick most of the time, he had talked to them only casually on the trip, but now he direly needed masculine companionship. Diffidently he joined the noisy group clustered around the man dispersing brandy.

"Here's one for you," said the barman genially. "It's on the house. We'll let Old Cap pay for it. He's rich."

A dark-skinned man, fashionably attired in a cutaway coat and a foulard tie, smiled pleasantly at Augustus.

"Your name, Sir?" he asked.

"John Augustus Sutter, Jr., *Señor.*"

The man stared at him incredulously. "Captain Sutter's son? But you don't resemble him in the least."

"I'm like my mother, everyone says. I've just come . . . from Europe . . . to be with my father." His hesitation, his air of apology were not lost upon the older man.

In a kindly voice he said, "My name's Colonel Stewart. I've known your father for some time. I represent the Russian-American Fur Company in San Francisco, the position Leidesdorff held until he died. I come to the fort once or twice a year to see your father on business. I'm waiting for him now to return from the mines." He did not add that he was here this time with the intention of attaching the fort and commencing suit to collect the long-overdue payment on the old Russian debt.

He turned toward two men standing near the bar. "Permit me, *Señor* Bennett and *Señor* McKinstry, to present to you Captain Sutter's son. I believe he calls himself Augustus." Colonel Stewart then explained in a paternal manner, "George McKinstry is a man you should know. He's an old friend of your father; in fact, his business manager."

To George McKinstry it was a relief to meet this well-mannered and intelligent young foreigner. For months he had been trying to unravel Captain's Sutter's involved business affairs, but whenever he tried to discuss them, the captain was either drunk or disinclined to talk business. The longer McKinstry chatted with Augustus, the more inclined he felt to be frank and open with him.

After a few drinks he invited Augustus to join him in the seclusion of Captain Sutter's office. "I must find out first where Mary is," said McKinstry. "She might overhear our conversation." He glanced into the untidy bedroom. "She's gone," Augustus called after him, "and taken all her clothes."

"Thank God," said McKinstry. "Now we can talk."

They sat until dawn discussing business. The older man explained in painful detail to Augustus the total amount of his father's indebtedness, some eighty thousand dollars. He insinuated that the Russians were about to attach the fort for debt. He told him that the one way to save the property was to have it transferred at once into the name of Augustus. He assured the young man that there was a reasonable expectation of repaying it from rentals of fort property and from the profits of various companies with which Captain Sutter was connected, if only he could be induced not to squander them on liquor and squaws. He then explained the possibility of selling off some of the land around the fort and at the new settlement of Sutterville, four miles below the fort, which had valuable river frontage.

George McKinstry was favorably impressed by the young man's response to what he had to say. They parted with the understanding that they would both make every possible effort to save the captain's ventures from collapse and to conserve his properties with their tremendous potential value for the benefit of the heirs.

For the next three days, Augustus Sutter mulled over the disordered papers in the office of his father. They lay everywhere. Valuable documents, including his priceless land grants, were stuffed carelessly into half-open drawers, or lay in jumbled piles in dark corners. The son's orderly Teutonic mind rebelled at the mad disarray. By working persistently, he was able to bring about a semblance of order. He sorted and classified. He could tell without adding them that the total owed was terrifically high. Notations made by the Captain on faded scraps of paper of amounts due him, made a less impressive pile. From the old dates on most of them, it was clear to Augustus that his father seldom bothered to try to collect. These evidences of his father's lack of business acumen made the son heartsick. He could see a fortune carelessly slipping away. Determination to save at least some of it for his mother and sister and two younger brothers obsessed him.

On every occasion he talked earnestly with the more substantial men who came and went; with his father's former clerk, John Bidwell, with sober old Major Hensley, with the clever lawyer, Peter Burnett. He listened carefully and determined to profit by their experience.

He had been at the fort less than a week when an Indian entered his father's house and said, "Come. Quick. *El Capitán*. He is here."

The young man rushed outside. He saw a middle-aged man slide heavily off a cream-colored mare and come toward him.

"Augustus, Augustus." He threw his arms around the boy's neck and kissed him on both cheeks. "Augustus, *Mein Sohn*." Tears streamed from his eyes.

Silently they drew apart. Embarrassment overwhelmed them. Augustus felt suddenly tongue-tied, for the man before him was a total stranger. He bore the marks of dissipation plainly on his bloated face. He was unlike the flattering picture he had built up in his mind. Miserable, the young man turned his head away.

"Well, son," said the Captain, equally ill at ease. "Tell me all about the family. Alphonse and Emil. What are they like? And Eliza. She was such a pretty little thing. Your mother is well, I trust?"

After the awkwardness of the first reunion had passed, Augustus told of his life in Burgdorf, his schooling, his determination to follow his father to America. He described the brothers and sister with affectionate warmth, telling of their eagerness to live in California.

Of his mother he said little. Consciousness of some unspoken difficulty between his parents made him reticent.

Then his father began to talk. Augustus listened, alert and fascinated. Inspired by his enrapt listener, Captain Sutter outdid himself in loquaciousness. He described the stupendous, bewildering, unbelievable changes that had taken place in the past few months at the fort and all over California. He told of industries paralyzed, towns entirely deserted, ships idle, fortunes made by illiterate miners overnight, the influx into California of emigrants from all over the world, the wave of lawlessness mounting.

More soberly he told his son of his fear of losing the fort. "I'm afraid of the new Russian agent who's replaced kind old Leidesdorff. McKinstry tells me he's about to begin suit in San Francisco to take over my property in payment for the Russian debt. I can see no way to avoid it."

"I have a plan," said Augustus eagerly. "Major Hensley and Judge Burnett and I worked it out while you were away."

"What?" His head jerked up in astonishment.

The boy smiled. "A plan to save the fort," he said simply.

"What is it?"

"First, you must transfer all your property into my name to avoid suit. No one can attach my holdings for debt. Gradually we'll pay off all back obligations. I'm sure I can do it, father."

"But how?" He stared incredulously at the eager face of his son.

"First of all, we'll rent every room here at the fort. I estimate we can make three thousand dollars a month from that alone. Then we'll sell off some land."

"What land?" He was beginning to catch some of the boy's enthusiasm.

"Lots near the fort. In the new town of Sutterville. Men are clamoring to buy property. The miners have no safe place to invest the gold they take out. Land values have fallen drastically in San Francisco and the Bay area. Miners are afraid to buy property there. But here, at the fort and close to the mines they would invest. We'll make a fortune out of land."

The wisdom and enthusiasm of his son warmed his heart. "It's a good plan. I'll sign the papers as soon as I can have them drawn up. Tonight, if possible."

The papers were drawn up, signed and notarized that same night.[1]

The event was concluded with considerable drinking, from which Augustus refrained. He had received from his mother and grandmother a puritanical upbringing; he neither drank, smoked nor swore; he went regularly to church. Captain Sutter was considerably annoyed at his prudish ways. After the last witness had departed, father and son entered the bedroom. The captain somewhat the worse for liquor looked silently around.

"Where's Mary?" he asked. "Her clothes aren't here."

Augustus raised his eyebrows. "She's gone. For good, I trust. She's a good riddance, father."

"Augustus, don't speak to me like that. Mary's no affair of yours. Besides, I don't like your sanctimonious manner."

"But father . . ."

"Drop it, I say. I won't have any son of mine tell me what to do."

"But father . . ."

[1] Actually months later.

"Augustus."

John Sutter lifted a choleric face toward his son. This son of his loins whose arrival he had so happily anticipated, now he stood before him, like a David come to sit in judgment upon him. Brandy numbed his mind; his thoughts were confused and belligerent. In an angry flash he recalled hazily his forced marriage to Nanette, the night before Augustus was born, the dreary years that followed, his quarrels with his wife, his escape from Burgdorf to America. Now Augustus was here. The others would soon follow: they would rise up to rebuke him, like Augustus. The same feeling of despair that he had so often felt in his youth returned. He suddenly felt smothered as if high mountains were closing in upon him.

He waved his arms savagely toward his son. "Don't stand looking at me like that, with those staring eyes. I won't have my son look at me like that. I want Mary. Where is she? I'm going to find her," he called, stumbling half intoxicated from the room.

In the full moonlight past drunken revelers and dozing natives he crossed the fort and headed out into the countryside. Instinct told me to take the trail leading to the Indian *rancheria* where Mary's tribesmen lived. He had not gone far when he saw two figures standing under a large oak tree beside the road. One was Mary; the other was that of a young brave who often hung around the fort. The man glided behind a tree as John approached. The woman did not move.

"Mary," said John in his most ingratiating manner. "Come back. I'll give you anything you want. A silk dress from Monterey. Combs for your hair. A silver necklace. Anything."

"No. No. Go back to your white *hijo*."

"Mary." He swayed drunkenly toward her.

She turned to run.

He snatched her wrists.

"Mary," he pleaded.

She struggled to free herself. "Go back. No. Never. White men no good. I hate them. Indian braves good men. I go back to my tribe." Sobs broke from her lips.

"Mary," John tightened his hold on her wrists.

She recoiled and tried to break away from him.

He dropped his right hand from her wrist, reached for his pistol, and pointed it at her. "Now will you come?"

From behind the tree an Indian head appeared. The next moment an arrow whirred past John's head missing it by inches.

He lifted his pistol and fired at random toward a dark figure gliding silently away.

"Mary." He leveled the pistol at her forehead.

She cowed in fright.

"Obey me. Get behind that tree." He shoved her violently ahead of him to a bower of thick underbrush where they would be undisturbed.

# CHAPTER XXIV

## BLACK HOURS

Augustus stood thoughtfully before Sam Brannan's bar in the fort on the first day of January, 1849, a bottle of brandy clutched tightly in his hand. *Aguardiente* was a drink he had never tasted before. Home training in Switzerland, his innate distaste for the drunkenness prevalent everywhere at Sutter's Fort, the indignation he felt when he saw his own father stagger home, intoxicated, had made him shun hard liquor in every form. But of late, the disorderly life at the fort, with its drunken brawls, its gambling for high stakes, and its highly-sexed half-naked squaws hiding out with the miners in secluded places, had had a demoralizing effect upon him.

Worst of all were the endless arguments with his father, that usually terminated in foul-mouthed quarrels. Although he did his utmost to control himself, Augustus was beginning to feel the strain of repressing the torrents of hatred against his parent. He had come to the fort from Europe full of boyish ideals and hero worship for the father who had become a romantic figure and the most important man on the west coast. He had expected so much of his parent: companionship, affection, understanding. He had found, instead, a man addicted to every kind of folly; a man with frontier standards of conduct which he could not understand, and the shock of learning the truth about his father's infidelities reacted disastrously upon him.

He was also gravely troubled about his parent's vindictive spirit toward him. Twice the Captain in the throes of intoxication and a flaring temper had told his son some blunt but illuminating facts. He had berated him for having been the cause of his forced marriage to Nanette. He had berated him for having attempted to restrain him from drinking, from spending his money as he chose, or from consorting with women like Mary. "You . . . you damned son of a bitch," he had stormed, aping the current slang at the fort. All this Augustus mournfully recalled, as he fondled the unopened bottle in his hand.

Of late his mind was acting strangely. He was beginning to have periods of nervous trembling. The muscles in his face contracted and expanded, as if pulled by invisible wires, a reflex movement Augustus could not control. Involuntarily the fingers of his hands tapped a kind of automatic tattoo on whatever they touched. At times he was feverish to the point of suffocation for no good reason at all; as suddenly his body would quiver and shake with cold as if it were packed in ice. He told Dr. Bates, the fort physician about it, but the old man merely shook his head. "You're the Captain's own flesh and blood, ain't ye lad? Well, what do ye expect?"

His father's son. Recalling the words Augustus smiled wryly to himself. He opened the bottle, took a sip, then a drink. It half choked him. He took a larger one. Needles of fire ran down his throat and into his stomach. Presently the burning sensation merged into one of exaltation. He drank some more. Depression vanished. Confidence returned. He skipped lightly around the room, the bottle held to his lips. He had never felt so happy before . . . never . . . never . . . never . . . that he could remember . . . remember . . . remember . . .

Sam Brannan, standing near the bar, eyed him coldly. Like father, like son, he thought. He leaned over and picked up the insensible youth from the floor, pouring a pitcher of water over his head. Augustus opened a bewildered eye.

"What's the matter?" he asked staggering toward the bar.

"Keep away," warned the irate Mormon, slapping Augustus viciously on the back. "Damn your young hide anyway. And never ask me to sell you *aguardiente* again." He led the teetering youth to a chair and thrust him roughly into it. "Sit down and cool off, Augustus, until you're fit to go home. I'd hate to have Old Cap see you like this."

Although Sam Brannan saw much of Augustus during the next few weeks, he never saw him drink again. The young man seldom left the fort but stayed close at hand as if doing penance, devoting all his efforts toward safe-guarding his father's interests. His one thought was to devise ways to pay off the obligations the Captain owed. He was especially interested in a plan Sam Brannan, Lansford Hastings, and Theodore Cordua laid before him to develop a townsite near the fort to be named Sacramento City. He hesitated, however, knowing the Captain hoped to sell out at a good profit land already surveyed and divided into lots four miles below the fort on the Sacramento River which he had named Sutterville. He bragged constantly about his new namesake, even writing glowing accounts to friends in Switzerland about the great city named in his honor. Yet his father was constantly away at the mines, and creditors were pressing for payment. Desperate for funds, Augustus agreed to the proposal. He did not write his father a line about the new venture, but hired a man to sell lots at prices ranging from two hundred and fifty to five hundred dollars each. The more valuable sites along the river sold readily to miners anxious to find a way to invest surplus gold. Then as lots rose in value, speculators began to make sizable purchases. Sacramento City was thriving. Each dollar taken in Augustus carefully hoarded to pay off the family debts. He hoped his father would be proud of what he had accomplished.

The sale of land was progressing beyond Augustus' fondest hopes, when John stormed into the fort one day from Coloma. He flung his old army coat down on the table in the main room of his house where Augustus was studying a large map of Sacramento City and grabbed his son by the collar. He shook him until Augustus was too exhausted to speak.

"Lansford Hastings came to Coloma yesterday. He told me about Sacramento City. What does this mean? How dare you drive Sutterville off the map? The city named for me. I've a mind to kill you, Augustus." He dropped his son's collar and drew his pistol from his belt, pointing it at his son. "Come, what have you to say for yourself, Augustus?"

"No . . ." the words died out. Three men, Peter Burnett, Lansford Hastings and Theodore Cordua had just entered the room. Burnett snatched Captain Sutter's gun from his hand.

"Just a little drunk, ain't you, Old Cap?" Burnett raised his voice from a whisper and spoke so that everyone in the room could hear.

John's face flushed scarlet. "Give it back, Burnett."

The judge removed the bullets, pocketed them, and returned the weapon to John with a sarcastic bow. "Think twice before you shoot Augustus, Cap. They hang a man for that. Are you crazy, John? Or just drunk? What's happened, Augustus?" He looked kindly at the flustered young man, who could not take his terrified eyes off the gun now lying uncocked in Burnett's hand.

"Father's . . . indignant . . . because . . . we promoted Sacramento City. I don't . . . quite know . . . why." He stammered the words out slowly. "I was saving all the money . . . to . . . pay off his debts."

"Vain old ass," Peter Burnett muttered to Hastings under his breath. "Jealous of his son as all hell. Gives him no credit for what he's done, or for trying to pull Old Cap out of debt. All that bothers the old man is that Sacramento City wasn't named for him. He wants to see the name Sutter on everything: Sutterville, Sutter's Mining Company, Sutter's Merchandise House, Sutter this, Sutter that." They left the room, leaving father and son glaring at one another without speaking.

In the weeks that followed, bitterness was raising an impenetrable barrier between them. John's delinquencies affected Augustus deeply. He drank to forget them and in between bouts of drinking he was morose and dejected to the verge of melancholia.

For a time John ignored Augustus' fits of despondency. Finally, alarmed at his son's strange manifestations of inner misery, he consulted Dr. Bates. The kindly physician understood the nature of Augustus' distress and tried awkwardly to explain it to John.

"You see, Cap," he said, "frontier life is strange to Augustus. He was brought up in a sheltered way. All this bawdy life he sees around the fort is more than the lad can stomach, Cap. I reckon that's the trouble with him. He can't take it. But I don't like his drinking. 'Tain't like Augustus."

"What do you suppose it is?" He had come to rely more and more on his son's financial acumen and was worried for fear he might be seriously ill. "It's nothing serious is it?"

"Can't say yet, Cap," the physician replied. "But I've my suspicions." He tapped his forehead. "Something's amiss up here. Mebbe it's all my imagination. I hope so. . . ."

"But he was so eager to come to California."

"That's half the trouble. He's been disappointed, poor lad. It's gone to his head." Dr. Bates had too fine a sense of medical integrity to tell John what Augustus had confided in him, that the constant discord between father and son was reacting disastrously on him. Years of observation had taught him that shattered idols are hard to bear, and he sympathized deeply with the son.

"We'll have to find a way to stop the lad's drinking, Cap," he said. "His constitution can't stand it. No more than yours. I seriously urge you to stop drinking for a few months, John. Have some pity for your stomach. And your heart and your liver. If you keep on drinking, I doubt if you'll live to see fifty."

"I believe I'll stop. If only as a lesson to Augustus," John replied as they parted.

For a time John made some feeble attempts to establish a more friendly relationship with his son. He found that Augustus was interested in politics and California law and concerned over the lax way the country was being administered. They were discussing it one day in the fort office when John remarked, "I have an article here that will interest you, Augustus. Let me see . . . where did I put it?" He rummaged for a time in an untidy desk drawer, until he found it. "I knew I'd saved it. It's *The California Star* for February 13, 1849. The

article's by my old friend, Robert Semple. He presents
the matter clearly. Listen to this, Augustus:

"We have alcaldes all over the country, assuming the power
of legislatures, issuing and promulgating their *bandos,* laws,
and orders, and oppressing the people. The most nefarious
scheming trickery and speculating have been practiced by
some.

"Why should we endure this inefficient, military rule? It's
outrageous. We need new laws of our own."

John laid the paper aside and remarked, "There's
talk of calling a convention at Monterey this fall.
Brigadier-general Riley talked to me about it when I
met him at Coloma. Governor Mason was a good enough
man, but not capable like Riley. In the two months he's
been in California, he's been open-minded. He does the
best he can."

"Yes. It's no easy matter for a military man to serve
as governor, even if the position's only a temporary
one," Augustus replied.

"Riley sees our problems," continued John, "and is
trying his best to solve them. You know as well as I do,
Augustus, how he's toured all the placers and explained
to the miners the imperative need for new laws."

John talked on at length, discussing the latest menace
to the mining fraternity, the bands of outlaws called
the Hounds, a well-organized band of criminals, ex-
convicts from Australia and United States soldiers dismissed after the war, who were now roaming the country
robbing, killing and raiding with a brutality never
known before. Lawless as they were, they justified their
acts on the grounds that the United States laws forbade
foreigners from trespassing on public lands, and that
miners not born on U. S. soil, or naturalized citizens
were panning gold illegally. John mentioned many in-

stances of how they had descended on small groups of miners, and demanded their citizenship papers. When they could not produce them, the Hounds then took their gold, killing those who resisted. They also stole horses and cattle, and burned wheatfields for the excitement of it. "They are ruining California, Augustus," John said. "Unless we take matters into our own hands and soon, the Hounds will take over California."

"Unless the Squatters take everything first," replied Augustus.

"That's almost as serious," said John. "For us, personally, it's even worse. We'll have to pass new laws to control it."

"What of the hundreds who have moved to unoccupied land around the fort and won't leave?"

"The Squatters Association formed two years ago is an extremely powerful organization. No matter what I say they insist my land grants will never be recognized when the new Land Commission meets."

"That's ridiculous," said Augustus. "The lands were given you under Mexican law. Surely the United States will recognize just claims."

"You can't make the Squatters believe that," John replied. "They all swear the United States will win. They say land belongs to the colonists who develop it. That's their old contention about mining claims, too. They've settled all over my property. And no power on earth can get them off."

"Nothing but new laws and a strong police force. But when they will come, no one can say."

Mutual interests drew the two men closely together for a time; both worked soberly and diligently to protect their holdings. In the spring a decision was reached to accept an offer of $40,000 for the fort and to move to

Hock Farm, the country place up the Feather River.
John had been raising fruits and vegetables there for
some time and had also built several small structures
to house his workmen. These he now planned to enlarge.
He also designed a main house large enough to accom-
modate his family. Augustus was eager to have them
come out to California as soon as possible. Finances were
much easier now; the sale of the fort and town lots in
Sacramento City had materially reduced the Sutter
debt and each month Augustus was laying aside money
to pay their passage from Switzerland. He felt that
when his mother and sister and brothers arrived they
could all lead a normal, happy life at Hock Farm, and
that his father might abandon his licentious ways. The
amounts saved he entrusted to Heinrich Lienhard, an
honest Swiss settler whom John had employed for a time
at the fort and who had agreed to go to Switzerland
and escort the Sutter family to California. Late in June,
after enough money had been collected, he left San
Francisco for Europe.

In anticipation of his mother's arrival, Augustus
worked diligently to pay off the last debts. By mid-
summer they had dwindled to an insignificant amount;
in August the last one was paid. Peter Burnett, John's
financial adviser, secured a signed release from the largest creditors, the Russian agent, Suñol, Samuel French,
and the Hudson's Bay Company. He placed them in
Augustus' hands with the remark, "You have accomplished what I never believed could have been done,
Augustus. The Captain owes you a lasting debt. I only
trust he will repay you as you deserve."

"I have no right to keep my father's property in my
own name any longer, Sir," the young man replied. "As
you know, it was transferred to me only to protect us

from bankruptcy. Will you be kind enough, Major
Burnett, to see that the necessary legal documents are
made ready for me to sign. Tomorrow, if that is agreeable."

"I shall comply with your request. But unwillingly,
Augustus. You know as well as I do that your father
can't keep a dollar in his pocket. But try and persuade
him to give you at least a part of what comes in from
the sale of land to put away for the family," he said,
shaking hands with Augustus as he left.

A month or more later in one of those rare moments
when he displayed the slightest affection for his eldest
son, Captain Sutter invited him to a special supper
to celebrate the payment of the last debt. It was to be
their last dinner at the fort before the new owner took
possession. Augustus accepted with delight, for he hoped
the event would cement a closer relationship between
them. He still felt at times a timid sentimental attach-
ment toward his father and mourned the antagonism
between them.

Captain Sutter invited his closest friends, Judge Burnett, Major Hensley, George McKinstry, Theodore
Cordua, Lansford Hastings, and a few more, to help
celebrate. He ordered from San Francisco the choicest
of delicacies, many of them imported from France. His
guests dined bountifully on deer and fat bear meat, on
wild turkey, salmon from the Columbia River, and goose
liver from Strassburg. They had sturgeon and oysters,
crab and river trout. They gorged on pastries and fancy
desserts made especially for the occasion by a French
pâtisserie at the Bay and rushed by special messenger
to the fort. There was champagne and Burgundy, Rhine
wine, brandy and liquors. Eating and drinking began

at eight and lasted until midnight. But after twelve, drinks alone were served.

For a time Augustus refused to drink. Observing it, his father rose from his seat and shouted loudly at him. "Don't be a prude, Augustus. Have some champagne." He held out a glass of yellowish liquid that bubbled enticingly. "Try some," he urged. The hand holding the glass wobbled unsteadily as the Captain, flushed of face and with watering eyes, sat down.

One of the guests winked at Augustus. Another laughed uproariously. "Have a drink, son," another shouted.

An embarrassed flush made pink patches on Augustus' cheeks. His face began the nervous twitching he so dreaded. Someone shoved a full bottle toward him. He opened it gingerly. The cork popped and flew upward, then dropped onto his father's lap. The men shouted with glee. "That's a good omen, Cap. Your son's a chip off the old Swiss block. Ain't you, Augustus?"

The young man twisted nervously in his seat. Reluctantly he lifted the champagne to his lips. He hoped now his father would be proud of him. He drank until he could hold no more, until he lost all sense of what was going on around him. He remembered nothing except that the walls of the room were closing in on him.

It was long past midnight when the only two sober members of the party, Judge Burnett and Major Hensley, rose to depart. They glanced with amused tolerance at the drunken figures slouched down in their chairs. Augustus and his father, who had been sitting across the table from one another had now fallen across it, so that their heads almost touched.

"Liquor's a damnable thing, isn't it?" said Burnett,

glancing sadly at Augustus and Old Cap. "Let me see.
Wasn't it Socrates . . . or was it Aristotle who said, 'Ex-
cesses always breed disaster.' That excess carries in it
. . . what was it he called it? . . . Oh, yes . . . the tragic
flaw."

CHAPTER XXV

# THE AMERICAN OCCUPATION

THE GOLD RUSH began at the time the treaty of Guadalupe Hidalgo, ceding California to the United States, was signed. Excitement over the discovery of that precious metal overshadowed in importance events in Washington. Indeed, scant attention was paid to the adjournment of Congress, and its failure to provide its newly acquired land with a civil government. Californians accepted complacently the continuance of military rule, and the administration of obsolete Mexican laws. Belatedly they came to realize that these outmoded laws were inadequate to cope with the wave of lawlessness, brought in by the bandits, the thieves, the murderers and the gamblers that came in after gold was found.

With utter disregard for law these outlaws gravely menaced the lives and property of all those living near the Bay, Sacramento, and at the mines. Their activities increased at so swift a pace that General Bennett Riley, military governor of California, desperate at his inability to check banditry, urged Californians not to wait for Congress to establish a Territorial government but to call a convention at once, draft a Constitution and then apply for admission to the Union. He realized, even more than the people themselves, that with emigrants by the tens of thousands pouring into the country, under existing law no man's life was safe. By talking and making speeches in the northern cities and

at the mines urging people to act, he was finally successful in enlisting the interest of settlers throughout California. Because of his efforts in August, 1849, an
election to select delegates to attend a convention a
month later at Monterey was held at the fort. John
Sutter was one of six delegates elected to represent the
Sacramento Valley area.

John left Hock Farm and traveled to San Francisco
where he boarded a small steamer bound for Monterey.
He was delighted to find his old friend, David Spence,
waiting for him at the customhouse pier. The Scot took
John's arm and the two men started up Alvarado Street,
reminiscing as they went.

"Do ye remember the first time we met, mon?" said
Spence in the rich brogue he had never lost. "When ye
came to see Alvarado about that land grant?"

"Yes," John replied. "Somehow I can't realize it was
only ten years ago."

"And do ye remember Alvarado's banquet? And how
we bet he would win? We picked the wrong side that
time, mon. We're living through great times, John,
and unless I miss my guess, better ones are ahead of us.
I predict great things for California."

They walked along Alvarado Street until they
reached the Bull and Bear pit. David Spence hurried
John past it. "Let's go on up the hill, John," he said,
a twinkle in his eye. "I've a surprise for ye."

They went on until John felt Spence's finger pressing
his forearm. "Look ahead, mon." He indicated a magnificent building towering in the distance. "That's our
new Colton Hall."

Speechless, John gazed reverently at the great structure, built of local yellow sandstone. Its simplicity, its
classic façade thrilled him. Two stately flights of stairs

led from opposite sides of the street and joined at the front door. Above them was a colonnaded balcony.

"*Gott*," he finally exclaimed, "there's nothing like it anywhere in California."

"For a town of only twelve hundred people, it's not so bad, is it, mon? I think we have a right to be proud of it. Do you see those large windows on the second floor? That's the room where the convention's being held next week." After a thorough inspection of the town the two friends parted at the door of the Pacific Hotel where John had engaged quarters.

He spent the few days preceding the opening calling on William Hartnell, José Obrego, Thomas Oliver Larkin, and the seven-foot Kentuckian, Dr. Robert Semple, whom he greatly admired. Everyone was talking about the convention and how important it was for California.

On the morning of the opening session, groups of delegates from every part of the country gathered on the steps of Colton Hall at an early hour. At nine o'clock they streamed into the building and climbed the broad stairs that led to the large assembly room.

At one end of it, directly below a portrait of Washington framed by two American flags, stood the president's rostrum. The room itself was divided in the middle by an iron railing. Behind it were four tables, each seating twelve delegates. The other section of the room was reserved for spectators. Into it were streaming *señoritas* wearing high combs and black lace mantillas and whispering languidly together.

John recognized most of the American delegates as they took their places. He waved his hand in friendly greeting to H. W. Halleck, to Edward Gilbert of the *Alta California*, to J. Ross Brown, the official recorder.

He shouted words of welcome to Jacob Snyder, the surveyor and to his old friends, Stephen Foster and Rodman Price and Pacificus Ord. He glanced at the six native Californians, Antonio Pico, Jacinto Rodriguez, Pablo de la Guerra, Mariano Vallejo, José Carrillo and Manuel Dominguez, who were huddled in a far corner of the room, absorbed in conversation.

At the opening session Dr. Robert Semple was elected president. John Sutter and General Vallejo were appointed to escort him to the official chair. A tremendous ovation broke out as the ceremony was completed, for the Kentuckian was popular with everyone.

When it finally died down Dr. Robert Semple placing his great lean hands firmly on the arms of his chair for support, raised his seven-foot lanky frame laboriously from his seat. He smiled wanly, and placed his right hand with a curious fumbling gesture, upon his heart, as if its pounding disturbed him. He was pale with the significant bluish pallor of the ill.

Then, straightening his huge frame, he led the opening session of the Monterey Convention with strict adherence to Parliamentary form. His poise and acumen, mellowed by years of editorial experience on newspapers, injected a semblance of order into the loquacious, enthusiastic delegates. He rapped his gavel and called for order. Forty-eight pairs of eyes watched solemnly every move their erudite president made.

"We have gathered here," he said, "to make a constitution for California, to create a government for the people, by the people; to bring law and order to a turbulent land. There is much work to do. Let us proceed with dispatch. We shall begin with the declaration of rights."

Unanimous approval was voiced by the delegates.

"There is nothing about it you wish to discuss?" He paused briefly. No one replied. Semple turned to the secretary. "The Monterey Convention stands unanimously in favor of the United States Declaration of Rights."

Led by Semple, the delegates, during the weeks that followed and working often by candlelight until far into the night, reviewed in rapid succession the basic points important to Californians. They voted to prohibit slavery. They voted against divorce. They decided that judges should be elected by the people. They accorded married women the rights of property. They proposed to establish a liberal system of education. Despite their difference in race and background and viewpoint, the delegates worked with surprising harmony together.

But when the question of boundaries came up for discussion, discord rose among the delegates. Weary from long sessions, they spoke sharply to one another. More than once, after some used the foul language of pioneers and began to berate those who disagreed, President Semple was forced to rap sharply with his gavel to restore quiet. After heated discussions about including the Mormon-populated area of Salt Lake and the entire Great Continental Basin, the delegates voted to establish the east boundary of California between the Sierra Nevada and Salt Lake. The land thus incorporated included eight hundred miles of sea coast and had an average width of two hundred and fifty miles.

Later on, when the final business had been transacted John, who had favored including more land on the east, argued with Semple about it.

"No," said the lanky Kentuckian, "I'm obliged to disagree with Captain Sutter. What's the good of add-

ing all that desert to California? It's as useless as the
Steppes of Tartary. It's without water. There's no
tillable land, nothing but alkaline wastes. Why no one
could be induced to settle there, not while there is an
acre of good land near the coast."

John was unable to refute this convincing logic.
Nevertheless, he could not forgive the delegates for their
refusal to agree with him in his love of large boundaries
and vast expanses, even if he saw no immediate use for
them. If Semple surmised the thoughts passing through
John's mind, he made no comment, but merely said,
"Would you consider running for governor?"

Surprised, yet his face beaming with delight, John
replied with gravity, "But am I worthy of this honor?"

"That would be for the people to decide," Semple
replied. "But I think they might elect you. After all,
you're the most prominent man in California." Noticing
the absorbed look on John's face, he then directed the
conversation into lighter channels. "I suppose you're
looking forward to the ball tonight? I understand it's
to be a gala affair."

John crossed over to the window and looked out
across the harbor. Whalers, vessels belonging to the
United States navy, a few foreign ships and innumerable
small craft rode quietly at anchor. Each was flying the
Stars and Stripes in honor of the momentous occasion.
The sight of them gave John a new feeling of protection
and security. A lump rose in his throat as he watched
them. A moment later he turned and recrossed the room,
joining a group of delegates who were clustered around
one of the tables.

They were waiting to sign the scroll of the new constitution, which the secretary had just placed in President Semple's hands.

"Gentlemen," he said, "I believe Captain John Sutter's name should come first."

Several delegates stepped back to make room. John approached the table. He took the long-handled pen the secretary handed him. John Augustus Sutter, he wrote. The forty-seven remaining delegates signed in rapid succession.

When they had finished Semple called a young Mexican page. "Hoist the Stars and Stripes over Colton Hall," he said. Presently a single gun boomed out. "It's the fort gun. Listen," he said. Another rumbled, then another. The hills reverberated with the sound of gunfire as the shots continued. Ten . . . fifteen . . . twenty . . . thirty. . . . One for each state, Semple called out. Then came a pause.

"Listen again," Semple said. At that moment a tremendous cannon shot resounded across the bay. "Thirty-one. That's for California. Let's give three cheers for California. The new state." Hats were tossed in the air. The delegates cheered themselves hoarse. They stamped their feet. They whistled and sang and jostled one another with the familiarity of schoolboys.

In the street below Colton Hall a Mexican orchestra— flute, guitar and violin—struck up a tune faintly resembling *Yankee Doodle*. They followed it with *Hail Columbia*, equally poorly rendered.

John stepped out on the front balcony and applauded the musicians. Tears streamed down his face.

On the streets below crowds were gathering: festively attired Mexicans, *señoritas* in gala costumes, ragged children, a few Indians, groups of American marines off the gunboats in the harbor, an occasional foreigner. John watched them with moist eyes.

Directly below Colton Hall he saw an old *carreta*,

wheels creaking noisily and piled high with pine boughs, lumbering by. At that moment he was joined by Peter Burnett and General Vallejo.

"Those must be the decorations for the ball tonight," said Burnett. "By Jove. I've forgotten to bring my white gloves. Or patent leather boots. Perhaps I can buy some in Monterey."

"There's no use trying," General Vallejo said quietly. "The last pair was sold yesterday. For fifty dollars. Everything's gone, including white gloves. Why don't you try to borrow what you need from David Spence?"

At eight o'clock Montereyans began arriving for the ball. Colton Hall was filled to overflowing. Every Spanish costume in town had been appropriated for the event. There were exquisite Spanish shawls of rare black lace, gay flower-embroidered mantillas, bought in the days when the Spanish galleons plied annually between Acapulco and Manila, priceless heirlooms of the Serranos, the Carrillos, the Covarrubias, the Ortegas, and other proud old families. Most of the women also wore hoop earrings of gold that weighed down the lobes of their ears. High combs of tortoise-shell, red roses and carnations topped their elaborate coiffures. The brilliance of the Spanish costumes made conspicuously drab-like the dresses worn by the American newcomers, delicate pinks and blues and mauves and white embroidered muslins with an occasional crisp taffeta of simple elegance.

Suddenly a bugle sounded. "General Riley," called a voice. The crowds parted to form an aisle. Down it walked General Riley in full uniform, complete with medals, and wearing the gay sash he had won at Contreras. He bowed and smiled graciously as he walked slowly into the center of the room, his aides close behind.

Inconspicuously a few feet behind there came an old priest wearing a shabby cassock. It was Father Ramirez who smiled indulgently at his parishioners who crowded around him. He rarely attended worldly affairs like balls, but he deemed the event one God would surely condone.

In a pine-banked corner four musicians tuned their instruments. They watched Pablo de la Guerra, the master of ceremonies, for the signal to begin. Finally the delegate from Santa Barbara nodded. The orchestra broke with feverish animation into a waltz. Soon couples were moving sedately around the room, ears strained to catch the rhythmical beat, for the musicians' tones were scarcely loud enough to be heard above the chattering voices in the room. The waltz was followed by a quadrille, then a contra-dance, then more waltzes. From eight until twelve, the delegates and their guests danced.

At midnight a bugler announced supper. Breathless and flushed from exertion the dancers descended to the first floor, where a courtroom had been converted into a dining room. On long tables lay enormous platters of wild turkey, roast pig, beef, tongue, and pâtés and an assortment of bottles holding wines and liquors. It was a banquet such as Monterey had never seen before. Refreshed, the guests then returned to the ballroom and danced until five o'clock. As they left Colton Hall, weary and footsore, yet supremely happy, they all declared that it was the finest fiesta they had ever attended.

There remained only one final celebration, the banquet to be given by the forty-eight delegates in honor of General Bennet Riley, the man who proposed holding the Convention at Monterey.

It was held at the Old Pacific House on Lower Alvarado Street that night at eight o'clock. John was appointed toastmaster, an honor he accepted reluctantly. Making speeches was not his forte and he knew he was apt to break into German if he became excited, and so an hour before dinner he called Bayard Taylor, the official reporter of the Convention, aside and begged him to write his speech. "I'll give you a palomino mare from Hock Farm, if you will."

When the diners had finished, John rose and with the reporter's speech held firmly in his hand offered a toast to Riley. Addressing him he said, "General, I have been appointed by the Delegates elected by the people of California to form a Constitution, to address you in their names, and on behalf of the whole people of California, and express the thanks of the Convention for the aid and co-operation they have received from you in the discharge of the responsible duty of creating a State government. The Convention duly appreciates the great and important services you have rendered our common country and adds: Well done, thou good and faithful servant." As he finished he handed the General a small plush box.

General Riley opened it and removed the gold watch with his name inscribed upon it. For a time he was too overcome to speak. "Gentlemen," he began, "words cannot convey the gratitude I feel for this token of your esteem. I shall treasure it all my life."

"Speech, speech, Riley. We want a speech," several voices called out.

The General rose, his plain blunt face strained with emotion.

"Gentlemen," he said. "I never made a speech in my life before. I am a soldier, but I can feel, and I do feel deeply the honor you have conferred upon me today.

Gentlemen, this is a prouder day to me than that on which my soldiers cheered me on Contreras. I thank you from all my heart. I am satisfied now that the people have done right in selecting delegates to frame a Constitution. They have chosen a body of men upon whom our country may look with pride. You have framed a Constitution worthy of California. And I have no fear for California when her people choose their representatives so wisely. Gentlemen, I congratulate you upon the successful conclusion of your arduous labors, and I wish you all happiness and prosperity."

As he sat down, John reached over and gripped him by the hand. "This is the happiest day of my life," he said. "It's a day I'll remember all my life."

# CHAPTER XXVI

# SAN FRANCISCO DAYS

STANDING ON THE far end of the wharf at the foot of California Street in San Francisco, Augustus looked up at the long arm on top of Telegraph Hill, that signaled the approach of ships. Its position indicated that a small bark from Monterey was passing through the Golden Gate, and would soon dock. He turned his eyes in the direction of Clark's Point, watching for it to appear.

He had reached the city that morning on the *S.S. Sacramento* just in time to meet his father upon his return from the convention in Monterey, for he had important business to discuss with him. He had not seen his parent for several months and he dreaded the ordeal ahead. He did not have long to wait. A stiff wind soon carried the *Fremont* around the bend of the Bay and by the time Augustus reached the wharf she was preparing to dock. Captain Sutter, leaning on his gold-headed cane, was the first passenger to walk down the gangplank. They shook hands in awkward silence.

It was apparent to Augustus that his father was worn out after his strenuous work at Monterey and the trip by water, for he was invariably a poor sailor. But the Captain forgot his malaise the moment he began to talk about himself. "Did you know they want me to run for governor, Augustus? Yes. The first governor of California," he said as they walked down the long wooden wharf. "What do you think of the idea?" he asked pompously.

"I don't like it," the son replied. "If you ask me I advise you not to be a candidate. Campaigning's hard work. So is being governor."

"But think of the honor, Augustus."

"No. You're needed at Hock Farm. Things are going badly."

"What do you mean?"

"Cattle thieves have been taking everything we own. Squatters are settling on our lands everywhere. I can't get them off. They say the land belongs to them. They insist it belongs to the United States, and is free to settlers. They claim your land titles are fraudulent. That they will never be upheld by the Land Commission when it meets. No, father. We need you at Hock Farm."

"Perhaps so," said John moodily. "But if my friends insist on placing my name on the ballot what can I do? Besides it's a great honor, Augustus. You seem to forget that."

"Who are the other candidates?"

"Peter Burnett is the only one of any importance."

Still chattering about the political situation in California, the two men reached the end of the wharf and turned north on Montgomery.

"This city is changing so I scarcely know my way around any longer," observed John.

He looked with surprise at the new four-story brick building bearing the name W. H. Davis, which had an impressive double stairway leading up from balcony to balcony. They went on past stores owned by A. Swan, Runkel, Kaufman and Co., prominent merchants who carried large supplies of dry goods, and the house run by W. G. Kettelle, the auctioneer, until they reached a door bearing the name Sam Brannan, Real Estate. John looked inside but the office was empty.

"I'm sorry he's out. I've always liked Sam," John said. "I hear he's making much more money then he did at the Fort."

"Mormons are shrewd," replied Augustus, although he felt little enthusiasm for the ex-storekeeper of Sutter's Fort.

At the office of the express agents, Adams and Co., John stopped again.

"I have some business to attend to here, Augustus. Kindly remain outside," he said. He did not care to tell his son that he had bought from a French schooner deserted by her crew at Monterey a large consignment of champagne and red wines from Bordeaux, which he wanted to have shipped to Hock Farm, knowing Augustus would consider it an unnecessary extravagance.

Augustus waited patiently outside. He amused himself by watching an auctioneer across the street, standing on a barrel, hawking his wares.

"Eggs. Fresh eggs. Just in from the Islands. Six dollars a dozen."

No one made an offer.

"I'll bet they'd cost you a dollar apiece up at Delmonico's. Five dollars bid? Come. That's not enough. Six . . . six . . . did someone say six?"

"Six bid," said a Frenchman, shoving his way through the crowd to reach the barrel. "Here's the dough." He thrust a bag of gold dust toward the auctioneer. "I'll take twenty dozen, sir, if you please. And a few cabbages and potatoes. That is, if they're not too spoiled. The last ones you sold me at a dollar apiece rotted within a week."

Augustus was enjoying the auction immensely when he saw a shadow near by.

"Come, Augustus," said his father. "Don't stand here like an imbecile, gaping at the crowds. Don't forget, you are Captain Sutter's son. I don't care to have you seen mixing with this street rabble," he said crossly. "Come on. I want to see what new businesses have opened up here while I've been away."

Further down the street they came to Rowe's Olympian Circus, featuring Ethiopian serenaders. Crowds were standing in front of the canvas tents housing it. From within came the sounds of darkie voices. The two men listened for a time to the melodies of the old south, some familiar, some new.

"San Francisco is becoming more like an European city every day," said John, smugly.

After spending several hours strolling through the city streets, in mid-afternoon John boarded the *S.S. Sacramento* on his way back to Hock Farm. Augustus saw him safely aboard, then went on up Washington Street toward the Parker House, the new hotel where he was stopping. It was situated on the old plaza now renamed Portsmouth Square.

The day was warm and sunny, yet it carried with it the invigorating tang of fall. In the depressing hours just spent with his father, Augustus had been conscious only of the strain of carrying on an amiable conversation with his egotistical parent. But now, carefree and thrilled by the exhilarating pageant on all sides, he walked briskly up the street, swinging his arms in the carefree manner of a schoolboy as he went. This was his first visit to the city since his arrival in California. He was amazed at the changes that had taken place since gold was found.

Its population had increased to a spectacular degree; from a hamlet of 500 it had grown into a metropolis of 20,000, some said even more. In the harbor 500 ships swayed idly at anchor, deserted by their crews. All over the city houses and stores were being erected. There was a bedlam of hammering and the creak of moving lumber being set into place. Most of the buildings were being constructed of wood, but a few of the small shops were made of sheet iron and brick. He was amazed to learn that workmen were being paid from twelve to twenty dollars a day, and even at that price were not easy to find.

Yet the feverish building going on could not house the thousands pouring into the Bay area from all over the world. Most of them were forced to live in flimsy canvas tents near the waterfront, or in queer improvised shacks made of odds and ends of lumber, anything, in fact, they could find. The tent city, once only along the waterfront, was now being set up along the slopes of the hill, human beehives by the thousands.

By contrast certain sections of San Francisco, new as they were, Augustus observed, had a settled aspect. Dignified stores lined the streets near the plaza; there were also some excellent dining places and several gambling houses as well as two good hotels.

Augustus decided to go to Delmonico's for dinner. It was the most fashionable dining place in the city. Since most of the San Franciscans dined late, at the time he entered, six o'clock, the place was almost deserted. He was ushered to a solitary table by a supercilious head waiter who looked scornfully at his patron's rather unfashionable costume. Feeling lonely and uncomfortable in the ornate place, Augustus began to study the menu.

As he sat looking at it a sad-faced musician drew a discordant version of Gounod's *Ave Maria*, from a worn violin.

Meanwhile, a French waiter, in a white apron and cap, stood stiffly beside Augustus' chair.

"*Monsieur*, may I recommend the salmon trout," he finally said. "It came in from the Columbia River this morning."

"No," replied Augustus, "I don't care for fish. I'll have ox-tail soup first. Then a crab *pâté*. For an entrée . . . let me see . . . yes, venison steaks cooked *à la chausseur*."

"*Magnifique.* You'll not be disappointed, *Monsieur. C'est bien fait chez Delmonico. Pommes de terre? Pâtisserie? Et du fromage?*"

"Yes. That will be more than adequate."

He glanced with amazement at the exorbitant prices charged for everything. The meal would cost at least twenty dollars. I could have dined at Tong Ling's Chop Suey House for a dollar, he thought with ingrained Swiss thrift.

The French cooked dinner, served with a flourish, proved excellent in all respects. A gourmet like his father, Augustus knew and appreciated fine cookery and the meal was like nothing he had tasted since he had left Europe.

"My compliments to *Monsieur* Delmonico and my deep thanks to your chef," said Augustus slipping a modest tip into the waiter's hand, as he finished.

He was about to leave his table when he saw a pretty Italian girl, elaborately dressed, enter. She went over to the Italian musician who laid his violin aside.

"*Bambina mia*," he said, as she kissed his cheek.

Smiling amiably in the direction of Augustus, the musician pushed the girl toward his table. "The young man looks lonesome, *bambina mia*," he said.

After a brief conversation she induced Augustus to accompany her to see the sights. They started down a side street toward the waterfront. As they walked, *Bambina mia* cast amused glances at the embarrassed young man. He peered nervously in the direction of the dimly-lit tents and shacks they passed. Harsh voices, feminine shrieks and strains of gay music filtered out into the night.

"Where are you taking me?" asked Augustus.

"To Sydney Town," she replied. "We'll have fun there. We can stop at the Bear's Head."

She led him to the Sydney Town bar on Montgomery Street at the base of Telegraph Hill. It was a large establishment built of wood. From the second story dim lights cast a faint glow through curtained windows, but the main entrance door opening on Montgomery Street was closed and barred. Opening a panel near the entrance, *Bambina* pushed a concealed bell.

A tousled head appeared from an upper window.

"Who's there?" asked the head.

*Bambina mia* flung the hand a kiss.

"Baby. I'll be right down."

The man shut the window with a bang and a moment later opened the front door. It disclosed a long, empty hallway, lit by a lantern hung at the far end.

"No," said Augustus, looking at it suspiciously. "I won't go in. I'll wait here until you come back."

"That don't go mit me." A burly hand reached out and clutched him by the collar. "Step inside, my dear young man."

*Bambina* laughed merrily at her friend's ironic ways. "He's rich," she whispered. "He has all his meals at Delmonicos."

"Baby. You make me hungry," said the man, pushing Augustus along the hallway and up the dark stairs. "You'll join us in a quiet little game, dear boy?" he said mimicking the elegant voice of the croupier at El Dorado. "We play for small stakes, dear boy. Yes. Very small stakes," he said.

*Bambina mia*, trailing behind, clapped her hands in glee. "Sydney Duck, I could fall in love with you," she said.

"And why not?" Still holding Augustus by the collar, he leaned over and smacked her noisily on the lips. "Baby," he exclaimed. "Baby." At a closed door he knocked daintily, aping a woman's touch. "It's *Bambina mia*," he said, mimicking the Italian woman's voice.

The door swung open. Rounds of applause came from a group of Australians playing cards. "What prize this time, Sydney Duck?"

"Just a rich stranger," said Sydney Duck. "I don't know his name."

"Any jack?"

"Plenty." Sydney Duck pushed Augustus into an empty chair. "Put all your gold on the table," he said.

*Bambina mia* draped herself elegantly on the arm of his chair and watched Augustus take a money bag from an inner pocket and open it. She saw that he had at least five hundred dollars. She leaned boldly across the table and took out a few gold coins, slipping them into her bag.

"Baby." Sydney Duck reached over for the bag and dumped all the coins on the table. "None of that, *Bam-*

*bina*." She began to pout. He patted her cheek. "Why baby, you wouldn't cheat me, would you?"

The pouting increased. "You might give me a drink," she said peevishly, "a big, big drink."

"Very well, baby."

Sydney Duck poured a large glass of *aguardiente* and handed it to her.

"Drink that and be quiet," he said. "And no more lip from you while the game's on."

The men shuffled and dealt the cards. Unfamiliar with the game, Augustus followed instructions as if in a daze. After a few rounds his entire pile of gold had found its way into the gamblers' pockets.

"I have nothing more to lose, gentlemen," Augustus said. "I think, *Bambina*, we should leave now."

She giggled hysterically, for the liquor had gone to her head. "No. I want another drink first. I want another, Sydney Duck. And make it large."

He poured her a small one, diluting it with some water. "Little girl, it's time you went home now. Besides, we're expecting guests," he added, as the sounds of voices floated up from the hall below.

In a moment three swarthy Mexican women, arrayed in red slippers, red skirts and green blouses carrying deerskin sacks full of gold, entered. Ignoring *Bambina*, Sydney Duck began to flirt with the youngest woman.

Jealously *Bambina* looked on. "Another drink," she said, hoping to draw attention to herself.

The gambler, however, ignored her. She saw him put his arm around the woman and kiss her several times.

"Come," she said crossly, turning to Augustus. "*Vamos.*"

Unnoticed, they slipped out into Montgomery Street.

Out of range of the Boar's Head, Augustus turned to his companion. "They've won all my gold," he said miserably. "I haven't a dollar left."

"I'll show you how to get some," she replied.

She began to sing at the top of her lungs the popular Italian street song, *Caro Mio*. Clapping her hands she began to dance to her own improvised accompaniment. Miners in high boots, Mexicans and Chinese stopped to watch. She had a good soprano voice and sang with pathos and charm.

"*Bravo*. Why, it's *Bambina carissima*," called one of the men as she finished. Smiling at him, she opened her purse and held it out.

Some dropped gold coins, others gold nuggets into it. Then, humming the refrain, she continued along the waterfront with Augustus. They had not gone far when they heard the clatter of hoofs. Soon they saw a man wearing a black mask and riding a black horse gallop at top speed up Montgomery Street. He had a drawn pistol in his hand and kept turning around in his saddle to look behind. Presently a second rider appeared. He was riding even faster than the first. He, too, was armed. Loiterers in the street moved close to the store buildings and crouched down against them.

"It's the Hounds," screamed *Bambina*, in a frenzy of excitement. "They're after those Chilenos again. They met a week ago in their tent, Tammany Hall, and swore to kill every man, woman and child in Chiletown. My friend Willie the Rat, was lying on the ground behind the tent. He heard every word they said. They've killed ten already this week," she added. "Come on. Let's watch the fun!"

She started down the street calling merrily to the

HOCK FARM

Sutter's country place on the Feather River

bystanders to join her. When she finally looked back she saw Augustus rapidly disappearing in the direction of the Graham House. Shrugging her shoulders with a gesture of supreme disdain, she headed on toward Chile-town.

# CHAPTER XXVII

# OMINOUS PORTENTS

ALL DURING THE election excitement, John remained at Hock Farm, comparatively indifferent as to the outcome. More pressing affairs were absorbing his interest at this time. Squatters and cattle-rustlers both at Hock Farm and Sacramento City were making his life unbearable, and financial affairs were again becoming precarious.

Most annoying to John was the fact that a group of outlaws had recently established themselves on a small island across the river from Hock Farm, for the place had the advantage of being near the main roads that led to Sacramento City and the gold mines. The professed occupation of the bandits was to kill off John Sutter's cattle and steal his wheat. Each night they slaughtered as many cattle as they could market and, under cover of darkness, moved them in *carretas* to Sacramento City where they sold them to the local butcher shops, hotels and restaurants. They worked so skillfully and quietly that John could never catch them in the act. But diminishing herds were unmistakable proof of their nocturnal tactics.

John was sitting morosely over his ledgers in his office one day, when he heard his dogs barking furiously outside. He rushed to the window just in time to see some twenty masked men who were pulling up near his door. They jumped off their panting horses and pulled out their guns.

"Hello, Cap," the leader shouted. "Come on out."
He went over and pushed his booted foot inside the
half open door. "Out," he called, leveling his gun at
John.

Captain Sutter walked with cool deliberation out
into the yard. He saw twenty guns pointed directly
at him.

"Gentlemen, you can see that I am unarmed," he
said. "What can I do for you?"

"Cap," said the leader, "we've come for your wheat.
Sorry we must take it. But our animals are starving.
It's ours anyway. You raised it on soil owned by the
U.S.A."

"But gentlemen . . ."

"Quiet, Cap." said the bandit, placing his finger
firmly on the trigger of his gun. "Not a word out of
you. Come boys. Ready. Let's take the wheat. I'll
keep him covered while you work."

John looked helplessly on as the men raided the
grain stacked in the field a few hundred yards away.
After loading all the horses could carry they galloped
down the road, waving their hands merrily over their
shoulders. Their leader, keeping John covered, got on
his horse, then backed out of the yard and, wheeling
suddenly, galloped off behind his comrades.

Quivering with anger, John sank down on his doorstep and buried his head in his two hands.

"*Mein Gott.* It's those bastards again."

The next day he took the Sacramento-bound steamer
to report the affair to the American alcalde. The man
listened attentively while John described the theft of
his cattle and grain. Then he shook his head.

"Reports like this reach my office every day," he said.

"I'm desperate, Captain Sutter. I can get no help from Washington."

"But we must do something. We must protest. Lives and property are not safe."

"These dastardly Hounds are getting bolder every day," sighed the alcalde. "They even have a complete outfit of rifles and boats and butcher's tools. Yes. It's the Hounds. They steal and murder all the time."

"The cattle rustlers are the worst," John replied. "They've cleaned out most of the good herds in the valley. I'm told that some outlaws operating in the vicinity of Hock Farm have cleared as much as $60,000 apiece."

"I know it's outrageous, Captain Sutter . . . I sympathize deeply with you. But I'm helpless."

Upon leaving the alcalde's office John went to stay at the only comfortable place in Sacramento, the City Hotel.

Dinner that night was unusually excellent; the roast beef served was tender and sweet.

"Where do you get your beef?" he asked the waiter.

"It comes from some place along the Feather River, Cap. We get it in fresh every day."

John ate only a small portion of it, then told the man to remove his plate.

"You didn't like it, Captain Sutter?"

"No," growled John. "I don't like the flavor of Feather River meat. Something about it gags me."

Still harboring his grievances, John strode out into the night. Near the City Hotel and overlooking the river was the Eagle Theatre. It was housed in a flimsy canvas building and had seats for some four hundred spectators, including a fashionable tier of boxes. John went inside, had a glass of brandy at the bar, then found his reserved seat. He heard the overture being played by an orchestra of five; it was led by a curly-haired Italian who waved his arms frantically in an effort to produce out of his few musicians the effect of a full orchestra. By laboring feverishly on their instruments the quintet made up in volume what they lacked in skill.

Indifferent to their musical efforts, John studied the garish drop curtain absent-mindedly. As he watched it move slowly up, John sat forward in his seat.

When he came out, rain was falling heavily in great sheets, as if from a cloudburst. By the time he reached the hotel, he was drenched to the skin. Shivering with cold, John went into the lobby and warmed himself by the sheet-iron stove that threw out a comforting mellow glow.

The storm continued with such violence that he was forced to remain indoors for several days. Every street was hip-deep in mud and water, and since no merchandize could move in or out, business was suspended. In the eleven years he had lived along the river, John could not recall anything like it before. He sent word by river steamer to Augustus at Hock Farm not to expect him for some time. Secretly, he was glad of an excuse to remain away, not only was he enjoying himself, but several interesting business ventures had come up and through them he hoped to recoup some of his heavy losses suffered at the hands of the cattle thieves.

Over the Christmas holidays the skies cleared. Then, for several days early in January, one storm after another inundated the city to such an extent that the water reached the second floors of the large buildings and covered all small structures. In places the water was more than twenty feet deep. Sacramento City was demoralized. Thousands were without food or shelter. Small boats plied through rivers that had once been streets, moving stranded men and women to tall buildings and high ground, for a fee of twenty dollars an hour. Every available building that had more than one story was soon packed with starving refugees.

To add to the confusion Sacramento was glutted with debris. Dead horses, cows, sheep, dogs, tree trunks and household furniture jammed the river-streets. Some floated with the currents; others found temporary anchorage as they caught against the boughs of half-submerged trees, the chimneys of housetops, the edges of window ledges. Soon the fetid odor of putrefying flesh permeated the air.

Trapped on the second floor of the City Hotel, John watched the stricken city through a window. The rising river haunted even his sleeping hours; he was overwhelmed by the hidden force of the mighty Sacramento sweeping with herculean force beyond its banks, inundating the city.

As he watched the human tragedy, he could not bring himself to mourn his own personal losses, although he felt it was inevitable that the value of city lots, from whose sale he had derived so much revenue, would immediately drop.

But to his surprise, when the waters finally receded Sacramento City regained its normal sanguine outlook. Public meetings were held, funds were raised to build a great levee as protection against future floods, and the land speculators redoubled their efforts. City lots that had fallen during flood time, now sold for more than ever before. New commercial houses handling lumber, building supplies, food and clothing opened in boats along the riverfront where auctioneers, hawking cast-off merchandise from the Bay area, sold their goods with little effort.

Caught in this new wave of speculation, John began to plan new business enterprises. He even induced six friends of Swiss ancestry to join him in buying for seven thousand dollars what were called the Big Wheatfields northeast of the fort along the American Fork and the South Slough. As they sat one day toward the end of January in the main room of the City Hotel with the legal papers ready to be signed lying on the table before them, the front door opened and a beaming traveler, bag in hand, walked briskly in.

"*Gott im Himmel!* It's Heinrich Lienhard," shouted John, rushing over and clasping him warmly by the hand. "Where's my family?"

"There're all here. Safe and well. At the Graham House in San Francisco. Can't wait to see you, Cap. I don't need to tell you that."

"Little Eliza? Grown up, of course."

"As handsome a young woman as you'd care to see."

"And Emil? And Alphonse?"

"Fine young men, both of them. You'll be proud of your sons."

"And ... their ... mother .. ?"

"Also well," said Lienhard.

"I can't wait to see them," said John.

"The *El Dorado* is returning to the Bay tomorrow. I suggest we book passage on her at once."

An unusually swift trip down the river brought Lienhard and John to the Bay in less than twelve hours. Not wishing to witness the reunion of the Sutters who had been separated seventeen years, Lienhard left John at the door of the Graham House. A clerk led John to the room occupied by Mrs. Sutter and Eliza.

The door opened. He saw a lean, stoop-shouldered woman, careworn and faded with eyes as hard as flint. Her hair was pulled back into an unbecoming knot and she had on an old black dress fastened at the neck with an antiquated gold pin. He looked into the face of Nanette, cold, austere devoid of emotion.

"*Meine Liebchen*," he said with an attempt at gaiety. He kissed her on both cheeks. They were cold and unpleasant to the touch.

Nanette drew back in consternation, looking at him with cold appraising eyes, then kissed him lightly on the forehead.

"Come, children," she called in a loud voice. "Father's here."

The door leading into an adjoining room opened and two boys and a girl rushed out. They came running toward John and smothered him with kisses.

Their obvious joy at seeing him was like a tonic to John. A sensation of happiness, of pride in his children, of boundless affection for them came swiftly to him. Presently he held them at arms length, appraising them. There was slight resemblance to the tiny children he had last seen so long ago.

"Eliza. Why, you're a young lady now."

"I'm twenty-two, Father," she announced proudly.

He looked with pleasure at her lovely vivacious face, her eyes blue and sparkling like his own, her curly blonde hair, her proud carriage. She was attractively dressed and took, he could see, a keen interest in her personal appearance.

"Everyone at home says she looks like you, father," remarked Emil.

John smiled happily at his twenty-year-old son. He liked his quiet way, his respectful, courteous manners.

He was slim and dark; John saw that he was not so much a Sutter as a Dubeld.

"And you, Alphonse? How do you like California?" John asked as he turned toward his youngest, eighteen-year-old son.

"Why I like it Father, immensely. I'm glad we're all rich. We never had a franc to spare in Burgdorf. I wanted to go to the military academy. But I couldn't. I want to be a soldier."

He spoke swiftly with a hint of embarressment in his manner. He paused for breath then went rapidly on.

"I can't wait to see Hock Farm . . . and the Indians . . . and the gold mines. Can't we leave now?"

Several days later, the *Linda* pulled in at the Hock Farm wharf and gave three shrill blasts. Nanette Sutter stood gravely at her husband's side, eager for her first glimpse of her new abode. "There it is," said John.

He pointed toward a dignified white mansion, set in a grove of shade trees. A pillared porch extended across the front of the entire floor. An upper porch, its roof supported by four white pillars adorned the center of the façade, giving it a Greek-like appearance, at once classical and sedate. Above it was a belfry in which hung a large alarm bell. A series of smaller buildings were grouped near by.

"Do you like it, Nanette?" asked John.

Tears dimmed her eyes. "It's wonderful, Johann," she replied. "Why, it's like a palace."

"I call it *El Palacio*," he said.

As the steamer tied up to the dock, a crowd of loiterers gathered.

"Where is Augustus?" asked Nanette. "I don't see him anywhere."

She scanned the crowd of white men and Indians with wistful eyes.

Just then she saw a young man wearing buckskin trousers and an old flannel shirt coming toward the boat. He wore a brown felt hat pulled low over his eyes; a bowie knife dangled from his belt. His unsteady gait indicated that he was drunk.

"That man looks like a disreputable miner," said Nanette disparagingly. "I'm glad my boys don't drink. I don't want drunkards like that around our house."

The man weaved his unsteady way toward them, looked up, and waved his hat.

"That man," said John, "is your son, Augustus."

# CHAPTER XXVIII

# FALSE DAWN

Boisterous laughter filtered through the walls of the Stinking Tent Saloon, the Sacramento City rendezvous on the riverfront. From the ranks of the Squatters' Association meeting there in its nocturnal session, high-pitched voices rose excitedly.

"Old Cap Sutter's land ain't worth a gold slug." The shyster lawyer drove home his remarks to the members he was addressing. "No . . . sir . . . They ain't worth a penny, his land titles ain't valid."

"How do you know they hain't?" drawled a frowsy Missourian. "Tell me that. Proofs what I aim to git."

"Holy Moses, man. Don't ye trust me?" the lawyer replied with a show of offended dignity. "Else why did ye hire me to guard yer interests?"

"Proof's what I'm aiming fur," said the Missourian, clinging stubbornly to his point.

"Then ye'll git it. And straight from the shoulder, too. Jist larnt it today."

Biting off a plug of tobacco, he chewed with tantalizing deliberation, as if enjoying the suspense plainly apparent in the faces of his audience.

"Quit yer dawdling. Tell what ye heard," growled a miner.

The lawyer adjusted his florid red tie.

"Gimme time, my friend," he said. "Jist gimme time."

Restless feet shuffled on the ground; excited whispers circulated.

The lawyer held up his hand for silence.

"I jist larnt that Old Cap don't own a spek o' land in Sacramento. Or in Sutterville. Never did. Seems like old J. J. Voiget, who surveyed it, didn't git his lines right. South boundaries all wrong. New Helvetia line should o' bin four mile above the old fort. Boys, ye all know the south lines of the Alvarado grant is 38°, 49′, 32″ n. latitude. Old Cap himself admits it. Boys, that lies miles beyond here. Squat where ye want. Old Cap—God himself—can't stop ye. Sacramento City belongs to the good old U.S.A."

Laughter and applause greeted the speaker as he sat down.

From the rear of the tent a more cultivated voice with a marked Bostonian voice inquired. "Sir, what of the men who call themselves land speculators and who control a large part of Sacramento City? On what legal grounds do they base their claims?"

The shyster lawyer jumped to his feet. "On swindle and fraud, that's all."

"But what of our own laws? The Treaty of Guadalupe Hidalgo, I understand, guaranteed the sanctity of property rights."

"Bosh." Unequal to legal intricacies into which he was being drawn, the lawyer sat down.

There began among the assembled squatters animated arguments as to their respective rights. Organized to further the interest of penniless emigrants and criminals who had no funds with which to buy land, they had become one of the most powerful, the most feared groups in all California. Their professed purpose was to filch from John Sutter what land they could. They made no secret of their intentions.

John was gravely concerned over the inroads on his property. They had squatted on his domains all the way from the fort to Hock Farm. They had erected tents, established residences and defied all attempts to remove them by drawing bowie knives and guns. By bribing the officials of Sacramento City they had removed the one danger of being ejected by the law.

Desperate, John formed an Anti-Squatters League by way of protest, but it was ineffectual. All he could hope for was that before long a United States Land Commission would be sent out to establish the validity of land grants issued under Mexican rule. Meanwhile, denied legal protection, he had no choice but to watch men occupy his land, and rob him of his wheat and livestock.

Not John alone, but everyone who had bought property for speculation and did not occupy it themselves, was equally at the mercy of the squatters.

In Sacramento City outlaws in bands of ten or more roamed the streets after dark, robbing and insulting every prosperous-appearing man they met. They made their headquarters in one of the six saloons frequented by prostitutes that lined the riverfront where they could watch the steamers land and miners carrying sacks of gold disembark.

Important business was often transacted over the drinks served at the local bars, and stool-pigeons, belonging to the Squatters Association, regularly reported to their leaders what they overheard. But not even the squatters could entirely disrupt the mounting business activity of the young metropolis. Stores and large buildings were going up all the time, and prices

of lots continued to soar. Merchandise was even sold
from "store vessels" lined up along the riverbanks,
that carried the miscellaneous supplies needed for the
eight thousand or more local residents.

John met the ominous rumors he heard at Sacramento City bars by indulging heavily in drink. He
could afford to, for money was still coming in large
amounts from the sale of land which speculators bought
from him, despite squatter activities. He gambled recklessly and bought lavishly: imported wines and cham-
pagnes brought by sailing ships around the Horn
from France, choice foods from all over Europe, books,
costly and pretentious furniture for Hock Farm, an
expensive piano for Eliza, a curiosity in California.
Expenditures of a thousand dollars a night were com-
monplace. He often spent that much for a banquet
for his friends. He had full control of his property
again and Augustus was powerless to check his father's
ribald extravagances.

The six months that followed the arrival of the
Sutter family from Europe were a time of open-handed
hospitality and riotous living at Hock Farm. Eliza
and the youngest son, Alphonse, fell gaily into their
father's prodigal ways. But Augustus and his tight-
lipped mother were disturbed.

If Augustus dared to protest, his father waved him
aside. "You do not know how to spend money, Augustus; everyone expects me to be hospitable. Everyone
thinks I am fabulously rich. The richest man in California. You forget you are a Sutter, Augustus."

After a few arguments that ended in bitter quarrels,
John said a month later to his son, "I can't endure the
sight of you any longer, Augustus. I think you will be
happier away from me. I'll stake you to a business in

Sacramento City. I've decided to have you go into partnership with the Wetzlar brothers and old Doc Bates. I'll supply all the capital."

Sullenly Augustus acquiesced. Attacks of dizziness were bothering him again and after each fresh quarrel with his father he was physically ill for several days. He knew only that he hated his father, hated Hock Farm, Sacramento City and all California. He began to turn over in his mind the idea of leaving it.

"Very well, father," he replied morosely. "I'll go to Sacramento City on the *Linda* next week."

"Say nothing to your mother about it yet," said John. "We're having one of our large parties on Sunday and she may need you to help her cook. She has to do most of it herself, you know. These Indians can't be trusted to make anything fit to eat."

"*Mutter* works far too hard," said Augustus. "Even more than when we were so poor in Burgdorf."

"*Himmel.* I supply her with enough servants. She can have more if she wants. We have the entire *rancheria* of Hock Indians right at our back door. They're docile, good-natured devils. Far better than most of the migratory white trash overrunning California."

"If you consider Indians servants," replied Augustus tartly, "I don't. They're untrained and filthy. I can't stand the sight of them in the house."

He thought with disgust of the young unmarried girl not yet fifteen who came and went familiarly through his father's quarters.

"They suit me," John replied with that air of injured dignity that so annoyed Augustus. "Be sure to meet the steamer when she docks early Sunday morning, and fire the cannon twice. I desire to impress my guests."

Although he disliked his father's Sunday gatherings

intensely, Augustus met the *Linda* as she docked. He
fired the cannon himself and then signaled to the brass
band playing loudly aboard to precede the guests who
disembarked noisily at the small Hock Farm wharf.
They nodded casually to Augustus who led the way to
the main door of the house where his father stood waiting to receive them. He was meticulously attired in a
cutaway coat, a striped yellow waistcoat, and gray
trousers. He had a red rose in his buttonhole and carried
his gold-headed cane.

"This is indeed a great pleasure. Come in ladies and
gentlemen," said John, smiling and bowing *"Mi casa es
su casa,* as the Spanish say. You might like to have me
show you my rose gardens. They're one of the sights of
Hock Farm."

He then led them through his rose gardens and out
into the vineyards beyond. "These are better grapes
than they raise in France, ladies and gentlemen. I
merely repeat what a distinguished Frenchman, Pierre
Charles de Saint Amant, told me when he was my guest
last week. Prince Paul of Wurtenburg said the same
thing."

The Captain raised his voice as he always did when
mentioning important visitors.

Presently he invited his guests to be seated at the
long wooden tables spread under the shade trees. He
took his place in a special chair elaborately carved and
provided with a scarlet cushion, at the head of the
largest table. Nanette was not in evidence.

"My wife presents her compliments, and begs you to
forgive her absence," he said regally. "She is ill with a
severe headache."

Overhearing it, Augustus gave a wry smile, then hastened out to assist his mother, hot and weary as she

General Sutter in His Seventies

bent over the stove. He was glad of an excuse to avoid the flattering obsequious crowds who fawned on the Captain in exchange for a bountiful supply of food and drink.

"Where are Emil and Alphonse?" his mother inquired, in a dull, colorless voice. "I didn't see them with your father."

"They've gone away for the day, I believe. I saw them saddling their horses this morning." He did not add that he had exchanged some harsh words with them about their too frequent visits to the huts of young squaws. "I presume they'll be back before long."

"And Eliza?" asked Nanette. "She's at the party," Augustus replied.

He thought with disdain of his gregarious sister always in evidence, over-dressed, giggling and flirting and preening herself, as she aired her charms for the benefit of every eligible man.

"Yes. Eliza's at the party, *Mutter.*"

Upon this particular Sunday Eliza had retired to a small table for two placed under a rose arbor far from the crowd. Her piano teacher, a handsome young Swiss called George Engler, was with her. From the day he had come to Hock Farm to instruct her brothers in mathematics and music, she had been in love with him.

"*Gott*, Eliza," he said. "I can't live without you."

"Hush, George," Eliza giggled nervously as she looked around.

The nearest table was only ten feet away, the guests were watching the young couple curiously.

Defiantly he reached under the table and caught her hand.

"*Liebchen.* I'm mad about you. You must marry me. I know you love me, Eliza."

"Of course I do." She giggled nervously as he pressed his foot against hers. "But father won't consent. You know he won't."

"Yes. I know," said Engler sadly. "Yesterday I asked him for your hand, *Liebchen*."

"What?" Eliza stopped giggling and looked at him. Her face momentarily drawn with fright. "You don't need to tell me what he said, George. I can guess."

The young man's eyes devoured her. "You're rich. I'm poor, Eliza. That's enough."

Eliza stamped her foot indignantly on the ground.

"He wants me to marry a rich husband, I know. Someone prominent. Like the president of the United States. Or an ambassador . . . or something. He doesn't care . . . if . . . I'm in love with you."

Tears welled up in her eyes. A few guests, hearing the commotion of raised voices, glanced curiously her way.

"*Liebchen*, don't cry," Engler pleaded. "Just say you love me . . . that you'll marry me."

His voice, wild and turbulent, carried over to the listening guests. Several winked at one another and smiled.

Eliza wiped her eyes. "I love you. I love you. I love you," she said.

"You'll marry me?"

She nodded.

"Where? When?" Engler half rose from his seat and leaned toward her.

She motioned him back.

"Not here, George . . . please. I don't know yet how we'll manage. Father will never give in, I know."

"But your mother? Won't she help us?"

"*Meine Mutter? Nein.* She acts strange all the time.

It's been that way ever since she reached California. She says she's sick. I know, it's not that. I think . . . sometimes she quarrels with father . . . when we're not around." Eliza spoke in a frightened whisper.

"About what?"

"Mostly Augustus. And father and the Indian squaws . . . and his drinking . . . and spending so much money all the time."

Engler shrugged his shoulders with a gesture of disdain. "Let's run away, Eliza. It's the only way I know. This is no place for a sweet girl like you anyway. We'll elope. That's what we'll do."

Eliza sank back limply into her seat.

"I wouldn't dare. Father would kill me. With those dreadful pistols of his . . . Besides . . . He says I'll be the richest girl in the United States some day. He's promised to name a city for me . . . Eliza City . . . across the river from Hock . . . a Swiss engineer has drawn all the plans for it. And father says he'll put a large sum of money in my name when his land grants are confirmed by the Supreme Court in Washington. Just now, he's short of cash, he says. But he has enough to buy himself anything he wants. I notice," she observed maliciously. "And I don't want to be poor all the rest of my life the way we were in Switzerland. Do I, George?"

George David Engler cursed silently between clenched teeth. The lying old sot, he thought. Then he looked with compassion at the pretty, trusting, unsophisticated Swiss girl sitting across the table. He knew of her father's ambitions for her. He was aware that designing foreigners as well as every eligible young man in California was angling for the hand of Old Cap's only daughter. He also knew, as Eliza did not, that the Captain was heavily in debt again and that he had borrowed $10,000 on Hock Farm the week before. "Scoundrel," he said under his breath.

"What did you say, George?"

"I started to say *Liebchen*, that your father was the most amazing man I've ever known. But come. The guests are beginning to look our way. Run into the house and wash your face while I get my music. I've promised your father I'll play the Chopin ballades and a few Strauss waltzes for his guests."

As Engler went indoors, John rose from his seat and addressed his guests in his most perfunctory manner. "I am happy to say I have engaged a most talented young musician from Switzerland to play for you to-day. He is one of the foremost artists in Europe. *Herr* Engler," he called.

Presently through an open window came the stirring notes of Chopin's *Polonaise.*

In his room upstairs Augustus listened as he packed his bag with nervous quick gestures, then slipped downstairs. The final chords of the dramatic ending were rising to a last climax as he moved quietly out of a side door and to the corral where his horse was saddled and waiting. He jumped into the saddle. He slapped his stallion's rump viciously with his riding crop and galloped down the road toward Sacramento City.

Augustus could not remember exactly what took place after he reached there. He had a feeling that either he fell from his horse and hurt his head or that he was slugged and drugged in the Stinking Tent Saloon. When he regained consciousness, he found himself in the house of his old friend, Doc Bates. The physician was standing by his bedside. "Well, son. Feel more like yourself now?" he said.

Augustus ran one hand across his bandaged forehead. "What happened?"

"I don't know, son. They carried you here from the Stinking Tent Saloon."

"Last night?"

"Two months ago, Augustus," the doctor replied gravely. "But you're almost well now. Another day or so. . . ."

"Does father . . . know?"

"I thought it wiser not to send word to him," Doc Bates replied.

He had witnessed too many distressing scenes between father and son to have any illusions as to the real state of their feelings.

"*Gott.* You're a saint, Doc. Look here. I'll tell you something. I'm leaving California . . . I'm through with it . . . I've had enough."

"And where do you intend to go, son?"

"Maybe Mexico. Maybe New York. I don't much care where."

"Any money, son?"

"Yes. I have enough. In the Wells Fargo Bank. In San Francisco."

"Good," said Doc Bates. "I believe it's the wise thing to do, Augustus."

"Don't tell father."

"I won't, son."

He reached into his hip pocket and took out a heavy leather bag, which he laid on the pillow beside the invalid. "This will get you to San Francisco. I must go now. There's been more trouble at Coloma. Two miners killed and several seriously injured. They've sent for me. Write to me, son," he called over his shoulder as he left the room.

Two days later Augustus reached the Bay. It was a sunny mild day in early May. He walked slowly along Montgomery Street and on toward Portsmouth Square, where he engaged a room at the Parker House. After a good dinner he went to bed at an early hour.

He was dreaming happily when he heard the fire gong ring. The clatter of fire engines followed. He rushed over to the window. Half way down the block he saw sheets of flame.

"Where's the fire?" he yelled.

"Dennison's Exchange. Reckon them Sydney Duck's bin a cackling again," the man called out cynically.

"Incendiaries? Why the last one was only a week ago," cried Augustus.

"Stimulating fer business," the bystander replied. "I'm a carpenter meself. Always like work. I aim ter ask twenty dollars a day tomorrow marnin. Reckon I'll git it, too."

Augustus hurriedly dressed and went down to join the hundreds of spectators who jammed the plaza. He watched three fire brigades roughly push their way past the excited spectators.

"Come lend a hand with these buckets," called a fireman to a bystander.

"Nope," he replied.

"Dammit. Come and help."

"For three dollars an hour, I will."

"All right. But hurry."

The fireman formed a bucket brigade extending across the plaza to the water supply near the customhouse.

"Get back there," he ordered the crowd. "The walls of the Exchange might go."

Augustus watched the red and yellow tongues of fire as they shot out and licked the roof of the banking house of Palmer, Cooke and Company. Soon he saw them swerve to catch the offices of the Alta California, then move on around the square. Until then the firemen had succeeded in keeping the sparks off the Parker House, but now the flames were moving toward its roof. Augustus rushed into his room and grabbed his bag which contained all his worldly belongings and the money he had drawn out of the bank that afternoon. He carried it down a side street and headed for the docks in the south end of the city, intending, should the fire spread, to hire a skiff and row out to one of the larger vessels anchored in the bay.

He walked rapidly to the Market Street wharf. There he sat down on its far end, satchel in his lap, watching the red glow spread across the sky. From his vantage point he could see that the entire city bounded by Montgomery, Clay, Dupont and Jackson streets was a seething mass of flames. As the fire swerved toward Telegraph Hill crowds of pimps and prostitutes, drunkards and gamblers began to desert their haunts and move down toward the shore. Many were carrying furniture and clothing and jewelry they had looted from stores in the path of the flames. Several of them joined Augustus on the Market Street wharf. He saw two of them, a man and woman look curiously at his satchel. In the semi-darkness the woman moved over and tried to engage him in conversation. Recognizing the voice, he looked up. "*Bambina mia*, get away," he cried out, shoving her roughly aside.

"None of that, mister," said the man.

Augustus shoved him violently and, bag in hand, ran along the wharf to Market Street.

"Stop thief," called *Bambina mia*, following close behind.

By this time her companion had scrambled to his feet

and was close on their heels. Rays of light in the east
indicated that the sun was about to appear. It broke
over the horizon just as Augustus reached the end of
the wharf. At the foot of Market Street he suddenly
stopped. A man in a black frock coat and an austere
black hat was addressing a group of men and women
standing quietly around him.

"And the Lord said unto them . . ."

Augustus listened, then elbowed his way for safety,
close to the speaker. He glanced back and saw that
*Bambina* and her shifty friend were afraid to follow.

"It's Reverend William Taylor, the famous street
preacher," said a bystander.

"This city of iniquity, this den of sin and vice, this
Sodom and Gomorrah. . . . Flee, all of you who value
your lives. Flee, all of you who hope to save your souls
from eternal damnation. Flee. Before it is too late. Go
back to your homes, your wives, your children. Abandon
this frenzied search for gold. Go back home. Go. And
may God have mercy on your souls."

As he finished and the crowds began to leave Augustus turned to a sailor standing beside him.

"What boats are scheduled to sail tomorrow?" he
inquired.

"The *El Dorado*," the man replied. "She sails at two
for Acapulco. I'm booked as first mate."

"Good," said Augustus. "Find a skiff and take me
aboard."

## CHAPTER XXIX

# TWILIGHT

FOUR MONTHS AFTER California was admitted to the Union, Congress passed a law to settle private land claims in California.[1] It was destined to clarify the legal ownership of disputed lands occupied by squatters irrespective of the protest of the men who had held them under the land grants allotted during the Mexican regime. Every land grant in California was under its jurisdiction and claimants were requested to present their cases.

John welcomed the Congressional move and felt certain he would have no difficulty establishing his rights. He was fully confident that his two grants, the New Helvetia, given him in 1841 in Monterey by Governor Alvarado, and El Sobrante, issued in 1845 by Micheltorena at Santa Barbara, would soon be indisputably his own. He was reading the San Francisco paper one day in his room at Hock Farm when he suddenly looked up and remarked to Nanette, "I see hearings before the Land Commission will start in January. They're to be held in San Francisco."

"So it's come at last. Now you can get legal title to your land. Two hundred and twenty-nine square miles. That's more than most princes have in Europe, Johann." She gave him a sarcastic look. "Only there princes have both land and money. Money. I wonder how it feels to have a dollar in your purse."

[1] March 3, 1851.

He shrank back at her barb. "Nanette. I'm not responsible for all this squatter trouble. They're just too many of them to fight. Besides, they're organized. They have shrewd, shyster lawyers, the best in California."

"It means litigation, doesn't it? You'll need good attorneys to represent you before the Land Commission, won't you, Johann?"

"Yes. I can't avoid a certain amount of expense, Nanette."

"Does that mean we'll have to mortgage Hock?"

"Not necessarily."

He had never told her he had already sold all his holdings except Hock Farm to land speculators for $6000 and that their home was also mortgaged. He had also concealed from her the report the squatters were circulating around Sacramento: that his land grants had been incorrectly surveyed and did not include Sacramento City or the fort. For he knew that if that were true, he had sold enormous amounts of land he did not own, property on which he had paid thousands of dollars in taxes while squatters paid neither rent nor taxes, but enjoyed free ownership. The burden of this knowledge weighed heavily on him; he could feel himself breaking under the strain.

He glanced at Nanette. Her shoulders drooped as they had ever since the day Augustus had gone off without saying a word to anyone although later he had written his mother from Acapulco, saying he intended to remain there and go into business.

John resumed his perusal of the news. He read with interest about the public indignation over the wave of murders at the Bay and the formation of the Vigilantes, an organization of prominent citizens pledged to check crime. Seven hundred members had joined the group. They had elected Sam Brannan to head them. They were said to be rounding up the convict gang from Australia, and had already deported fifty of the worst criminals. Sam Whittaker and Rob McKenzie, the leaders, were in jail.

The noise of horses outside came through the open window. John flung his paper aside and began to walk restlessly back and forth across the floor. "There's Eliza and that beggar, Engler, again," he said. "Quite time they returned. It's growing dark."

"Be kind to them, Johann. I know he's poor. But they're in love."

"Let them get over it. I'll never consent to their marriage. Eliza Sutter can marry anyone she likes. It would be an honor for any man to marry into the Sutter family. It's the most prominent one in California."

"Johann. Do stop bragging. Mother Dubeld always said it indicated feeble-mindedness."

"*Gott*, Nanette. How you women do babble."

At that moment Eliza and George Engler entered the room.

"*Popchen*," she said, kissing his bald head.

Eliza's demonstrations of affection always flattered John.

"You are prettier than ever, Eliza," he said, patting her rosy cheeks.

"We've something to say, *Popchen* . . . to ask you . . ." Embarrassed, she stopped. . . . "You tell him, George."

"*Monsieur* Sutter, I beg you for . . . the hand . . . for permission . . . to marry . . . Eliza," he stammered. In the stiff European manner he bowed formally before John.

John glowered at the mild-faced Swiss teacher. "No. I forbid it. Eliza shall never marry you. How dare you suggest it. You rascal you. Get out. Leave Hock Farm at once," he said, pushing Engler toward the door.

With a despairing backward glance at Eliza who was crouching, pale and frightened, beside her mother, George David Engler went sadly out into the night.

Eliza's love affair paled into insignificance beside the one thing that absorbed John's waking hours: the validation of his New Helvetia and Sobrante grants. He mortgaged Hock Farm to the hilt to employ able attorneys to defend his case.

In January, 1852, the United States Land Commission began its hearing in San Francisco. John attended many of the meetings, listening to the arguments. Every landowner around the Bay was vitally concerned with the outcome. Many cases were thrown out of court because the records were incomplete. It worried John considerably. The original copies of his own grants had been destroyed in the office of a San Francisco legal firm the year before in one of the huge incendiary conflagrations that devastated that city every few months.

He left the Bay in March only long enough to attend the wedding of George Engler and his daughter. Worn out by their pleading and that of Nanette, he grudgingly gave his consent to an elaborate ceremony at Hock Farm. To drown his chagrin he drank heavily and escorted the bride to the improvised altar with unsteady steps.

He was glad of the excuse his land cases afforded to make frequent trips to San Francisco. It was the liveliest place on the entire coast, barring none. The only other accessible city, Sacramento, was recuperating from another disastrous spring flood caused by broken levees after a rainfall of thirty-six inches, and an even more devastating fire in the late fall which destroyed two-thirds of the city and a loss of five million dollars. Now in the throes of rebuilding, most of the saloons and dives and the one theater were closed. There was talk of moving the new capital there and opening a library and some schools. He found it unbearably dull.

But San Francisco was an exciting place. It was far away from Nanette, the Squatters, the land speculators and the usurers who charged five per cent a month. At the Bay he was esteemed and revered as the man who held *La Llave de California*—the Key to California. San Francisco honored him for it; indeed they made him Major General of the California Militia. Handsomely uniformed and bemedaled he rode at the head of all official processions, seated with the utmost dignity on his white stallion. He was never happier than when the crowds cheered madly as he rode by. He often wondered whether Napoleon himself received warmer or louder applause.

Slowly, for John indulged in long periods of inactivity, months merged into years. He grew grayer, heavier, balder. He never ventured out without a cane. His shoulders sagged, his lids had a way of half closing over his eyes. He moved with difficulty, dragging his great bulk at a slowed gait. He spent more time at Hock Farm. Eliza, divorced, was back at home; the two boys Emil and Alphonse passed their time between Hock and the mines.

John was sitting under the trees one day when a rider brought him a sealed communication from the Bay. He knew from the return address upon the envelope that it was from the Land Commission in San Francisco. His hands shook so violently that he was afraid he could not open the envelope. Slowly he slit it open with his penknife. He peered at the contents. "*Gott im Himmel.*

We've won. Nanette. Eliza. The Land Commission concedes the validity of the New Helvetia and Sobrante grants. They say they were issued in conformity with Mexican law." [2]

But within the week he learned that the Squatters Association had appealed the case to the U.S. District Court of Northern California.

For an interminable length of time, John's case now jammed its overburdened files. At first he was impatient; finally he resigned himself with a melancholy apathy to the outcome. Financial difficulties continued to harass him. He had already mortgaged Hock Farm so heavily that he could not always pay the interest when it came due. Past days of prodigal hospitality were distant memories. The cases of *aguardiente* he once kept conveniently at hand were now too costly for his depleted purse. But habitual sobriety irked him; he missed the momentary exhilaration of prolonged drinking.

He had neither the means nor the inclination to develop Hock. The model school he had planned to establish there, the introduction of new vines and fruit trees from Europe, his plan of breeding superior herds, all were abandoned. His listless indifference disturbed Nanette, for he sat most of the time in the kitchen watching her work.

"We might go to San Francisco and see Alphonse," she said to him one day. "It's a dangerous city and I don't like to leave him there alone all the time."

"No. We can't afford it," he replied. "Come, Nanette. Just remember the children are grown up. You seem to think they're still babies."

She clicked her knitting needles and held her tongue. Supported by his gold-headed cane, John limped out

[2] Decision of May 15, 1855.

of the kitchen, slamming the door loudly behind him, as if to divert his thought from the shabby poverty into which they had sunk, and began to water the scraggy rose garden.

John was pruning dormant grapevines one mild day in January when the *Linda* brought him word that his two grants had been confirmed by the District Court.[3] He was jubilant until he realized that the Squatters would never rest until the case was decided at Washington.

"If I only had the money to fight it," he moaned to Nanette. "But everyone in Sacramento is after me. I suppose you know that the city allotted $5000 of tax money to send a lawyer all the way to Washington to fight me. These squatters are no better than common thieves. If I only had a little money . . . then I could go to Washington. I'd fight them myself. If I only had a little money . . . not much . . . not much . . ."

With inward bitterness Nanette recalled the money he had squandered. She thought of his puerile extravagances: gold nuggets under the plates of dinner guests, champagne, money gambled away, yet she did not chide him for it. She had come to feel for the broken man a maternal sympathy, if not respect. "Johann, sell off that land you own at Ross."

"It wouldn't bring enough," he replied. "I tried once years ago."

"These past months have made considerable difference in land values. Look at San Francisco. And Monterey. Prices of real estate are the highest they've ever been in California."

"It's no use, Nanette. Ross is too far from the Bay. And there's no gold there."

[3] On Jan. 14, 1857.

John did not know how he could raise the money for a new trial. He finally induced his lawyers to give him credit. Meanwhile, he waited restlessly at Hock Farm, meeting each river steamer, hoping for official mail from the east. When it finally came, he learned that the former decision made in California had been partially reversed. The New Helvetia grant had been allowed but the larger Sobrante had been declared invalid on the ground that Governor Micheltorena was away from the seat of government at Monterey when he made it, it had not been legally executed, and that it was made solely for services rendered.

John collapsed and went to bed for a week. Nanette nursed him dutifully, although she deprived him of the brandy he craved. When he got up he seemed feeble and considerably older. Desperate for funds, John sold the remains of his Ross and Bodega holdings for what they would bring.

To lighten her household labors, Nanette closed off all but three rooms of the big house. Some of the older Hock Indians were still living on the old *rancheria* near by and refused to leave Old Cap even when he could no longer pay them. Then John and Nanette settled down to await the final decision of the United States Supreme Court at Washington.

It came sooner than they had anticipated. They were sitting near the stove in the kitchen at Hock Farm one day in the year 1858 when an aged Indian brought in the mail. John was so agitated that he could not read the verdict. Quaking with apprehension, he handed the letter to Nanette. Blank-faced and outwardly calm, she studied it. Washington admitted the legality of the New Helvetia, but denied the validity of the Sobrante claim. For a moment the normal throbbing of her heart seemed to stop. How can I tell him? she thought. She glanced sideways at John. He was watching her with the look of a tortured beast. "*Johann, Liebchen.*"

He knew from her voice, from the affectionate words he had not heard from her lips since the first year of their marriage, that the case was lost. He sank back in his chair and buried his head on his arms. Nanette neither moved nor spoke, but stood mechanically by her cookstove, the Supreme Court decision clutched tightly in one hand.

"Johann," she finally said, "the court has done us a grave injustice. I am positive this great government intends to protect the constitutional rights of its citizens . . . liberty and justice for all. But perhaps this decision comes from a higher court. Perhaps it is God's way of punishing those who defy his holy laws."

Then suddenly memories of long years of suffering, of trying to keep her family together, long years of watching bitterly her husband's moral delinquencies, his financial mismanagement, his abuse of her favorite son, Augustus, came back to her. Her calm deserted her. A frenzy she could not control came over her. She walked over to her husband, slouched down in an orgy of self-pity, in his chair. She shook her hand violently in his face. "God's vengeance . . . God's vengeance . . . God's vengeance."

She threw the document in his face. Then laughing hysterically, she rushed from the room.

When the full significance of the situation dawned on him, John did not know which way to turn. He knew that sale of land from the New Helvetia grant, although confirmed, was inadequate to cover the losses sustained by the sale of vast land holdings covered by the Sobrante, unconfirmed. He was faced with the tragic situation of having disposed of property valued at several hundred thousand dollars which the Supreme Court held he had never owned. Bankrupt, all he could do was to appeal to the California legislature for aid, on the grounds of the services he had rendered the country.

Meanwhile, he lived on at Hock, virtually penniless, except for some little support provided by his sons, discouraged, and in ill health. For days he felt too weak to do even the light gardening tasks he habitually performed. Nanette withdrew bitterly into a grim-mouthed silence. She seldom talked, but worked or knitted incessantly. Except for her young grandson whom Augustus, after a disastrous marriage to a Mexican woman in Acapulco, had sent to his parents in California to be educated, she had no companionship. Eliza had married again, this time to Dr. Franz Link, and gone to Acapulco to be near Augustus. Alphonse, after adventuring with Walker, the filibuster, in Nicaragua, had died under mysterious circumstances in Nevada City. Emil, now in business in San Francisco, came only occasionally to Hock.

Time dragged slowly by. Friends in the state legislature worked for the relief of Old Cap. Eventually they induced the California legislature to appropriate $15,000 for General Sutter's relief, payable in small monthly installments. It was given not on the grounds of relief, but rather as a refund of taxes paid on the Sobrante grant at the time John considered it his own.

Seven years after the Supreme Court decision that so altered his life, John was lying in bed one morning reading Rousseau's *Emile*, when he heard a crackling sound. Then he smelled burning wood.

"Nanette," he called to his wife asleep beside him. "You'd better look at the kitchen stove."

She got up and as she opened the bedroom door, flames leaped up at her. "Johann," she screamed. "The house is on fire. The hall. The wall's gone."

Slamming the door she rushed over to the closed window and flung it open. "Quick. Let's get out," she gasped.[4]

From a safe distance they watched the flames pour from the second story, from the roof, from one corner of the lower floor. John stared dully at it. "*Gott*," he sobbed, "Hock's gone. Why didn't it take me, too?"

He left Nanette, white and speechless, clutching her dressing gown around her thin body, and the stolid-faced Indians looking on. Unsteadily he walked to the river and out onto the wharf. He stood at the far end looking down at the water. Again, as it had before, the thought of suicide came over him. He leaned far out over the river, watching its gentle ebb and flow. He thought of plunging into it, into oblivion. He took a step nearer. Paralysis gripped him. He could not walk. He stared like a man hypnotized. His eyes focused themselves on the rippling waters. His mind seemed suddenly to weaken. He could not recall what water it was. He felt himself slipping down . . . down . . . down . . . Yet his feet seemed riveted to the wooden planks of the wharf. He looked dizzily at the stream idling by. Was it the Rhine he saw?

[4] On June 2, 1865, Hock Farm burned to the ground.

## CHAPTER XXX

# ROAD WITHOUT END

WEARY AND TRAVEL-WORN, John and Nanette stepped off the train at Washington a year later and drove in a dilapidated hack toward the corner of "E" and Tenth Streets, bound for Mrs. Graves Boarding House. As the vehicle bumped along the rutty roads Nanette observed for the hundredth time, "What a wonderful son Augustus has been to us, Johann. Sending money as soon as he heard Hock had burned to the ground."

"*Ja*," replied John, glum and uncommunicative as usual with Nanette.

"And now this trip to Washington. Congress will give you what you ask. I know they will, Johann. You haven't lost the petition, have you?"

"*Nein*. It's here."

He slapped a bulging vest pocket that gave his well-groomed figure a slightly slatternly aspect. Then he took it out and began silently to read. He was soon wholly absorbed in the vital document which he had come East to lay before Congress.

Nanette, meanwhile, glanced contemplatively at the rows of brick and wooden houses they passed. Most of them were dingy, with faded coats of paint. Indeed all Washington had a deserted aspect she disliked.

"You'd think the war wasn't over yet," she remarked, pointing to an especially dilapidated dwelling. "Look at that one, Johann. The roof's caving in. And most of the glass is all gone."

360

Ignoring her, he read on.

"And don't forget, Johann. You promised to show me the place where Lincoln was assassinated. The poor man."

The excitement of travel had changed amazingly the usually reticent Nanette who chatted incessantly with such animation that John, unable to concentrate, was forced to lay his paper aside.

He withdrew now to the far side of the hack and gazed silently at the strange sights of the nation's Capital which he had never visited before. He dreaded the ordeal ahead of him. He knew the time was inopportune to press his case. He knew that Washington was in the throes of post-war confusion, a disorder enhanced by the sudden death of its president, Abraham Lincoln. He knew that the financial collapse of the South, after the emancipation of its one source of cheap labor, the Negro, had serious repercussions in the Capitol. He was aware too, that dissatisfaction over Lincoln's successor, the opinionated and intemperate Tennessee Democrat, Andrew Johnson, contributed still further to political chaos. He turned over in his mind the many vital problems Congress had to solve: what to do with the emancipated and bewildered Negro; how to revive the bankrupt cotton plantations in the South; extending the railroads to the Pacific; settlement of the endless Indian wars that prevented colonization of the West.

Yet, despite political complications in Washington, John felt some of the old buoyancy surging through his veins, some of the courageous spirit of the pioneer. He felt confident he would somehow win his case. His request was a just one. He had only to get it before Congress. They could not fail to compensate him hand-

somely for the staggering loss of the Sobrante that had
bankrupt him.

He resumed the perusal of his petition. "Petition of
John A. Sutter to the Honorable Senate and House of
Representatives of the 44th Congress of the United
States. Praying compensation for lands owned by him
in California and held under Mexican grants, which
were settled upon and occupied by settlers from the
United States, under the plea that it was public land,
after the conquest of California, and indemnity for the
seizure and destruction of large quantities of his livestock by parties of emigrants from the United States."

He had been working diligently on the petition for
some time. In it he had recounted briefly his trip to the
west coast, and showed with what difficulty he had made
a settlement in the wilderness. He described the building
of the fort and the taming of the local Indians. He told
how he had supplied trappers with furs in exchange for
food. He described in detail acquisition of the Alvarado
and Sobrante grants. He recounted how he had sown
wheat, raised livestock, opened a sawmill and induced
settlers to live permanently in the Sacramento Valley.
He elaborated upon the part he played in the Gold Rush
and how he had aided the United States to acquire
California.

He had remembered to include what William T.
Sherman had said about him, "To Captain Sutter, more
than to any single person are we indebted for the conquest of California." Then he reminded Congress that
although the Treaty between Mexico and the United
States guaranteed full protection to the lives and property of Californians yet this Sobrante grant, of 97,000
acres had been taken from him by the Supreme Court,
a grant worth a million dollars. This was done even
though he had paid out in taxes, lawyers' fees, expenses

of litigation, and miscellaneous expenses 350,000
dollars.

The weeks following the Sutters' arrival in Washington were unhappy ones, because John was unable to get
his petition before Congress. He had hoped to have a
bill claiming relief and indemnity introduced the first
week, but he was brushed aside by Senators who considered John Sutter of minor importance in the political
treadmill. Nevertheless John climbed the capitol steps
daily, imploring every influential senator and congress-
man he met to hear his case. It was several months before
he finally got his petition into the hands of the Senate
Committee on Claims.

For a time John found living at the capitol mildly
exhilarating. Almost every day he met someone who had
known him in California when he was rich and important and who paid him the deference that meant so much
to him. Homage and flattery invariably restored his
self-confidence and he gloried in the adulation of old
friends. He was especially pleased when Frank Buchser,
the famous portrait painter, asked him to sit for him.
When the picture was unveiled in the painter's studio,
crowds of old friends gathered to celebrate. To John's
delight, they called him the Grand Old Man of California, and reminded him of the gay days at Sutter's
Fort. John went home to his hotel that night feeling
younger than he had for weeks.

"Nanette, they haven't forgotten me," he said. "Yes.
My friends all remember me. They're grateful for the
help I gave them when they were poor emigrants. No.
They haven't forgotten me. I'm sure they haven't,
Nanette. Perhaps my life hasn't been wasted after all."

Nanette looked grimly at him for a time. It was
always difficult for her to forget how John had neglected

her. But old age had made her more tolerant, for she knew now that John, poor and half-ill, leaned on her for support, and pity for him softened her harsh ways. "*Ja* . . . Johann . . . you have lived a useful life," was all she said.

After months and years of delay the Bill for the Relief of John A. Sutter reached the Senate floor. The Senate Claims Committee looked unfavorably upon it, however, and it did not come up for a vote.

Postponement of his case weighed heavily upon John. He began now to age rapidly, his gait slowed and he suffered excruciatingly at times from gout. Disappointment left telling traces on his face and he began, for the first time, to experience a keen distaste for Washington.

Worried over John's frailty, Nanette wrote in distress to her favorite son, Augustus, "I think Johann will not live very long unless I find some way to get him out of Washington."

Augustus' reply was full of constructive comments. Knowing his parents had spent one or more summers at Lititz, Pennsylvania, he urged his mother to take the generous sum he enclosed and move there. He also offered to supply enough money to build them a house, provided they would assume the responsibility of taking care of his children, whom he did not wish to educate in Acapulco.

Nanette burst into tears of joy when the letter reached her at their hotel. "*Ja*, Johann," she sobbed. "You see now what a fine son our Augustus is . . . And to think how you treated him at Hock. Johann . . . aren't you ashamed?"

"*Nein*," he roared gruffly at her. "Of what should I be ashamed?" He stamped out of the room, eyes suspiciously moist, to conceal from Nanette his deep gratification at his son's magnanimous offer.

That spring [1] the Sutters moved to the quaint Moravian town of Lititz to their new home, a sturdy red brick structure, with a slate roof. To Nanette's intense joy it was equipped with a modern cook stove and running hot and cold water. Although nearing seventy, the Sutters were as excited as children over their new abode. They welcomed their grandchildren from Acapulco with delight, happy to have young ones in the house to divert them.

In the months and years that followed, John and Nanette lived in monastic seclusion, seldom paying visits and never entertaining. Occasionally John went to Washington to try to have his petition reintroduced, but without success. Lobbying made little impression on the politicians of Washington and John found his own self-confidence growing weak. He realized suddenly that he had been in the east ten years and yet nothing had been accomplished. The pension allowed him by the California legislature had been stopped and his pride rebelled at accepting a larger allowance from Augustus. Downcast and helpless, thoughts of suicide taunted him from time to time, especially when he walked, as he so often did, along the banks of the Potomac in springtime.

His spirits were suddenly revived by the electrifying news that reached him one day at Lititz, that the House Private Land Claims Committee had under consideration a bill granting him $50,000 for his services to the country and for losses sustained by the Supreme Court's adverse decision in the Sobrante grant. He began again to haunt the corridors of the Capitol building striving,

[1] 1871.

by personal contact, to induce Congress to vote upon the measure.

Another three years passed by and still John's claim lay buried under stacks of unfinished business. Finally, ill with rheumatism and a serious kidney ailment, he decided to enlist the aid of the Associated Pioneers who numbered among their ranks many of his old California friends.

Aware that Old Cap was failing fast, the Pioneers rallied to his support. They had copies made and distributed to politicians of what J. Ross Browne wrote about John Sutter when he addressed the Territorial Pioneers in San Francisco not long before.

"The series of events which resulted in the acquisition of California by the United States may be said to have commenced prior to 1845. Without going into unnecessary details, the Mexican government, under the Presidency of Paredes, found itself in the beginning of the year, on the eve of war with the United States. The department of California was in an exposed condition and already the explorations of Lieutenant Frémont and others were attracting attention to the Pacific Slope.

"At that time John A. Sutter, a native of Switzerland, who had served in the armies of Napoleon, was a resident of California. This brave adventurer had established a ranch or farm near the banks of the Sacramento River. In order to ward off the attacks of hostile Indians he had erected a strong defense work, then and now known as Sutter's Fort. Generous in his hospitality, as he was brave and enterprising, Sutter received with open arms the adventurous Americans who crowded across the plains at that period. He furnished them with provisions and aided them with his teams over the difficult passes of the Sierras.

"Enamored with their conversation which breathed the spirit of liberty, he made a rendezvous of his fort. The Mexican government was prompt to resist the threatened invasion of the Americans. Don Andrés Castillo, a Mexican officer of note, was dispatched to California in order to negotiate with Sutter for the possession of his stronghold. Castillo was empowered to pay as much as $100,000 for it, and actually offered Sutter in addition several fine tracts of Mission lands, now worth millions.

"But Sutter, with an unselfish devotion to our interests, rejected all these tempting offers. He is now old and poor. His lands have been taken away from him. The Legislature of California has grudgingly given him a pittance of $250 a month to enable him to prosecute his claims at Washington; but the General Government has never recognized his service."

By this and personal approach, they were instrumental in getting a new memorial before the Senate in a few months.[2] John's confidence in gaining redress now soared to new peaks. Ill as he was, he left Lititz and went to stay at the Mades Hotel in Washington.

From then on, events moved swiftly to a climax. That April a bill for his relief received a favorable report from the House Committee. Toward the end of the same month, the Senate Committee on Claims gave their stamp of approval. In fact, it was openly acknowledged by many Senators and Representatives that Sutter's Sobrante claim was valid according to Mexican law, and it was conceded that John had suffered damage of at least one million dollars. Its sponsors assured him the bill would be passed before Congress adjourned in June.

Happier than he had been in years, John stayed quietly on at the Mades Hotel, waiting for the bill to pass. He believed it was only a matter of a few weeks; it was election year and politicians were anxious to get home to campaign for votes. He amused himself by re-reading the books he loved: Goethe, Voltaire, Rousseau, Scott. He wrote long letters to relatives and old friends in Switzerland, letters bubbling over with confidence

2 In January, 1880.

that he would win his case. He spent long hours in his rocking chair, recalling bygone days in California, his old friends. New life seemed to surge up in him. He was nearing eighty but he wrote Nanette that he did not feel a day over sixty-five.

Fifteen years of pressing his case in Washington had mellowed John. He had not tasted liquor for a long time, but drank only occasionally a small glass of wine. He lived a life of the utmost moderation, going to bed at nine and rising regularly at five. He was more kindly toward Nanette; there were moments when he was mildly affectionate to her. The years had left their impress upon him. His hair was thin and entirely white; he was bent and crippled with rheumatic pains. Young at heart, as he felt, to the world he was just a sick, broken, old man, given to dozing in the sun. He rested contentedly in his rocking chair for days at a stretch. Sometimes he dozed, sometimes he read, but most of the time he sat lost in thought. Peace such as he had never known before invaded his heart. He sat waiting . . . waiting . . . always waiting. . . .

The early days of June came and went without a word from Congress, whose members were rushing to bring to a close the forty-sixth session in days of exhausting heat. On the sixteenth, leaving piles of unfinished business, Congress suddenly adjourned. John read the news in the morning paper, panic in his heart. He dragged himself from his chair, took his cane, and made his way to the Capitol, hoping desperately that his bill had passed. As he went, a sudden dizziness half-blinded him. He moved slowly ahead, leaning on his cane. With lagging steps, he trudged toward the Capitol, pausing now and again to rest. A hot wind, muggy and oppressive, made the glare of the Washington pavements almost unendurable. On the sidewalk near the Capitol steps he met one of the bill's sponsors, a prominent senator, who was leaving for the train, bag in hand.

The senator read the question in John's deep-sunk eyes. "General Sutter . . . I am sorry . . . indeed I am . . . You see . . . we had so much to do . . . at the last. . . ."

"Then . . . then . . . it didn't pass?"

"We never got to it, General . . . It's still on the table . . . but we'll get to it the first thing in the fall . . . No reason to worry, general . . . no reason at all. . . ." With a reassuring smile he patted John on the back and, calling a cab, drove swiftly off toward the railway station.

A sensation as of smothering made John gasp for air. Breathing heavily he dropped down on the broad steps.

"Better let me take you home, sir," said a cabby standing near by waiting for fares. "Washington's hot as hell. No wonder you're exhausted, Sir, sitting there in the broiling sun."

Gently he supported John to the cab. "Where to, Sir?"

John sank back against the seat with closed eyes, breath coming in labored gasps. "Mades Hotel."

Although he was conscious, he had no sensation of time, of place, of sound, as the cab sped along the Washington streets. A numbing despair cast its pall upon him. He felt no desire to resist it, no desire even to live.

At the Mades Hotel, attendants half carried him to his room and put him to bed. He did not protest, but obeyed them like a tired child. He wanted only to sleep . . . sleep . . . sleep. . . .

"Pull down the blinds and don't disturb me," he mumbled.

"You're not ill, are you, Sir?" one of them inquired.

"Not ill, only tired, very tired."

John lay there in bed all the next day, refusing all food and sipping only a little brandy which he kept with him for emergencies. It was the first drop of it he had tasted in years; he had almost forgotten how good it was. It warmed him and blurred the torment within him. Pleasant memories of the past flitted in and out of his mind. His beloved Rhine. The Sacramento. The day gold was discovered. Miners coming into the fort, bags of gold in hand, drinking, gambling. Hoisting the American flag over the fort. The convention at Monterey with Riley thanking him for the gold watch. And . . . Eliza in her wedding gown. Who was it she married? His mind struggled to recall the name. Oh yes. The President of the United States. The only person fit to marry the daughter of the great Captain Sutter, richest man in California, and monarch of New Helvetia.

Suddenly he heard the sound of running water. Was it the Rhine? Or was it the Sacramento he heard? With herculean effort, he lifted himself out of bed and went over to the window, trying to find it. When he got there the sound had stopped. "Nanette, Nanette," he called. "Where are you, Nanette?"

Then the room went black before his eyes. He groped his way to a desk near by and sat down. Presently the black veil seemed to lift. As it did so, he remembered that Nanette was at their home, in Lititz. He had forgotten to write her as he had promised. He must write to her now, this very moment. He had something important to say. What was it he had to tell her? Some bad news, he knew, but he could not remember now what it was.

His shaking fingers fumbled around the desk. They came upon paper, a pen. But these seemed to glide away when he tried to hold them. He redoubled his efforts. A gray veil fell across his eyes as if far away ...*Meine Liebchen*...Then the black veil enveloped him, once more. Through it he heard the sound of rushing waters; he knew that it was the Rhine, here in the room at his side. He felt himself being drawn into it ... floating gently off into space.